FRANCIS BACON

FRANCIS BACON

FRANCIS BACON

THE FIRST STATESMAN
OF SCIENCE

By
J. G. CROWTHER

LONDON
THE CRESSET PRESS
MCMLX

First published in Great Britain in 1960
by The Cresset Press, 11 Fitzroy Square, London, W.1
Printed in Great Britain by
Western Printing Services Limited, Bristol

More substitutes might be found for Galileo than for Bacon. More than one could be mentioned, who, in the place of the former, would probably have done what he did; but the history of human knowledge points out nobody of whom it can be said, that, placed in the situation of Bacon, he would have done what Bacon did; no man whose prophetic genius would have enabled him to delineate a system of science which had not yet begun to exist!

JOHN PLAYFAIR

CONTENTS

The Incomparable Verulam   I

Part I
FOR MANKIND

1. *The Conquest of the Universe*   21
2. *The General Staff*   28
3. *Strategic Objectives*   37
4. *Can Scientists be Statesmen?*   41
5. *The Organization of Science*   44
6. *Dawn*   47
7. *Preliminary to Planning*   61
8. *How it is to be Done*   89
9. *Dialectic*   97
10. *Limitations of the Mind arising from Social
       Being*   101
11. *The Statesman of Science*   106
12. *The New Method*   116
13. *Natural Histories*   128
14. *The Principle of Conservation*   131
15. *The Prolongation and Renewal of Life*   137
16. *The Dissemination of Scientific Knowledge*   144

Part II
FOR HIMSELF

17. *Bacon's Origin*   153
18. *Formative Years*   158
19. *An Unofficial Officer*   165
20. *Defending Parliamentary Rights*   173
21. *No Place for the Unsubmissive*   179

22. *Private Interests and Public Affairs*   187
23. *Rebellion*   198
24. *Prosecution*   205
25. *Statesman or Scientist?*   213
26. *The Planned Life*   225
27. *Becoming a Statesman*   236
28. *Friendship*   247
29. *The Ladder of State*   253
30. *Earning Promotion*   265
31. *Chequered Ascent*   272
32. *The Lawyer Strikes Back*   282
33. *Two Conceptions of Discovery*   289
34. *Against Appeasement*   294
35. *Infinite Business and the Abuses of the Times*   298
36. *The Summit*   302
37. *The Fall*   307
38. *Criminal or Invalid?*   324
39. *Bacon and Coke*   332
40. *Entrance Halls of a Better Life*   338

     References   352
     Index   355

PLATES

FRANCIS BACON   *Frontispiece*
After Paul van Somer

I   FRONTISPIECE OF THE INSTAURATIO MAGNA

II   TITLE OF VALERIUS TERMINUS
The list of contents and the word 'Philosophy'
are in Bacon's own hand   *Between*
                                           pages

III FRANCIS BACON AT THE AGE OF TWELVE   *48–49*
'two years younger than Her Majesty's happy
reign . . .'
*After a coloured bust belonging to the Earl
of Verulam*

IV Bacon's Father and Guardian
NICHOLAS BACON
BURGHLEY
Attributed to Marc Gheeraedts

V   Bacon's Earlier Masters
ELIZABETH I
Attributed to Marc Gheeraedts
ESSEX   *Between*
                                          pages

VI Bacon's Later Masters   *160–161*
JAMES I
By Daniel Mytens
BUCKINGHAM

VII Bacon's Rivals
ROBERT CECIL
Attributed to John de Critz
EDWARD COKE
By Cornelius Jansens

ix

Foreword

As the four hundredth anniversary of the birth of Francis Bacon in 1561 approaches, his genius and significance shine more brightly than ever. He has long been recognized as one of the greatest of men, but there has been little agreement on the true nature of his greatness.

It has always been clear that Elizabeth was a ruler, Burghley a statesman, Shakespeare a dramatic poet and Drake a seaman, but what was Bacon? He was in part writer, lawyer, statesman, philosopher and scientist, but he was not primarily any of these. Today, his combination of statesmanship with science is seen to be the deepest aspect of his genius. He was the first to propose the continual improvement of human life by the systematic development and application of science, not as a utopian dream but a practical policy.

He entered politics with the aim of securing the power necessary to carry it out, besides satisfying his personal ambition. He fared with spectacular success and dramatic failure. In the course of his effort he struggled with the problems of the relations between intellectual and practical life, which confront scientists and society so acutely in the second half of the twentieth century.

Through his combined effort in science and politics Bacon became the first of the new type of man essential in a scientific age, the Statesman of Science, who is not primarily concerned in making scientific discoveries, but with the organization and utilization of science, and its proper integration in the rest of human life.

Bacon struggled with these problems on an epic scale, and thereby became the greatest prophet of the modern world.

In this book, the evolution of his ideas and the course of his extraordinary life are traced, and their significance expounded. The threads of science and politics in the complex skein of his career are unravelled. They are the beginning of the fabric of the modern scientific age, and the starting-point for the investigation needed to discover how science and scientists should be governed, and govern themselves, so that human society, and life itself, are developed to the highest point, and do not end in self-destruction.

Bacon's ideas and aims were unintelligible to nearly all of his contemporaries. They have become better understood at different periods, according to the historical and scientific conditions of the times. A wave of appreciation rose in the third quarter of the seventeenth century; in the middle of the eighteenth century and in the second quarter of the nineteenth. In the second half of the twentieth century a new wave is rising as the consequence of the headlong development of science, and the acute questioning of its place and management in human life, which this has caused. Bacon was a modern Prometheus who bartered his good name to bring science to the aid of humanity. He suffered thereby, but emerged a creator of the future.

The social and moral problems of science and the scientist arose in Bacon's life with the freshness of the newly-created. The consideration of his dramatic career provides one of the most illuminating ways of approaching our own great problem: what are we to do with our science and our scientists? Only the statesmen of science can tell us, and of these Bacon was the first and greatest.

Acknowledgments

THE first acknowledgment by a writer on Bacon must be, in a peculiar degree, to Bacon himself, who took pains to leave an exceptionally complete collection of his writings to posterity. These are very varied; they include not only polished major works but numerous drafts and treatments of those subjects and affairs which interested him, discussed at various times from different points of view. In a way he has already said a great deal of what can be said about his own works, but he has left his comments in a labyrinth of literature, from which his varying views on any particular subject are not easily assembled for comparative consideration.

He formed his basic notions in his youth and struggled incessantly with them during his life, discussing them over and over again, in perspectives that changed through his early, middle and later years. He made no less than twelve drafts of the *Novum Organum*. For this reason, it is necessary to examine his main ideas more than once, as his treatments at different times reveal significant differences. His thought was gradually built up in a great spiral, like those giant helical molecules which are now found to constitute the basis of living matter. As one goes up or down the structure, one returns over and over again to corresponding points on adjacent spirals, from which the perspective is similar, but never quite the same. Bacon is the best guide through the maze of his own thought.

Second only to Bacon himself, the writer is indebted to James Spedding, who devoted thirty years of careful and perspicacious labour to the editing and elucidation of Bacon's works and life. Spedding's texts and translations have generally been used in composing this book.

Spedding's interest in Bacon was aroused by the relations between Bacon and Essex. Bacon correctly perceived Essex's failings and warned him against them, intimating that it would be politically impossible to follow him if he persisted in them.

xiii

Spedding saw that Bacon had put the interests of the state above personal loyalty to an unsound statesman, and the commonly-received judgment on Bacon's behaviour in the Essex affair was mistaken. When he read Macaulay's review of Montague's edition of Bacon's *Works*, which appeared in 1837, he found it superficial. He began a new study, which led to the preparation of a new edition and commentary.

Spedding's independence of judgment, sensitive discrimination, experience of administration, and diligence enabled him to penetrate more deeply into Bacon's behaviour, and even to some extent into his scientific works, than others with more spectacular talents and greater theoretical knowledge.

The political and scientific events of the last hundred years have confirmed his general judgment on Bacon's character, and demonstrated that his doubts on the correctness of the opinions of current scientific authorities on Bacon's technical works were not unfounded.

This book is, in a sense, a path cut through the magnificent forest of Spedding's scholarship, in the perspective of the social relations of science, and under the light that recent developments in science and politics have thrown on the interaction between these two main strands of modern life. It is a contribution to the celebration of the hundredth anniversary of Spedding's edition of Bacon, as well as to the four hundredth anniversary of Bacon's birth.

Among recent works on Bacon those by Professor F. H. Anderson, Professor B. Farrington, and Miss Mary Sturt have provided valuable ideas, and I am indebted to Professor T. Kotarbinski, President of the Polish Academy of Sciences, for a copy of an illuminating article by him on Bacon's method.

Mrs. Margaret Sherwood Taylor has very kindly given me permission to quote from her late husband's *Century of Science*.

Permission has been received from *Country Life* for the reproduction of the portrait of Sir Edward Coke, in the possession of the Earl of Leicester, and from the National Portrait Gallery for portraits of Francis Bacon, Nicholas Bacon, Buckingham, Burghley, Robert Cecil, Elizabeth I, Essex and James I.

Plate II is a facsimile after the Harleian MS 6463. According to Spedding, who was expert on the handwriting of Bacon and his staff, the MS is in the hand of one of the staff, with corrections, erasures and interlineations in his own. Spedding expresses the opinion that the complete table of contents and the word 'Philosophy', which are written on the blank space of the title page, are also in Bacon's own hand.

The portrait of Bacon as a boy of twelve is reproduced from Volume VI of Spedding's edition of Bacon's *Works*. It was engraved by F. Holl from a drawing by Arthur Hughes from a coloured bust belonging to the Earl of Verulam.

The chief works which have been consulted are given in the list of references. I wish to record my indebtedness to their authors for the information I have gained from them.

J. G. CROWTHER

The Incomparable Verulam

Bacon proposed 'a total reconstruction of sciences, arts and all human knowledge . . . to extend the power and dominion of the human race . . . over the universe'. This was to be done in the first place to enable mankind to achieve 'the serene tranquillity of abstract wisdom', which can only be obtained by 'building in the human understanding a true model of the world, such as it is in fact, not such as a man's own reason would have it be'. It required 'a very diligent dissection and anatomy of the world', which would not only provide the means for understanding it, but also for extending 'the limits of the power and greatness of man'. Thus 'the true and lawful goal of the sciences is none other than this: that human life be endowed with new discoveries and powers. . . . To speak plainly and clearly, it is a discovery of all operations and possibility of operations, from immortality, if it were possible, to the meanest mechanical practice.' In his project, 'truth therefore and utility are here the very same things: and works themselves are of greater value as pledges of truth than as contributing to the comforts of life'.

Bacon conceived his project as concerning the *whole* universe, not only that of matter and physical things. It comprehended 'mental operations, logic, ethics and politics'.

All the phenomena of the universe, including the mental and social, were to be explored by means of an improved method of investigation, and according to a plan. This improved method consisted of deriving laws from experiments, and then making further experiments under the guidance of these laws. In his own words, it was 'not to extract works from works or experiments from experiments (as an empiric), but from works and experiments to extract causes and axioms, and again from those causes and axioms new works and experiments, as a legitimate interpreter of nature'.

Bacon conceived not only the planned development of science,

B   I

but also the planned development of society, on the basis of material possibilities and the scientifically ascertained facts of the human mind and social life. He was the first to outline the chief aims of modern man, which are taking shape so swiftly in the twentieth century.

As his work becomes more and more significant, it repays attention with ever-increasing interest. Some of his main conceptions which seemed not to be clear, or appeared to be irrelevant or wrong, or merely fantastic, are now found to be closer to the ideas of today than to those of the last three centuries.

His main achievement is the conception of a programme for a scientific age, and a method of carrying it out. This is the function of a statesman of such an age, a man who guides the aim of science, which has become the primary instrument in modern life. He is the first example of the new kind of statesman required for organizing a society in which scientific activity and human life are one. As human activities become more and more scientific, the leadership of mankind will devolve more and more on such men, who are not primarily scientists, but statesmen of science, who understand and foster it, and guide its utilization for the benefit of the human race.

Bacon conceived the idea of an improved method of discovery in his youth. The possession of this idea led him to consider what might be done with it. He saw in it a key to all knowledge, which made a complete investigation of nature possible. His mind therefore moved to the consideration of how, being in possession of the key, the complete investigation of nature should be organized, and what should be done with the result. How was human life to be managed in the light of the knowledge that was coming to it? How was man to govern his scientific destiny?

He became preoccupied with this question, so that in his later years it took precedence over his concern with method, in which he had at first been chiefly interested.

Bacon's proposals for the planned development of science as the means for raising the dignity and greatness of man made a profound impression on his immediate successors. The *Record* of the Royal Society of London opens with the statement that 'the foundation of the Royal Society was one of the earliest practical fruits of the philosophical labours of Francis Bacon'. Thomas Sprat, who published the first history of the Royal Society in 1667, only five years after the granting of its charter, said that 'some of Bacon's writing' gave a better account of the aims of the Society than anything he could compose.

The founders of the Society acquired from Bacon the conception of a systematic investigation of nature, by a group of men who had formed themselves into a corporate body for the purpose. They had found in Bacon's *New Atlantis* the sketch of a new social order based on planned research by teams of research workers. Without accepting Bacon's greater scheme, they did adopt the notion of planned research by scientists banded together in a corporate body. This, however, was merely a society within the existing social order, and not at all a new social order based on science. The Royal Society is a private society. The society of scientists in the *New Atlantis* is in control of the whole social order.

Though the early founders were influenced by the *New Atlantis* and adopted from it the name of 'fellows' for their members, the scope of their society was much narrower than that of the one which Bacon had in mind. Consequently, Bacon's ideas faded from the leading place they had had in the beginning of the Society as it developed along its own essentially narrower lines. After a hundred years, the ideas of Bacon had receded from the forefront; after two hundred years, members paid merely perfunctory tributes to his memory, and after three hundred years, many of them doubted whether he had had any real influence at all on modern science.

This was not unnatural after the abandonment of Bacon's aim of pursuing science and the improvement of man's condition as an indivisible unity, and the concentration on the discovery of facts and theories, without reference to their bearing on the rest of life. Bacon would not have recognized in the professional scientific societies of today the embodiment of the comprehensive scientific social order which he envisaged. It was quite another thing, and the doubts whether Bacon really had any influence in the creation of modern scientific societies, though not correct are not unintelligible. His aims were on an altogether wider and greater scale.

The foundation of the Royal Society of London was a realization of only a part of Bacon's aims. The realization of yet another part, and again only a part, was the compilation of the great French Encyclopaedia, a universal dictionary of arts, sciences, trades and manufactures, under the editorship of Diderot and d'Alembert. The first volume was published in 1751 and, together with its successors, provided much of the intellectual stimulus which contributed to the French Revolution. Diderot and d'Alembert made the source of their inspiration for the idea of the Encyclopaedia very clear in their famous preface. They ascribe it to Bacon, Descartes, Newton and Locke, and say:

'At the Head of these illustrious Heroes we deservedly place the immortal Francis Bacon, Lord High Chancellor of England; whose works, though justly esteemed, are too little known, and deserve Perusal more than Praise. To consider the just and extensive Views of this prodigious Man; the Multiplicity of his Objects; the Strength of his Style; his sublime Imagery; and extreme Exactness; we are tempted to esteem him the greatest, the most universal, and most eloquent of all Philosophers. It is to this great Author we are chiefly indebted for our Encyclopaedic Plan.'

Bacon's influence may have been more widely and deeply realized through the French Encyclopaedia than through the Royal Society. But the most complete realization of his aims, so far, is to be found in the new socialist states, where social life has been reorganized on scientific lines, and science is pursued according to a comprehensive plan, for the endowment of human life 'with new discoveries and powers'.

Bacon's project for the conquest of the universe and the scientific organization of human life has generally been regarded as a phantasy, and dismissed as such. The events of today show, however, that it was a sublime prevision of the future. We have to accept his magnificent conception not as a wonderful fiction but a concrete outline of what is to be.

Bacon's earlier grand conception of science for the benefit of the human race was accompanied in his later years by a lower, narrower conception of the utilization of science for profit. It emerged rather clearly after his fall, when he was making desperate efforts to secure interest and material support from James and Buckingham, in order to meet his debts. This narrower conception of science for profit made him an anticipator of the capitalist attitude to science. But this later conception was secondary to the main stream of his thought.

The word 'profit' rarely occurs in Bacon's early works. In these, the development of science is to be for the benefit of the human race, and not for any individual's profit.

The narrowing of Bacon's conception of a universal organization of science and the social order into the formation of a society within the social order is a parallel to the narrowing of outlook from science for the benefit of the human race to science for profit.

Bacon's early and primary conception belongs to the base of civilization, while his later and secondary conception of science for profit belongs to the transient ideological superstructure of the capitalist period.

In his primary conception, Bacon does not belong to the capitalist period, but to the socialist society of the future. S. R. Gardiner pointed out that 'Neither of the great English parties which were so soon to spring into existence could claim him as their own; and as long as the influence of those parties continued to lay its spell upon history, his memory was left without a champion.' He leaps over the last three centuries, and is closer to non-egalitarian socialism than any other system that has predominated since his day.

The confusion of Bacon's sociological aims with the formation of a society of persons within an existing social system has been accompanied by a similar confusion with regard to his new method of making scientific discoveries. Bacon nowhere gives a complete example or description of his method, though he says it is clear in his mind. In his later years, however, he seemed to be less confident of its completeness than he had been in his youth, when he first thought of the idea.

Meanwhile, the method of research clarified and perfected by Galileo, became generally adopted, and has remained the characteristic research method of modern science. A common belief arose that it was fundamentally the same as Bacon's, and the fellows of the Royal Society changed over to it entirely, almost without comment on the differences between the two methods.

Galileo's method, seen at its most brilliant in his discovery of the laws of motion, consists in the exact measurement of particular cases by experiment, and then the discovery of a mathematical formula, by an effort of the imagination, by which all the particular cases can be described, and any other of the same kind forecast by mathematical manipulation of the formula. The correctness of deductions from the formula is then tested by experiment, and if these prove to be wrong, fresh experiments conceived in the light of what has already been observed, are made to secure further facts, which may inspire the conception of a more correct theory or formula. If this also proves inadequate, the research may be continued in the same way until an adequate law is found.

This method of discovery depends on the imagination as an essential link. It requires a faculty of guessing how a series of measurements can be accurately described or subsumed in a law or formula. Bacon described it as 'learned sagacity'. Often the investigator starts with the assumption that the phenomena under investigation behave according to a particular mathematical law. He then makes experiments to see whether the phenomena do in fact fit the law. If they do not, he may see how, while in process of making the comparison, the assumed law should be changed in order to make it fit.

The role of the imagination in the conventional method of scientific discovery is very important, and perhaps crucial. For this reason, the method is in this feature akin to artistic creation. It depends very much on the talent or genius of the individual scientist. Different scientists give very different descriptions of how they have actually made discoveries. The eminent mathematician Hadamard has collected accounts by various mathematicians of how they made well-known mathematical discoveries, to try to elucidate the psychology of mathematical discovery. Hadamard's investigation has shown that mathematicians seem to know little more about how important discoveries are made than poets about how to write great poetry. Either they can do it, or they can't.

Intense mental concentration on a number of particulars seems to have an essential part in it. Isaac Newton used to sit for hours on the edge of his bed half-dressed, without moving, trying to find a solution to a problem. Pasteur made copious notes of experiments and observations, and then went into 'brown studies' for hours, as if he were in a trance. During these concentrations, his staff moved on tiptoe and spoke in whispers, and he was not to be disturbed. James Watt's great and many inventions generally came to him after severe attacks of migraine.

In these cases, at least, it looks as if the mind were juggling with a lot of particulars, and trying to find a pattern into which they would fit. One can almost hear the wheels of the brain working.

This method of discovery depends pre-eminently on personal

ability, and is individually only roughly predictable. One can say that a number of well-trained clever men, provided with facilities, will certainly make useful progress in the investigation of a wide range of problems, but there is very little certainty in the forecast of whether any individual will discover any particular thing, or what he will discover.

Soon after the Royal Society was founded, this became the accepted method of research. Bacon's method, as described by him, appears very different. He conceived it as a procedure in which every step was to be conscious, and which, when applied to any subject with due diligence would extract the laws which govern its phenomena. It would have had the effect of transferring the business of finding the pattern among particulars from the obscure operations of the imagination to a logical procedure, every step of which was clear to the consciousness.

If it could have been completely worked out, it would in principle have made it possible to conceive a machine which could be operated to discover the laws governing any aspect of natural phenomena. 'My way of discovering sciences goes far to level men's wits; and leaves but little to individual excellence; because it performs everything by the surest rules and demonstrations.' Nevertheless, other things being equal, 'the growth of (sciences) comes from great wits'. He considered that the method of discovery was itself a subject of research, and capable of improvement thereby. 'I that regard the mind not only in its own faculties, but in its connection with things, must needs hold that the art of discovery may advance as discoveries advance.' He conceived the art of discovering arts, or the science of science.

He gave an example of the application of an incomplete form of his method. This was to the phenomenon of heat. The use of his method, even in its imperfect form, enabled him to conclude that 'heat is a motion, expansive, restrained, and acting in its strife upon the smaller particles of bodies'. This is a rough conception of the dynamical theory of heat; no mean conclusion.

The imperfect method exemplified in this research consists of a comprehensive enumeration of every kind of manifestation of heat, and then the extraction from each kind of the features special to it, by a system of exclusions. The material for investigation is increased by the performance of experiments arising out of this procedure, and this additional or new material is now subjected to exclusions and experiments. Finally, a principle common to all the manifestations is extracted. This example of the imperfect method consists of a process of induction sharpened and guided by experiments. In it Bacon made use of his imagination, for his conception of heat as a motion acting on the smaller particles of bodies is an imaginative picture of something that he could not see. He did not leave any description of an automatic method of discovery, in which imagination plays no part; he almost certainly did not succeed in discovering this. But an important part of his achievement was to conceive that the method of discovery was itself subject to improvement, and might be improved continually, producing in the course of time an instrument of investigation the power of which would exceed that of the method we now know and use.

Bacon did in fact accomplish a very considerable technical achievement in elucidating and making clear and conscious a considerable part of the logical process which is carried out largely intuitively when a scientist is engaged in making a discovery. In the course of doing this, he made the most important contributions since Aristotle, up to his own time, to the development of inductive logic.

But he under-estimated the complexity of the task of working out the process of discovery, and it will probably be a long time before this is tolerably completed.

At the end of the seventeenth century, before the Galilean method had been generally adopted, some of the greatest scientists still had a deeper grasp of Bacon's conception than has commonly occurred since. Most prominent among these was Robert Hooke, whose status as a scientist has always been high, and increases with time. He was overshadowed in his own day by Isaac Newton who was more Galilean in his method, though on fundamental questions of his natural philosophy he was careful not to commit himself. Hooke's view of Bacon's method of discovery was published in 1705, after his death. He said that according to it the human intellect 'is continually to be assisted by some method or engine which shall be as a guide to regulate its actions, so as that it shall not be able to act amiss. Of this engine no man except the incomparable Verulam hath had any thoughts, and he indeed hath promoted it to a very good pitch.' Hooke appreciated this conception of a method of discovery which was capable of development, like science itself. He proposed that its power should be increased by the addition of a technique which he called 'philosophical algebra'. He said that he could not 'doubt but that if this art be well prosecuted and made use of, an ordinary capacity with industry will be able to do very much more than has yet been done, and to show that even physical and natural inquiries as well as mathematical and geometrical will be capable also of demonstration; so that henceforward the business of invention will not be so much the effect of acute wit, as of a serious and industrious prosecution'.

In this, as in many other things, Hooke has proved himself a man in front of his time, for the tendency of today is to develop the idea of the calculating machine, revived by Babbage and the inventors of electronic computers, which will take over more and more the business of research, and convert the discovery of new facts and theories from a process of individual inspiration and craftsmanship into one of mass-production of discoveries by machines, along industrial lines. The question whether it is possible to construct a calculating machine which can think is now seriously discussed. After the passage of two-and-a-half centuries, the circle of acceptance has nearly completed a revolution, and the idea of Bacon and Hooke is coming into its own again.

The pregnancy of Bacon's thought in this field is seen in his contribution to 'information theory'. He discovered for himself that information can be conveyed in two symbols, like the pair of symbols used by a modern electronic computer, which performs all its calculations only with o and 1. He illustrated how this could be done.

'Nor is it a slight thing which is thus by the way effected. For hence we see how thoughts may be communicated at any distance of place by means of any objects perceptible either to the eye or ear, provided only that those objects are capable of two differences; as by bells, trumpets, torches, gunshots, and the like. . . .'

Bacon's conception of method was not erroneous, but was incomplete. He was over-sanguine in believing that he had perfected so grand an idea as the systematic production of discoveries by machine methods in his own lifetime, when generations of effort might well be needed. 'I have provided the machine, but the stuff must be gathered from the facts of nature.' He spent his last years hurrying on this collection, but he realized that the complete explanation of nature would take much longer than he had supposed. Six months before he died, he wrote that he tried to carry his work as far as he could because he worked 'for posterity; these things required ages for their accomplishment'.

His conception of the possibility of a comprehensive method of discovery was probably one of the causes of his critical attitude to the work of his greatest contemporaries, such as Gilbert and Galileo. He remarked that scientists 'spend their labour in working out some one experiment, as Gilbert with the magnet', and that 'he has himself become a magnet; that is, he has ascribed too many things to that force . . .'. Gilbert produced a theory of the motions of the universe in terms of magnetic force.

Galileo's discoveries with the telescope were 'all indeed noble, so far as we may safely trust to demonstrations of this kind; which I regard with suspicion chiefly because the experiment stops with these few discoveries, and many other things equally worthy of investigation are not discovered by the same means'.

Bacon's criticisms of Gilbert and Galileo have occasioned much surprise and condemnation. They follow naturally from his conception of a method of research which discovers not only particular things and theories, but reveals the complete explanation of all nature. Bacon was not satisfied with a method which advanced only in darts here and there, and not simultaneously on all fronts. The Galilean method could result only in a lop-sided advance, in which a great deal was learned about a few things, and nothing about others equally important. It has provided us with a mass of insufficiently organized knowledge, some of it extremely potent and very dangerous, in which the research necessary in 'ethics and politics', as well as in physical science, for the discovery of how this knowledge may be safely utilized and controlled, has not been carried out. Bacon may have distrusted the conventional method of research because he foresaw the kind of situation in which we now find ourselves.

Bacon did not exhibit much skill in the Galilean method of research. His own doctor, William Harvey, who had studied in Padua when Galileo was in his prime, and became one of the greatest masters of his method of research, discovering the circulation of the blood by its means, does not seem to have influenced him. Bacon left no reference to Harvey's discovery, but he made a remark about the strange ideas of his doctors. He may have been thinking of Harvey. Harvey's opinion of Bacon's ideas on science has been recorded in a famous note by John Aubrey, who said that Harvey had told him that he much esteemed Bacon for his wit and style, 'but would not allow him to be a great Philosopher. He writes Philosophy like a Lord Chancellor'. Aubrey said he was 'speaking in derision'. In his own works Harvey refers to Bacon as 'learned'.

Today we see that one of Bacon's greatest merits was that he wrote on science like a Lord Chancellor, that is, an experienced and responsible statesman, and not as a clever specialist skilful in solving particular technical problems. Nowadays there are large numbers of skilful specialists capable of solving technical problems by the conventional method, but few heads of states who can administer science as an integral part of modern life and the basis of social development.

Aubrey is an invaluable authority because he is so often the only one, but he is not a very reliable reporter, and it is impossible to say how exact his record of Harvey's comment is, and how far it was coloured by subsequent conversations with later scientists, when the Galilean method had been more widely accepted.

Assessing the comparative merits of Bacon and Galileo, the eminent mathematician John Playfair, who had a leading part in reviving English mathematics at the beginning of the nineteenth century, remarked in 1824 that more than one scientist in history could have done what Galileo did, but no other man in history could have done what Bacon did. Galileo was essentially a great technician and specialist, whereas Bacon was a universal figure, combining work for the destinies of science and of the human race in a unique manner.

Bacon first thought of the possibility of discovering a new method of discovery while he was still a young student at Cambridge. He was disgusted by the degenerate Aristotelianism in vogue, and conceived that a better method of discovery must be possible. He found hints of how to discover this better method in the work of Peter Ramus, of whom he probably heard much when he was in Paris, attached as a youth to the British Embassy. Ramus had defended for his doctorate at the Sorbonne the thesis that all Aristotle's propositions are wrong, and had suggested an improved system of logic. Bacon saw how to develop this idea, and thereby succeeded in advancing inductive logic substantially beyond the stage in which it had been left by Aristotle.

After conceiving an improved method of discovery and making some progress in developing it, he considered for what purpose it might be used. It seemed to him that its most important use was to find out all those things which could be of benefit to man. The new method was to be used for solving all the problems of nature, of which the problems of life were a part. It was to be applied to the elucidation not only of the workings of living organisms, but also of human society.

At about the age of twenty-three, 'with great confidence', he described this double conception of the new method, and the uses to which it was to be put, under the 'magnificent title' of *The Greatest Birth of Time*.

He pursued the notion ever after, 'believing that it proceeded from the providence and infinite goodness of God'. He felt confirmed in this because the ardour and constancy of his mind in this pursuit never grew old nor cooled, even after forty years, because 'it seems, by reason of its infinite utility, to enjoy the sanction and favour of God, the all-good and all-mighty'.

We shall follow Bacon in his attempt to realize this great idea of developing and utilizing science for 'the glory of the Creator, and the relief of man's estate'. This had two main but in his opinion inseparable parts, one concerned with the development of science, and the other with the art of government. He therefore studied the nature and possibilities of science and practised politics simultaneously. He aimed at being a whole man, to qualify for dealing with the total problem of mankind.

In spite of the attractions of ambition, his inclination was towards the contemplative life. At the age of thirty-one, which he regarded as already 'somewhat ancient', he informed his uncle Lord Burghley, in the course of soliciting him for a government appointment, that he confessed to 'vast contemplative ends', and that he had 'taken all knowledge to be his province'. He had, however, the most 'moderate civil ends', and only wanted 'a place of any reasonable countenance', which he needed because it would 'bring commandment of more wits than a man's own', and this would be of great assistance to him in reforming science.

Bacon wondered why this application for a position in the civil service was unsuccessful. In spite of his intelligence there were stretches of imperceptiveness in his behaviour which appeared to be somewhat abnormal. He was sometimes naive, and he could be ridiculous. His English prose, in its simple words, reflected a passionate desire to be clear. He said that 'Words are the footsteps of reason', a phrase which echoes the measured tread of his style. It was fundamentally unsuited for deception. His presentation of devious policies in a transparently clear style was unconvincing, and was one of the causes which made people distrust him.

Bacon's mental characteristics are less baffling to the modern psychologist than they were to his contemporaries and successors.

When he was forty-five, and had not yet received his first official appointment, he said in a letter to Sir Thomas Bodley that since he had been 'of any understanding' his mind had in effect been absent from what he had done, and 'in absence are many errors', which he willingly acknowledged. The greatest error which led to the rest was that, 'knowing myself by inward calling to be fitter to hold a book than to play a part, I have led my life in civil causes; for which I am not very fit by nature, and more unfit by the preoccupation of my mind'.

Bacon thought of following the example of Bodley, who had withdrawn from politics into private life after, like Bacon, being deceived by Sir Robert Cecil. Bodley had retired to Oxford and founded the Bodleian Library, which Bacon described as 'an Ark to save learning from deluge'. Bacon played with the idea of seeking some similar position, as head of Westminster School, Eton, Winchester, 'Maudlin College in Oxford', St. Johns College in Cambridge, and especially Trinity College in Cambridge. This would enable him to command more 'wits and pens', and he thought of approaching the King, the Archbishop of Canterbury and the Lord Treasurer to explore the possibilities.

Fortunately, and just not too late, James I appointed Bacon Solicitor-General, and saved him from withdrawing into academic life, where his career could have been relatively of only secondary importance. As a man of affairs, and continuing his scientific studies, he was able to learn from practical experience the technique a scientist must possess if he desires to obtain the political power necessary to ensure the proper utilization of science in the state. He became the first statesman of science, with the kind of qualifications required in the government of a scientific age. He thereby made a contribution higher in kind than any which can be made by an academic scientist as such.

He rose to be Lord Chancellor, or chief minister under James, and attempted the twin task of administering the country and starting the systematic development and utilization of science. He showed the way towards the solution of our own great problem; the proper utilization of science in human life. But he failed to secure any immediate collaborators. He tried to pursue his twin tasks alone, and ultimately broke down, revealing incidentally some of the weaknesses that beset the scientist in acquiring and exercising political power. He depended far too much on securing the confidence and attempting to influence a few powerful persons, such as the King and his favourites. His habits of intellectual concentration inclined him to concentrate on individuals, and disqualified him for mixing with ordinary men. He recommended his isolation and lack of friends to the King as a qualification for political advancement, but it prevented him from becoming a political leader. When he failed to convert the King to his own views on the rôle of science, he found himself with no other means for getting his ideas carried out. This applied to his political as well as his scientific policies. He provided James with numerous constructive proposals, which had little effect. He was unable to form parties to pursue his programmes. This failure illustrates the importance of collective action for securing the development and utilization of science.

Bacon learned enough of statesmanship to draft a statesman-like programme for science. This was the explanation of his extraordinary influence on those scientists in succeeding centuries, such as Boyle and d'Alembert, who had experience of the world as well as of the laboratory and the study. Scientists exclusively interested in experimental and theoretical research did not understand the chief point of Bacon's work. Harvey told Aubrey that Bacon wrote on science 'like a Lord Chancellor'. But this was the very essence of Bacon's achievement, that he did not write on science narrowly from the technical point of view.

Though Bacon provided the first statesman-like programme for science, he had no immediate success in introducing it, because of his lack of personal political power. Planned science and planned society could not be carried out without the appropriate political instruments. It would have been too much to have expected Bacon to have created these, in addition to the programme.

Scientists today have the same kind of political difficulties as

Bacon in attempting to secure the adequate development and utilization of science. The lack of experience in politics, together with continued scientific effort produce a strain which is liable to cause them to break down on difficult problems of behaviour. Bacon placed loyalty to the state above loyalty to friends. He had to choose between Buckingham, who was James's favourite and executive, and departure from political life, which would have frustrated his unique achievement in combining science and politics. His decision to serve Buckingham as long as Buckingham virtually ruled the state was the condition which enabled him to learn statesmanship from experience. He bought this essential experience at great cost, as Buckingham insisted that Bacon should influence the course of justice in favour of his relatives and friends. Considering the pressure to which Bacon had to submit from a corrupt Court, the concessions he made were remarkably small. But they provided the lever for his personal political overthrow, though not until his main achievement had been accomplished.

The scientist-politician of today, the statesman of science, is also confronted with difficult moral problems. They may not be specifically the same as those that troubled Bacon, but they spring from the same fundamental conflicts between personal interest and social duty, which arise in every scientist who tries to be simultaneously a good research worker and a good citizen.

The call for the fullest development and application of science, for the endowment of laboratories, the education of scientists and the provision of good working conditions and salaries, is now widely understood. The vast possibilities for the improvement of human life by the advance and use of science have been extensively explained and appreciated. The greatest difficulties now are not in getting the possibilities of science understood and creating the necessary organization for achieving them, but in solving the moral and social problems of how to behave within the organization, and in the crucial region where science and politics interact.

In the past the scientist usually evaded all responsibility for the social effects of his discoveries. He could do this with impunity, because the effects were often not very great, and in any case slow. But he cannot do this now, because his discoveries are having a very much more comprehensive and quicker effect, and can cause immediate catastrophe. He cannot, without crippling his own human nature, avoid making moral decisions on the way in which his discoveries are used.

Bacon's programme for science, and his demands for all those means for its advancement, are pursued and echo through the world. But today, the significance of his moral difficulties transcends even these.

As the first scientist to enter politics on a major scale primarily for scientific ends, he was the first to wrestle on this scale with the moral difficulties of the scientist in politics. How far should a scientist make concessions to morality to obtain political power, if the future and the survival of the human race are at stake? What if his only hope of preventing the destruction of humanity rests on accommodating himself to the Buckinghams of this world? Should he retire from politics, and leave the Buckinghams to blow the world to pieces? Or should he enter the fray, even at the risk of being polluted?

Bacon, who entered politics to obtain the political power to use science for the restoration of man to his position before the fall, struggled with problems of political behaviour which trouble the scientists of today who wish to see their work used for the good of mankind. He believed that man could be saved only by those who loved him. He held that those who loved mankind must, because of this love, accord the first place in dignity to the pursuit of science for the benefit of man. This was the highest sanction for engaging in scientific research.

To him, the pursuit of science merely for its own sake was a selfish activity. This did not mean that he was opposed to the pursuit of pure science. He regarded this as a duty to the Creator, to reveal all the depths and subtleties of His glories, and also as the primary key to the applied science which would solve mankind's particular problems and satisfy man's needs.

Bacon's message to the scientist of today is to take his part in politics and social life, and fight for the proper development and use of science for the benefit of mankind, even if, in the course of the struggle, he suffers injuries, material and moral. Bacon chose the course personally dangerous to himself, and did not escape all the dangers that beset him, but it was the only course by which modern man can save himself, and the human race.

For this reason, he is the greatest prophet of the modern world.

In his pursuit of political place and power he deviated in the direction of personal ambition, though he never lost the guidance of his deepest inspiration, which ultimately brought him through all situations to serve science rather than himself. His ambition for himself and his ambition for mankind were sometimes conflicting, and sometimes mutually supporting. He oscillated dangerously between them.

He believed that 'magnificence' was essential in the style of life of the statesman of the first rank. It was a necessary part of statesmanlike dignity. The notion was not congruous with the ideas of the rising merchant classes. They tended to measure all things in cash values, and regarded Bacon's 'magnificence' as vanity. He inherited little wealth and had no business interests or aptitudes. He fell into accepting gifts to support a style of life which was not understood or approved by the classes who were coming to power and forming public opinion. The gifts he accepted had no fundamental influence on his administration of justice, as he had not accepted them with that end in view.

But all social transactions were being regarded more and more from the contract and business point of view. They were evaluated according to the new business ethics. The persons who gave Bacon gifts with the intention of influencing his decisions in pending legal cases were extremely angry with him because their payments had no effect. They regarded him as a scoundrel not because he had accepted their gifts, but because he gave nothing in exchange; he broke his contracts. He had had the audacity to treat their gifts as if they had had no exchange-value. The businessmen were outraged. They regarded him as the most dastardly kind of swindler, a person who undermined the system of business morals. He was particularly hated and held in contempt by Lionel Cranfield, the only new businessman to achieve high place under James. Bacon, for his part, described Cranfield as a 'base fellow'; he did not believe that businessmen should be admitted to the ruling class.

Though Bacon had not the qualities required to create and lead a party, he paid a great deal of attention to the principles of propaganda as a means of influencing opinion. He drafted his ideas in various styles, to try by experience which would be the most effective. He used the imagination to depict a society which was scientifically organized, showing what kind of institutions it would require. His *New Atlantis* is an essay in forecasting the future and thereby inspiring it, which he called 'feigned history'.

C

It is a major example of the art that has latterly been so much debased under the name of 'science fiction'.

He tried to spread his ideas by systematic expositions of science for the reading public. He pursued this 'dissemination of scientific knowledge' as a means of preparing men's minds for understanding and acting upon his proposals for a scientific human society, an age of science.

In spite of his utmost efforts, Bacon succeeded only partially in combining his ambition for himself and for mankind in a harmonious unity. As high political place was necessary for the accomplishment of his aims for mankind, his desire for place was prompted by mixed motives, one of personal ambition and the other of public good. In his political career his personal ambition often predominated, though never wholly.

The imperfect integration of his life caused him to pursue his two ambitions, in spite of himself, to a considerable extent in separate compartments, oscillating from one to the other. His career can be seen as the outcome of the conflict between these two motives, sometimes reinforcing, sometimes frustrating each other.

In this book, the account of his life and work has been presented in two parts. The first part, *For Mankind*, expounds and analyses his proposals for the development of science and its application to the conquest of the universe for the benefit of man. The second part, *For Himself*, describes the sequence of events in his life, and deals especially with his personal ambitions and problems.

PART I

For Mankind

1. *The Conquest of the Universe*

BACON pursued his project for the conquest of the universe with inflexible tenacity throughout his life. As his personal difficulties increased, so did his determination. Like Milton, who studied his works, he spent his last years in political defeat, but worked with redoubled intensity on the furtherance of his great project for the human race.

In his younger days he drew up a plan of campaign, in which he defined the strategic objectives of mankind, and the intellectual tactics which it must pursue to attain them. As a lawyer by profession, he attempted to secure the acceptance of his plan by expressing it in terms of the ideas and beliefs of his contemporaries. He represented it as the restoration of man to his place before the Fall when he was master of the world. Man by his expulsion from the Garden of Eden had been committed to a life of work; only by labour in the sweat of his brow could he secure his bread. Bacon pointed out that this principle of work contained the means by which man could retrieve his original position, provided that it was systematically developed. He therefore proposed that 'work' should be taken seriously and developed systematically as the means not only for supplying man's needs but for mastering the world. It should not be undertaken in the spirit of a reluctant beast, but in that of a being of intelligence.

Work undertaken intelligently becomes science. Thus the development and application of science was the means by which man could retrieve his original position. Following God's precepts and with His benevolent approval, man could, if he set about it, convert the universe into a new Garden of Eden of which he would be master.

Bacon therefore called his project for the conquest of the universe the *Great Instauration*, which meant the restoration of man through science to his place before the Fall. He believed that he had thereby made his project completely conformable with the Christian religion, so that it could not be justifiably opposed on religious grounds, and should be supported by the Church as strengthening religion.

This mode of presentation in terms of religious conformity had a considerable effect during the first hundred years after the publication of his plan. Religious men such as Robert Boyle, and scientific divines such as Thomas Sprat found it helpful to have at hand a justification of scientific research in terms of religion. But later on the word 'instauration' fell out of use, so that few, even among scientists, know what meaning Bacon gave it.

Bacon's presentation of his ideas in modes acceptable to his contemporaries has had the effect of disguising them from ourselves who have different modes. Yet Bacon's conscious concern with presentation has made him one of the forerunners of the modern art of propaganda. In his attacks on Aristotle and Plato he experimented with different modes of presentation, trying a persuasive style in one draft, and in another 'discoursing scornfully of the ancients', on the principle that an aggressive self-confidence might make more impression on those readers who are apt to take a man at his own valuation and assume that if he speaks peremptorily he must be right. His early editor Peter Shaw wrote in 1733 that one might 'be at a loss to know what the author was driving at in this piece'.

Today, we have no difficulty in seeing that he was trying to find different forms of presentation to appeal to different types of reader. His conscious attention to the technique of presenting his ideas in terms of contemporary beliefs contributed to his great success as a propagandist. In some ways he was even too successful. Many readers were left with the impression that he had not only been the chief advocate of the cultivation of science and of converting the method of scientific research into a conscious process, and had launched mankind into the modern scientific era, but that he was also the inventor of the method of scientific research at present in use, the instrument by which science has been brought to its present condition.

When science was mainly an affair of amateurs and academics, and not socially of immediate importance, propaganda for science did not seem very important. The attitude of the majority of scientists, who were independent gentlemen or professors, was that science was an affair of pure curiosity, which the scientist pursued entirely at his own will, and that the public could take it or leave it.

One of the most vigorous expressions of this point of view was given by Liebig, who in his earlier years, without reading Bacon closely, had accepted the common misconception that he was the creator of the modern scientific method, as well as the chief propagandist for science. In his later years he read Bacon more thoroughly, and discovered that he was by no means a scientist after his own pattern. He found that Bacon had only a limited appreciation, and seemed to have only an incomplete understanding of the modern scientific method. He felt that he had been deceived. He noted numerous errors in Bacon's experiments and scientific information, and that he was not a scientist in his own sense. Liebig conceived scientific discovery in terms of the effort of the individual; it was the result of something that went on in one man's mind. His attack on Bacon's notion of discovery as the result of a co-operative mechanical effort is all the more interesting because Liebig's own work was one of the principle contributions leading to modern team research. By his invention of improved methods he increased the speed of chemical analysis by a factor of a hundred and, as Hofmann pointed out, helped to make it possible, through the simplicity of his technique, for men of modest talent to do useful work in research in organic chemistry. This provided the technical conditions for the creation of the modern chemical industry.

For Liebig, too, the skill of the individual scientist was far more important than propaganda for science. Today we are forced to qualify this view. For us, propaganda for science in the development and government of human affairs is as important as technical skill, and Bacon comes into his own again.

While Bacon's adoption of modes of presentation appropriate to his age promoted his great early success, it also contributed to the later misunderstandings. As the fashion in beliefs changed, the old mode became a hindrance to the communication of his ideals in a new age. The news-editor of our times would find the Conquest of the Universe a more suitable title than the Great Instauration.

In 1620, when he was fifty-nine years old, and Lord Chancellor, he published an outline of his plan as an introduction to his chief work, the *Great Instauration*. The largest and most complete part was devoted to his new method of research, the

Novum Organum. Consequently, the book came to be known not by its original title, but by the title of this part. The passing-over of Bacon's general conception, and concentration on his technique was characteristic of the narrowing of outlook as science became more specialized. It has caused much confusion in understanding him.

Most of the book consisted of an exposition of his method, which was to replace the old one described nearly two thousand years before by Aristotle in the work entitled the *Organon.* His method was therefore the *New Organon,* or *Novum Organum.* Bacon had been utterly disgusted by the degenerate Aristotel-ianism which was taught in Cambridge, and chose this title to describe the method he had worked out to supersede it. By calling it the *New Organon* he gave honour to Aristotle himself.

The *Novum Organum* was only a means to an end. The end itself was the *Great Instauration.*

He wanted to make his general plan known, though he had made only preliminary contributions towards carrying it out, in case he should not have a subsequent opportunity, owing to absorption in state affairs, ill-health, mischance or death. It was drawn up in six parts. The first was to consist of a review of existing knowledge, the second of his improved method of scientific discovery, the third a natural history of the universe, the fourth the results of a general application of the improved method of discovery, the fifth provisional results pending the perfection of the method, and the sixth the philosophy that arises from the performance of the five preceding parts.

He explained that the first part, containing a 'summary or general description of the knowledge which the human race at present possesses', had not yet been composed, though some account of it was to be found in the second book of his *Advance-ment of Learning.*

He did not propose merely to survey these regions in his mind, 'but to enter them like a general who means to take possession'. After 'having thus coasted past the ancient arts' his next point, in part two, was 'to equip the intellect for passing beyond'. He proposed to advance, armed with a new intellectual weapon, which would raise and exalt the mind, so that it would be 'made capable of overcoming the difficulties and obscurities of nature'. This was 'a kind of logic; though the difference between it and the ordinary logic is great; indeed immense. For the ordinary logic indeed professes to contrive and prepare helps and guards for the understanding, as mine does; and in this one point they agree. But mine differs from it in three points especially; viz. in the end aimed at; in the order of demonstration; and in the starting point of the enquiry.

'For the end which this science of mine proposes is the invention not of arguments but of arts; not of things in accordance with principles, but of principles themselves; not of probable reasons, but of designations and directions for works. And as the intention is different, so accordingly is the effect; the effect of the one being to overcome an opponent in argument, of the other to command nature in action.'

He regarded his *Novum Organum* as a considerable contribution to the second part of the plan, exhibiting the 'art itself of interpreting nature, and of the truer exercise of the intellect'. It did not, however, expound the art 'in the form of a regular treatise, but only in a summary digested into aphorisms', or short pithy maxims.

He outlined his conception of a natural history for the third part of the plan, 'such as may serve for the foundation of a true philosophy', in his Preparative towards a Natural and Experimental History, or *Parasceve*. It would be a work of very great size, labour and expense, requiring the participation of many people, and the support of kings or popes. 'The materials on which the intellect has to work are so widely spread, that one must employ factors and merchants to go everywhere in search of them and bring them in.' He thought that while he had not the strength to perform this labour, he might be able himself to carry out the intellectual work, and he held it to 'be somewhat beneath the dignity of an undertaking' like this that he should spend his own time 'in a matter which is open to almost every man's industry'. With sufficient help, he believed the compilation of this preparatory or *mother* natural history, though vast, might be completed in his own lifetime. Though the compilation did not require more than moderate abilities, it was absolutely essential for the advancement of science, for 'if all the wits of all the ages had met or shall hereafter meet together; if the whole human race had applied or shall hereafter apply themselves to philosophy, and the whole earth had been or shall be nothing but academies and colleges and schools of learned men; still without a natural and experimental history such as I am going to prescribe, no progress worthy of the human race could have been made or can be made in philosophy and the sciences. Whereas on the other hand, let such a history be once provided and well set forth, and let there be added to it such auxiliary and light-giving experiments as in the very course of interpretation will present themselves or will have to be found out, and the investigation of nature and of all sciences will be the work of a few years. This therefore must be done, or the business must be given up. For in this way, and in this way only, can the foundations of a true and active philosophy be established; and then will men awake as from deep sleep, and at once perceive what a difference there is between the dogmas and figments of the wit and a true and active philosophy, and what it is in questions of nature to consult nature herself.'

Bacon provided a catalogue of 126 subjects of which particular histories should be made. These covered the mineral, vegetable, animal and human species, and the chief physical and biological sciences, including psychology and mathematics. About one-third of his subjects were practical, from cookery to wool manufacture, and from agriculture to metal-working; but' I care little about the mechanical arts themselves; only about those things which they contribute to the equipment of philosophy.'

This catalogue of subjects provided the French encyclopaedists with much inspiration. In it are hints towards the foundation of new sciences. There should be a 'History of the Figure and External Limbs of Man, his Stature, Frame, Countenance and Features; and of the variety of the same according to Races and Climates, or other small differences.' Here comparative anthropology is foreshadowed.

Bacon compiled several sections of this 'natural and experimental history for the foundation of philosophy'. He believed that the whole of the natural and experimental history required for the third part of his plan could be covered in about six times the length of Pliny's *Natural History*. His own writings contained about one-twentieth of what he estimated would be necessary to cover the whole of natural history. He succeeded in writing his histories of the Winds; Life and Death, and Dense and Rare, together with some prefaces and notes for others. He spent the last months of his life in compiling a further large volume on natural history, which he called *Sylva Sylvarum*, or a collection of collections of data and information. It was a summary of contemporary popular works.

Thus he had provided a substantial contribution to the first three parts of the plan. On this basis it would be possible to proceed to the fourth part. 'And now that we have surrounded the intellect with faithful helps and guards, and got together with most careful selection a regular army of divine works, it may seem that we have no more to do but to proceed to philosophy itself.' Yet the matter was so difficult and doubtful that examples of his method should be set forth, 'in which the entire process of the mind and the whole fabric and order of invention from the beginning to the end, in certain subjects, and those various and remarkable, should be set as it were before the eyes'.

This proved so 'difficult and doubtful' that Bacon did not succeed in supplying any such 'actual types and models'. None of his works can be identified as definitely forming a contribution to part four of his plan.

Part five was to include such things as he had himself 'discovered, proved, or added—not however according to the true rules and methods of interpretation, but by the ordinary use of the understanding in inquiring and discovering'. As these conclusions had not been 'discovered and proved by the true form of interpretation', he would not bind himself to them. He did not leave any contribution to part five.

As for the sixth or final part, this was to contain the result of the application of his new method of discovery to all phenomena of the world. But he was unable to deliver this because 'the completion however of this last part is a thing both above my strength and beyond my hopes. I have made a beginning of the work— a beginning, as I hope, not unimportant:—the fortune of the human race will give the issue;—such an issue, it may be, as in the present condition of things and men's minds cannot easily be conceived or imagined. For the matter in hand is no mere felicity of speculation, but the real business and fortunes of the human race, and all power of operation. For man is but the servant and interpreter of nature: what he does and what he knows is only what he has observed of nature's order in fact or in thought; beyond this he knows nothing and can do nothing. For the chain of causes cannot by any force be loosed or broken, nor can nature be commanded except by being obeyed. And so those twin objects, human Knowledge and human Power, do really meet in one; and it is from ignorance of causes that operation fails.'

2. *The General Staff*

WHILE Bacon was making 'collections of collections' of data for the composition of 'divine works', he also outlined the social and political organization which would be required for carrying out his project, which was not the business of one man, of however great genius, but of the whole human race. He sketched this in his *New Atlantis*. 'This fable my Lord devised', wrote his secretary Rawley, 'to the end that he might exhibit therein a model or description of a college instituted for the interpreting of nature and the producing of great and marvellous works for the benefit of men. . . .'

In it he envisaged a General Staff directing mankind's conquest of nature, and organizing human society on scientific principles. He supposed that the new social order had been worked out in an isolated land in an utterly unknown part of the South Sea. A European ship, with a crew of fifty-one, had sailed from Peru for China and Japan, but had been caught by calms and contrary winds and been driven off its course. The ship's company, finding themselves 'in the midst of the greatest wilderness of waters in the world', and their victuals exhausted, feared they were lost and prepared for death. They prayed that they might reach land, and next day about evening, they saw clouds which raised their hopes. On the following morning land was sighted, 'full of boscage', and within an hour or two 'the port of a fair city; not great indeed, but well-built, and that gave a pleasant view from the sea'. They 'offered to land', but many people on the shore 'without any cries or fierceness' forbade them to do so. A boat put off, whose officer came aboard their ship 'without any show of distrust at all'. He presented them with a scroll in Hebrew, Greek, Latin and Spanish which read: 'Land not, all of you; and provide to be gone from this coast within sixteen days, except you have further time given you. . . .' But 'if you want fresh water, or victual, or help for your sick, or that your ship needeth repair, write down your wants, and you shall have that which belongeth to mercy'.

They were troubled by the denial of landing, but comforted on finding that the people 'had languages and were so full of humanity'. They informed them that one-third of their company were very sick, and if not permitted to land, would be in danger of their lives. They offered money and merchandise in exchange for supplies, but these were not accepted, nor scarcely noticed.

Some hours later 'a great person' came in a boat towards the ship. He told them that he had been 'Warned by the Conservator of Health of the City that he should keep a distance' in case their sick men were infectious. On being assured that they were not, he said that they could come ashore and stay in the Strangers' House.

They found this had good hospital facilities and an excellent store of supplies, as very few visitors came from abroad. In fact, there had been none for thirty-seven years. They offered the personage a gratuity, but this was refused, as he said 'he had salary sufficient of the state for his service'.

After they had been comfortably settled in, they were told that 'ye are to know that the custom of the land requireth, that after this day and tomorrow . . . you are to keep within doors for three days. But let it not trouble you, nor do not think yourselves restrained, but rather left to your rest and ease. You shall want nothing, and there are six of our people appointed to attend you, for any business you may have abroad.'

They gave 'thanks with all affection and respect, and said "God surely is manifested in this land"'. A tip was again offered, and again smilingly refused. Soon after, dinner was served, 'which was right good viands, both for bread and meat: better than any collegiate diet that I have known in Europe'.

On the next day they reviewed their position. They thanked God for their deliverance, and in gratitude every man felt called upon to 'reform his own ways'. Yet they could not refrain from remarking that they had been confined, though courteously, for three days. 'Who knoweth whether it be not to take some taste of our manners and conditions? . . . for these men that they have given us for attendance may withal have an eye upon us.' The company spent their 'three days joyfully and without care' and their sick 'thought themselves cast into some divine pool of healing, they mended so kindly and so fast'.

There appeared 'a new man that they had not seen before'. They 'saluted him in a very lowly and submissive manner'.

thinking that they might receive from him 'sentence of life or death'. He proved to be the Governor of the House of Strangers, and informed them that 'the state has given you licence to stay on land for the space of six weeks', and he intimated that they need not worry about future extensions of their visas, 'for the law in this point is not precise', and he had no doubt that he would himself be able to secure any such further stay as they might desire. If they had any request to make they were to 'hide it not', and they would find that they would not be disappointed. They were, however, not to go more than a mile and a half from the city 'without especial leave'.

The next day the Governor visited them again, and told them that the island on which they found themselves was called Bensalem. Owing to its solitary situation, and 'the laws of secrecy which we have for our travellers, and our rare admission of strangers, we know well most parts of the habitable world, and are ourselves unknown'.

The company were extremely curious to know how this could be, and summoned up courage to ask the Governor for an explanation. Notwithstanding all the remote discoveries and navigations of the last age, Europe had never heard the least rumour of this island. 'This we found wonderful strange; for that all nations have inter-knowledge one of another either by voyage into foreign parts, or by strangers that come from them . . . it seemed to us a condition and propriety of divine powers and beings, to be hidden and unseen by others, and yet to have others open and as in a light to them.'

The sailors commented that there appeared to be somewhat of the supernatural in the island, but it was of the angelical rather than the magical variety. They continued to be deeply interested in the 'laws of secrecy touching strangers'. They asked the Governor most tactfully for further light on it. He said that there were some particulars which it was not lawful for him to reveal, but there would be enough that could be revealed to give them satisfaction.

He described how, three thousand years ago, navigation of the world had been much more common than in their time. Many men had found 'the great Atlantis, that you call America'. The population was large and flourishing. Then came a catastrophic inundation, by which it was 'utterly lost and destroyed'. There were left only a few mountains above the flood.

'So as marvel you not at the thin population of America, nor
at the rudeness and ignorance of the people; for you must
account your inhabitants of America as a young people; younger
a thousand years, at the least, than the rest of the world, for that
there was so much time between the universal flood and their
particular inundation. For the poor remnant of human seed
which remained in their mountains peopled the country again
slowly, by little and little; and being simple and savage people,
(not like Noah and his sons, which was the chief family of the
earth) they were not able to leave letters, arts and civility to their
posterity; and having likewise in their mountainous habitations
been used (in respect of the extreme cold of those regions) to
clothe themselves with the skins of tigers, bears, and great
hairy goats, that they have in those parts; when after they came
down into the valley, and found the intolerable heats which are
there, and knew no means of lighter apparel, they were forced to
begin the custom of going naked, which continueth at this
day.'

They were able, though, to 'take great pride and delight in
the feathers of birds' which had risen in 'infinite flights' to the
mountain-heights at the time of the inundation.

Bensalem's chief traffic and commerce had been with the old
Atlantis, so the disaster had greatly reduced her connexions with
other nations. It had been followed also by a decay in the art of
navigation. Consequently, 'that part of intercourse which could
be from other nations to sail to us . . . hath long since ceased,
except it were by some rare accident, as this of yours'.

The cessation of 'that other part of intercourse, which might
be by our sailing to other nations' had, however, quite a different
explanation. Their ships and navigators were as many and great
as ever: 'therefore why should we sit at home?'

Nineteen hundred years before, they had had a king, 'whose
memory of all others we most adore; not superstitiously, but as
a divine instrument, though a mortal man; his name was Solamona; and we esteem him as the lawgiver of our nation. This king
had a *large heart*, inscrutable for good; and was wholly bent to
make his kingdom and people happy.' He took into consideration how sufficient and substantive this land was to maintain itself without any aid at all of the foreigner; 'being five thousand
six hundred miles in circuit, and of rare fertility of soil in the
greatest part thereof'. He saw that it had sufficient resources to

be developed, and support a new social order without depending on, or being in contact with, other countries. Recalling 'the happy and flourishing estate' wherein the land then was, and that it might in a thousand ways be altered for the worse, but scarcely in any one for the better, he inclined to isolationism.

He therefore, 'doubting novelties, and commixture of manners', made the strict control of the admission of strangers one of the fundamental laws in the constitution. But he ensured that it should be administered with all humanity, making provision for any entering by accident and in a state of distress, as the ship's company had already seen from their own experience.

As, however, this king considered it against humanity to detain people against their will, and against policy that they should return and report to their own countries about the existence and condition of Bensalem, it was laid down that strangers should be offered 'very good conditions and means to live from the state'. They were to be retained not by force, but by their own choice in favour of the better conditions and more attractive life. The struggle to secure their adhesion was transferred from the field of force to that of ideology.

So successful were they, that in several ages no ship that reached them had ever returned, and only thirteen persons in all that time had chosen to return in one of their own ships. They were so few that probably nobody believed what they reported when they got home.

The citizens of Bensalem were, however, completely prohibited from travelling abroad, except on a special kind of official mission; thereby they succeeded in 'preserving the good which cometh by communicating with strangers, and avoiding the hurt'.

In explaining this, the Governor told them that the most preeminent of all of Solamona's acts 'was the erection and institution of an Order or Society which we call Salomon's House; the noblest foundation (as we think) that ever was upon the earth. . . . It is dedicated to the study of the Works and Creatures of God. . . .'

While voyages abroad were in general banned, one exception was made. Every twelve years two ships were sent out with 'a mission of three of the Fellows or Brethren of Salomon's House; whose errand was only to give us knowledge of the affairs and state of those countries to which they were designed, and especially of the sciences, arts, manufactures, and inventions of all the world, and withal to bring unto us books, instruments and patterns of every kind . . .'.

The Fellows had to stay abroad for twelve years, until picked up by the next mission. Meanwhile, they busily collected scientific knowledge and equipment, buying 'such things and rewarding such persons as they should think fit' from 'a good quantity of treasure'.

After hearing these delightful things, none of the ship's company wanted to go home. All took themselves 'now for free men', and 'lived most joyfully'. They went about in the city and were treated 'with such humanity, and such a freedom and desire to take strangers as it were into their bosom, as was enough to make us forget all that was dear to us in our own countries . . .'.

They learned that the people of Bensalem were the most chaste in the world. With them there were 'no stews, no dissolute houses, no courtesans, nor anything of that kind. . . . As for masculine love, they have no touch of it. . . .'

While hearing in detail about the differences between Bensalem and Europe in the matter of love, the company was informed that one of the Fathers of Salomon's House was expected in the city. Such visitations occurred scarcely once in a dozen years, and the cause of this one was secret. The company were given a good place from which to see his entry into the city.

'He was a man of middle stature and age, comely of person, and had an aspect as if he pitied men.' He wore a robe of fine black cloth, and was carried on a rich chariot 'adorned with crystal, save that the fore-end had pannels of sapphires, set in borders of gold, and the hinder-end the like of emeralds of the Peru colour . . .'. He was attended by fifty young men 'in white sattin loose coats to the mid-leg, and stockings of white silk; and shoes of blue velvet; and hats of blue velvet; with fine plumes of divers colours, set round like hat-bands . . .'.

Presently the company were informed that the Father would be happy to give them an audience. He blessed them all, and then their leader remained to receive a gift.

'I will give thee the greatest jewel I have,' he said. For he would tell him of the nature and organization of Salomon's House. First, he would set forth the end of the foundation, second the preparations and instruments used in their works. Third, the functions to which Fellows were assigned, and fourth their institutions and customs.

D

'The End of our Foundation is the knowledge of Causes, and
secret motions of things; and the enlarging of the bounds of
Human Empire, to the effecting of all things possible.'

They had caves dug three miles deep for the production of
'new artificial metals', towers 'about half a mile in height',
which, when placed on mountains enabled meteorological and
astronomical observations to be made at a height of three miles.
A number of hermits chose to live in the caves and on the towers,
in order to study the reactions of the body, and discover new
knowledge for the curing of disease and the prolongation of life.

They had 'great and spacious houses', where they imitated
meteors, snow, hail, rain, thunder, lightning and generations of
bodies in air, such as frogs and flies.

Large orchards and gardens were kept, 'not so much in
respect of beauty, as variety of ground and soil'. In these they
practised grafting, of wild as well as cultivated trees. They made
'by art . . . trees and flowers to come earlier or later than their
seasons; and to come up and bear more speedily than by their
natural course they do. We make them also by art greater much
than nature; and their fruit greater and sweeter and of differing
taste, smell, colour, and figure, from their nature. And many of
them we so order, as they become of medicinal use.'

They knew how to raise plants from 'mixtures of earths without seeds', and how to make new plants, and 'make one tree or
plant turn into another'.

In the zoological department, they tried poisons on animals
to discover their value for surgery and medicine. They knew,
too, how to make animals taller or shorter, and how to alter their
colour. They made 'commixtures and copulations of different
kinds' which produced new animals that were not barren.

The food industry was extensively developed, providing
'divers drinks, breads, and meats, rare and of special effects'.
There was a far wider range of drugs than in Europe, and they
had subtle methods of distillation and separation by which they
produced substances of 'exact forms of composition', which were
identical with, and had the same properties as, drugs of natural
origin.

They had various medicinal arts unknown to Europe, and
many kinds of furnaces; also instruments 'which generate heat
only by motion'.

They had 'perspective-houses', where they investigated light and radiation. Bacon's imagination seemed to be groping here towards photography and the cinema, besides research on light. 'Out of things uncoloured and transparent, we can represent unto you all several colours; not in rain-bows, as it is in gems and prisms, but of themselves single.' One wonders at what stage in his development Isaac Newton read this, and what he thought of it.

They were well-equipped, too, with telescopes and microscopes.

In their sound-houses they had discovered new forms of music, and had 'certain helps which set to the ear do further the hearing greatly'. They had loud-speakers, and speaking-tubes, and artificial voices which articulated sounds and letters and imitated the notes of beasts and birds.

They had perfume-houses for investigating smells and tastes. 'We multiply smells, which may seem strange. We imitate smells, making all smells to breathe out of other mixtures than those that give them.'

They had engine-houses, for making all sorts of motions, and some swifter 'than any you have'. They had 'some degree of flying in the air', and submarines, and 'some perpetual motions'.

Such was the kind of equipment possessed by the Fellows.

Their duties were distributed according to the tasks which had to be undertaken. Twelve of them were engaged on voyages into foreign countries. They sailed 'under the names of other nations, (for our own we conceal); who bring us the books, and abstracts, and patterns of experiments of all other parts'.

They supplied a kind of Central Institute of Scientific Information, collecting everything obtainable from the outside world.

They had three fellows who searched the literature for experiments; three for all mechanical arts, and also for the liberal sciences, and for the practices which are not yet brought into arts.

They had three who tried new experiments, and three who drew out axioms or theories from the work of the previous four classes of fellows. Three more fellows looked into the experiments of the others, 'to draw out of them things of use and practice for man's life, and knowledge . . .'.

Yet another three fellows, 'after divers meetings and consults of our whole number', devised new experiments, in the light of the general review of what had been already done, aimed at more fundamental discoveries, 'more penetrating into nature than the former'.

Then there were three 'that raise the former discoveries by experiments into greater observations, axioms, and aphorisms'. These most exalted fellows were called 'Interpreters of Nature'.

In addition they had many students and apprentices, and numerous technicians, both men and women.

Finally, 'we have consultations, which of the inventions and experiences which we have discovered shall be published, and which not; and take all an oath of secrecy, for the concealing of those which we think fit to keep secret: though some of those we do reveal sometimes to the state, and some not'.

They had 'two very long and fair galleries', one for models of 'the more rare and excellent inventions', and the other with statues of the greatest inventors and discoverers. There was Columbus, and the inventors of ships, guns, explosives, printing, astronomy, metal-working, glass, silk, etc. 'For every invention of value we erect a statua to the inventor, and give him a liberal and honourable reward.' They had their museum of science and technology.

'Lastly, we have circuits or visits of divers principal cities of the kingdom, where, as it cometh to pass, we do publish such new profitable inventions as we think good.'

They had their Association for the Advancement of Science.

The Father had now completed his description of Salomon's House and its activities. He blessed the leader of the company, and gave him leave to publish his account 'for the good of other nations; for we here are in God's bosom, a land unknown'.

Bacon put his story aside at this point. *New Atlantis* is 'a work unfinished'. Rawley said that Bacon had intended to include in the fable 'a frame of laws' for the 'best state or mould of a commonwealth', but his desire to compile the Natural History, 'which he preferred many degrees before it', diverted him. He regarded this as a more urgent and practical contribution to his great project.

Spedding regretted Bacon's decision, and said that he would have given the Natural History ten times over for 'an account of the laws, institutions and administration of Bensalem'. He considered that there is perhaps no single work of Bacon's 'which has so much of himself in it'. Salomon's House was the vision in which he lived, not of an ideal world released from natural conditions, 'but of our own world as it might be if we did our duty by it; of a state of things which he believed would one day be actually seen upon this earth such as it is by men such as we are; and the coming of which he believed that his own labours were sensibly hastening'.

The account of the people of Bensalem is an account of his own taste in humanity, 'for a man's ideal, though not necessarily a description of what he is, is almost always an indication of what he would be, and in the sober piety, the serious cheerfulness, the tender and gracious courtesy, the open-handed hospitality, the fidelity in public and chastity in private life, the grave and grace-ful manners, the order, decency, and earnest industry, which prevail among these people, we recognize an image of himself made perfect, of that condition of the human soul which he loved in others, and aspired towards in himself'.

The noble scholar of the nineteenth century interpreted Bacon's story primarily in terms of the individual. For us in the twentieth century, Bacon's own explicit exposition indicates that two things are necessary, and of equal importance: a correct plan and method, and correct individual behaviour.

3. *Strategic Objectives*

THE volume containing the original publication of the natural history *Sylva Sylvarum* and the *New Atlantis*, which was issued by Rawley in the year after Bacon's death, was con-cluded with a list, placed immediately after the *New Atlantis*, of the main strategic objectives in the struggle for the conquest and utilization of nature. This was given the title 'Great natural achievements especially in respect to their use by man.' They were discoveries which, Bacon conceived, would be of the greatest benefit to man.

Sherwood Taylor made a striking comparison of these ob-jectives with what has since been discovered on their respective topics. He drew up Bacon's list in one column, and a note of corresponding modern discoveries, up to the year 1941, in a parallel column. Even in the few years since that date, there have been many more discoveries and the first practical use of many older ones, such as nuclear weapons, tranquillizers, vernalization, rain-making, nylon and plastics, and the development of television, showing how Bacon's prevision continues to be confirmed.

BACON'S PROGRAMME	OUR RESULTS
The Prolongation of Life.	Expectation of life more than doubled, perhaps trebled, since his time.
The Restitution of Youth in some Degree.	'Monkey-gland' (*c.* 1920): sex-hormones synthesized (1938).
The Retardation of Age.	Very marked; largely owing to reduction of chronic septic conditions, modern dentistry, cosmetics, and contraceptives.
The Curing of Diseases counted Incurable.	The wholly incurable diseases are to-day a minority.
The Mitigation of Pain.	Aspirin: local anaesthetics, relief of intractable pain by nerve-surgery.
More Easie and less Loathsome Purgings.	Introduction of phenolphthalein, 'fruit salts', etc., and the abandonment of violent purging in Medicine.
The Encreasing of Strength and activity.	Stature of children (and of the race generally) greatly increased by better feeding and more exercise.
The Encreasing of Ability to Suffer Torture or pain.	Anaesthetics and Hypnotism.
The altering of Complexions[1] and Fatness and Lean-ness.	Hormone therapy: administering of thyroid extract or drugs to influence metabolism.
The altering of Statures.	Administration of pituitary extract can produce giants. Thyroid extract makes cretinous dwarfs become normal.
The altering of Features.	Plastic surgery.
The Encreasing and Exalting of Intellectual Parts.	Little progress here, save in so far as Education has been scientifically organized.
Version of Bodies into other Bodies	The myriad marvels of organic chemistry: silk from wood, dyes from coal.
Making of new Species.	Genetic experiments: especially influence of X-rays on the fruit-fly Drosophila.
Transplanting of one species into another.	Turkey-legs have been grafted into chicken embryos.

[1] *Complexion* in Bacon's day meant 'constitution' or 'habit of body', not the condition of the skin.

BACON'S PROGRAMME	OUR RESULTS
Instruments of Destruction as of War and Poison.	High explosive, machine-guns, poison-gas.
Exhilaration of the Spirits and putting them in good disposition.	A discovery still urgently required!
Force of the Imagination either upon another Body or upon the body itself.	Psychological treatment of neuroses and hysterical symptoms.
Acceleration of time in Maturations and clarifications.	Artificial ripening of spirits?
Acceleration of Putrefaction.	The septic tank: compounds such as 'Adco' for converting green stuff into manure.
Accleration of decoction.	Use of high-pressure boilers in large-scale cookery, etc.
Acceleration of Germination.	Little, if any, advance.
Making rich composts for the Earth.	The fertilizer industry.
Impressions of the Air and raising of Tempests.	Still not possible.
Great Alteration of Induration, Emollition, etc.	Notions not shared by modern science.
Turning Crude and Watry Substances into Oily and Unctuous substances.	Synthetic oils from coke and water.
Drawing of new Foods out of Substances not now in use.	Glucose from starch and cellulose. Margarine from fish oils, etc.
Making new Threds for Apparel and New Stuffs such as are Paper, Glass, etc.	Artificial silk, bakelite, celluloid, etc.
Natural Divinations.	Weather forecasts.
Deceptions of the Senses.	Scientific conjuring. The stereoscope.
Greater Pleasures of the Senses.	Cinema, radio, new musical instruments, new dyes.
Artificial Minerals and Cements.	Artificial stone, Portland cement, cultured pearls and synthetic jewels.

Sherwood Taylor commented that little progress was made towards any of these objectives in the first two centuries after Bacon enumerated them, but much during the last hundred years. They show that Bacon had a remarkable power of prediction on the future of science.

One of the most interesting features of the list is Bacon's close preoccupation with the most human needs of man. He does not beg for supernatural powers to gratify contemptible desires. Nor does he wish to perform astonishing but useless feats to impress people, as a means of bringing them under his control.

He foresaw new things, and new varieties of things, which would contribute to the better health and greater happiness of man. He did not emphasize the endless multiplication of quantities of goods, or the development of mechanical power, though he did not ignore these possibilities. He devised a scheme for raising water from 'drown'd mineral works'. The first effective steam engine was invented less than a century later for pumping water out of flooded mines. But he did not visualize in any very specific form the industrial revolution, in which machinery was developed and power made available in ever-increasing quantity. He had an intuition of it in a more profound form. He deliberately chose the phenomenon of heat as one of the most far-reaching principles in nature, and most worthy of investigation. This choice has generally been looked on as an accident, but the study of heat led to the development of the steam engine, the science of thermo-dynamics and the modern conception of energy. Of all the phenomena which he might have chosen, he chose the most vital one.

In Bacon's earlier works the idea of utilizing science for profit scarcely exists. His dominating idea was the use of science for the benefit of mankind as a whole. It was a social and not an individual aim.

In his later works, and especially after his fall, his conception tended to become narrower and lower. He frequently emphasized how the application of science can increase personal advantage and wealth. He speaks of the 'profits' to be made by the application of science to production. He pointed out these possibilities in an attempt to recommend himself to patrons when he was overwhelmed by debt and disaster. It was in these circumstances that the idea of the exploitation of science for profit first becomes noticeable in his works. Thus two motives for the development of science are found in Bacon's thought: one for the benefit of mankind and the other for profit. Consequently, he can be seen as the forerunner of both of these motives. But the first was dominant in Bacon's work. He would have questioned the anarchy that was characteristic of the utilization of science and technology in the industrial revolution as it occurred. It would have been repugnant to his ideas of social order.

4. *Can Scientists be Statesmen?*

BACON starts his campaign with a review of the social status and characteristics of learned men. He has already told us that the true end of knowledge 'is the benefit and relief of the state and society of man'. For him, then, the natural and the social scientists must be among the foremost of the learned. He says that their status has been depressed by the envy of the ignorant; by jealous priests, arrogant politicians and the imperfections of the learned themselves.

The priests contend that over-much knowledge caused the fall of man, and that knowledge 'has in it somewhat of the serpent'. It was not 'the pure knowledge of nature and the universe' which caused the fall, but the knowledge of good and evil. Natural science was guiltless of man's unhappiness. Bacon strives to separate science and religion, and consign the latter to a dignified seclusion, where it is treated with reverence, but ignored in the real business of life, which is the conquest of the universe in the interests of man. To the end of his days, Bacon regarded himself as a devout Christian, but he interpreted Christianity so that it could not interfere with, but would be a help and a protection for, the project he had at heart. He attributed great importance to the separation, because, in his opinion, it cleared the path for the undisturbed development of science. It prevented science from being frustrated by ignorant fanatics. Those things which were God's should be rendered to Him with the utmost conscientiousness, but those things which were nature's should be investigated in their own right. In practice, the former could be discharged by the performance of conventional observances. This gave freedom from spiritual anxiety, and conserved mental energy for the mastering of nature.

The scientist who correctly appraised his intellectual position would be a strictly orthodox Christian, and zealots would have no right to distract him from his proper work.

The criticism of the learned by politicians was more far-reaching. They said that learning softens men's minds. It makes them unsuited for the exercise of arms. It mars and perverts 'men's disposition for matter of government and policy', through irresolution caused by too great variety of reading, and by a peremptoriness arising from a too strict interpretation of principles, that is, from sectarianism. They lack a sense of proportion, tending to apply the lessons of major events in history to minor matters. They quote examples from the past which are too dissimilar from the events of their own times to be useful guides. The tendency to occupy their minds with ideas not appropriate to practical affairs tends to produce in them a separation between their mental preoccupations and 'action and business'. The conflict between their thoughts and the practical problems before them, causes them to drift into a 'love of leisure and privateness'. This detachment of thought from intimate application to affairs leads to a 'relaxation of discipline' in the state, for every man becomes 'more ready to argue than to obey and execute'.

Bacon replies to this criticism of the shortcomings of the learned as men-of-affairs by pointing out that men of the greatest executive ability in history, such as Alexander the Great and Julius Caesar were thoroughly educated and intellectually accomplished men. Alexander was Aristotle's pupil. He appreciated science and provided the means for collecting the materials of Aristotle's great treatise on biology.

Bacon proposed, however, to give a demonstration on a lesser scale: 'a tablet or picture of smaller volume': Queen Elizabeth.

'This lady was endued with learning in her sex singular, and rare even amongst masculine princes; whether we speak of learning of language or of science; modern or ancient; divinity or humanity. And unto the very last year of her life she accustomed to appoint set hours for reading, scarcely any student in a university more daily or more duly. As for her government, I assure myself I shall not exceed if I affirm that this part of the island never had forty-five years of better times; and yet not through the calmness of the season, but through the wisdom of her regiment. For if there be considered on the one side, the truth of religion established; the constant peace and security; the good administration of justice; the temperate use of the prerogative, not slackened nor much strained; the flourishing state of learning, sortable to so excellent a patroness; the convenient estate of wealth and means, both of crown and subject; the habit of obedience, and the moderation of discontents; and there be considered on the other side, the differences of religion, the troubles of neighbour countries, the ambition of Spain, and opposition of Rome; and then that she was solitary and of her self: these things I say considered, as I could not have chosen an instance so recent and so proper, so I suppose I could not have chosen one more remarkable or eminent, to the purpose now in hand; which is concerning the conjunction of learning in the prince with felicity in the people.'

It is, in fact, dangerous for states to be managed by 'empiric statesmen'. These are like lawyers whose knowledge is based on practice in the courts, without wide reading. They do not know what to do when they are confronted with a case of a kind of which they have no previous experience. The politician without a knowledge of science does not know how to deal with problems involving science.

The politicians who are ignorant lack the detached judgment arising from a universality of view, and tend to judge everything from within their own narrow experience. They 'refer all things to themselves, and thrust themselves into the centre of the world'.

The relation between politics and learning, seen in outstanding individuals, is shown in an even more striking way by the comparison of historical periods. The greatest feats of arms and statesmanship have always been performed when learning was at a peak. This was true in Greek and Roman, and other outstanding ages. The concurrence in learning and arms is 'yet more visible in times than in persons, by how much an age is greater object than a man'. Bacon saw plainly that society is greater than the greatest individual. For the same reason, the cooperation of many men in learning was essential, because 'the wit of one man can no more countervail learning than one man's means can hold way with a common purse . . .'.

One of Bacon's strongest arguments for the fitness of the learned for statesmanship was from the history of governments during the minority of princes. These have often been conducted by learned men, and 'it is almost without instance' that such governments were disastrous. In many cases, in spite of the great drawbacks of the system, they have 'excelled the government of princes of mature age'.

Learned men surpass merely practical men in affairs because they only 'love business for itself'. They are interested in it as 'an action according to nature'. They look at it from the point of view of a natural philosopher, they see it from the scientific point of view. They approve participation in affairs because it is a healthy exercise for the mind, and enjoy it as such, and not for what is obtained by it. Consequently, they of all men 'are the most indefatigable' in carrying out a policy if it 'can hold or detain their mind'.

The most determined statesmen are those who are deeply versed in social philosophy, and are engaged in carrying out policies based on a profound study of the principles of nature and society. Only a statesman who is also a scientist can qualify for the highest achievements in statesmanship.

5. *The Organization of Science*

BACON proceeded to review, 'in a style active and masculine', what had been done hitherto by 'kings and others' for the increase and advancement of learning.

He assumed that all the 'greatest and most difficult works' had been achieved through 'amplitude of reward', together with 'soundness of direction' and 'conjunction of labours'. Of these, soundness of direction was the most important, and was more effective than accumulating institutions and staffs, and ordering them to work. He felt compelled to observe that most of those who had founded institutions, though deserving honour for what they had done, had mainly been concerned with their 'own magnificence and memory', rather than with the progress of learning. They had augmented the number of learned men rather than advanced the sciences themselves

To advance learning it was necessary to provide institutions, literature and men. The institutions required buildings, suitable revenues and endowments, privileges, and constitutions, all tending 'to retirement and quietness of life, and a release from cares and troubles'. They should be equipped with libraries of important books, together with new editions and 'faithful translations'.

The staff should consist of two parts, all adequately remunerated; lecturers on existing and developed branches of knowledge, and research workers in those parts of learning which have not yet been sufficiently investigated.

On considering the many noble colleges in Europe, he found it strange that they were 'all dedicated to professions, and none left free to the study of arts and sciences at large'. Men rightly believed that learning should be of use in action, but this did not mean that 'philosophy and universality' are idle and unprofitable studies, for it is from these that the arts and professions derive their 'sap and strength'. One of the greatest hindrances to the progress of learning has been the leaving of fundamental research as something to be done by the lecturer 'in passage' and by the way. Scientists should always aspire to the 'first prizes', which consist of additions to knowledge. They should not be content only with 'second prizes', such as teaching, expounding, compiling and abridging.

The dedication of colleges entirely to professional training has been inimical not only to the growth of the sciences, but prejudicial to states and governments. For these find that 'when they have to choose men for business of state', there is 'a wonderful dearth of able men'. This is because there is 'no collegiate education designed' for the required purposes, which might prepare men more suitably for 'offices of state'.

He particularly disapproved of 'the smallness of the salaries assigned to lecturers in arts and professions', especially among the English. 'For it is very necessary to the progression of sciences that lecturers in every sort be of the most able and sufficient men; as those who are ordained not for transitory use, but for keeping up the race and succession of knowledge from age to age. This cannot be, except their condition and endowment be such that the most eminent professors may be well contented and willing to spend their whole life in that function and attendance, without caring for practice.'

Indeed, says Bacon, 'lecturers in sciences are as it were the keepers and guardians of the whole store and provision of learning, whence the active and militant part of the sciences is furnished, and therefore they ought to have equal entertainment and profit with the men of active life'.

Besides having libraries, the new scientific foundations must also have laboratories furnished with suitable instruments such as telescopes, furnaces, etc. For it is certain that 'for depth of speculation no less than for fruit of operation', other aids besides books are required. It is true that gardens have been provided for medicinal herbs, and bodies for studying anatomy, but far more is needed.

'It may be held for certain that there will hardly be any great progress in the unravelling and unlocking in the secrets of nature, except there be a full allowance for expenses about experiments.'

Just as secretaries of princes are allowed an expenses account for exploring civil secrets, 'so the searchers and spies of nature must have their expenses paid, or else you will never be well informed of a great number of things most worthy to be known'.

It was necessary also to keep university organization and courses continually under review, to see whether the old courses 'may be profitably kept up, or whether we should rather abolish them and substitute better'. He thought that in his day scholars came 'too soon and too unripe' to such studies as logic and rhetoric, which caused them to be presented in a trivial manner, 'suited to the capacity of children'.

Besides improving universities in England, it was necessary for the progress of learning that there should be 'a closer connexion and relationship between all the different universities of Europe than now there is'. There should be a brotherhood of men of learning and illumination, as there is in religious orders. Hence, Bacon implied, science should enjoy the stimulation of international contacts and organization, and there should be international scientific unions.

Finally, suitable men should be appointed to inquire into the state of the sciences, and note those parts of knowledge that are backward and neglected. To this end, there should be 'a review and *census*' of the sciences, in order to see what should be done for their best development.

The provision of proper institutions and endowments for science were 'truly works for a king', but the survey of knowledge in order to mark its various deficiencies was open to 'private industry'. He therefore proposed to embark on such a survey, which might serve as a guide both to public action and private endeavours.

He proposed, as far as his strength allowed, to point out all those investigations which required to be undertaken, which might be done by some persons though not by all; those which could be done only by collaborative effort; those which could not be done in one man's life but in the succession of ages, and those which could be done by public effort and expenditure, but are beyond private means and endeavour.

He would be content if his efforts were esteemed only as a laudable wish. For as it is not possible to ask a sensible question without some knowledge of a subject, 'so it requires some sense to make a wish not absurd'.

6. *Dawn*

THE earliest draft of Bacon's ultimate plan for the development of science is a synopsis of twenty-two sections, entitled *Valerius Terminus of the Interpretation of Nature with the Annotations of Hermes Stella*. It was not published until more than a century after his death. It is in some ways the freshest and most brilliant of his writings, in the form of notes for his own guidance, rather than an exposition for general reading. He expresses his ideas more concisely than in later works where he deploys the argument at leisure, in order to present it as lucidly as possible.

Valerius Terminus was probably written in 1603, at a period when he had decided to withdraw from practical life, 'meddle as little as possible in the King's causes', and entrust his 'ambition wholly upon my pen'. Shortly afterwards he changed his mind, and wrote *The Advancement of Learning*, published in 1605, which, he hoped, would help to recommend him to James I, a king who was learned.

Bacon probably chose the surname *Terminus* for the supposed author to indicate that he had come to a definite decision on the scope and nature of his main work. He had not yet decided, however, to make all of his fundamental notions public, and *Hermes Stella* was to throw only so much light on these by guarded comments, as was considered to be socially desirable. Bacon notes in his own hand on the manuscript that no such comments have in fact been included.

In *Valerius Terminus* Bacon's notion of the Interpretation of Nature still retains the first place in his mind. He uses the phrase no less than eighteen times in a work only thirty-five pages long. But by 1603, the purpose for which the method was to be used had become as important to him as the method itself. He made an intense effort to explain the purpose as powerfully as he had striven to think out the method.

So it comes about that in *Valerius Terminus* Bacon gives an account of his contribution to the logic of discovery, which is his main technical achievement and the foundation of his chief work, and also expresses in phrases of unsurpassed power the purpose for which it is to be utilized.

The arrangement of *Valerius Terminus* is best considered in the order chosen by Bacon. His first chapter is devoted to the *Limits and end of knowledge*. He says that in aspiring to the throne of power the angels transgressed and fell, and 'in presuming to come within the oracle of knowledge man transgressed and fell', but in pursuing the similitude of God's love ('for love is nothing else but goodness put in motion or applied'), it is impossible for man to transgress.

Bacon's preoccupation with the fall, before he had reached even the first step of political power, is of striking psychological interest. His concern with this was prophetic in his own case, as it has also proved to be with regard to science, by which man is liable to fall a second time. A similar, or the same unconscious psychological motive was at work both in his political career and in his philosophy.

Milton also was concerned with the same fundamental problem. His *Paradise Lost* and *Paradise Regained* are another treatment of the subject dealt with by Bacon in his conception of man's recovery of his position in the world before his fall. But whereas, according to Milton, man was to recover his position through faith, according to Bacon he was to 'give unto faith that which unto faith belongeth', but he was to recover his position in the world by scientific works. The intermingling of divine and human knowledge had caused infinite prejudice, and each was to be rigidly kept to its proper sphere. Bacon's conception of how man should recover himself was vastly more inspiring than that expounded in *Paradise Regained*. The difference in character of their solutions was influenced by differences in their religious convictions as well as in many other factors.

I. FRONTISPIECE OF THE INSTAURATIO MAGNA

Valerius Terminus

of the Interpretation of Nature
with the Annotations of

Hermes Stella

A few fragm^ts of y^e first booke, 2^t

1 The first chapter entier, ~~touching~~ Of
  ~~ye endes and limites of knowledge~~

2 A portion of the xj^th chapter ~~of the
  scale~~

3 A small portion of the ix^th chapter
  ~~being an Inducem^t to ye Inventorye~~

4 A small portion of the xth chapter
  ~~being the p^t^ face to ye Inventorye~~

5. A small portion of the jb^th chapter
  ~~being a preface to ye inward Elenches
  of the mynd~~

II. TITLE OF VALERIUS TERMINUS
The list of contents and the word 'Philosophy' are in Bacon's own hand

Of the Interpretacon

6 · A small portion of the iiij^te chapter ~~of the injoint's of knowledge in generall~~

7te A small portion of the vi^te chapter ~~of ye division of Cyences~~

8 The vij^th chapter Entire

9 A portion of the viij^te chapter

10 The viij^th chapter Entire

11 Another portion of the ix^te chapter

12 The Abridgm^t of the 12. 13. 14 . 15 . 16. 17.
18. 19. 21. 22 . 25 . 26te chapters
of ye first booke

3 . The first chapter of ~~the~~ a booke of
the same argum^t wrytten in Latine
and destined ~~for~~ to be ~~traditionary~~ separate and
(not publiste.

Nome of y^e Annotations of Stella
are sett down in these fragments.

Philosophy

ff · ff. 26. — · 1603 . B . 45^r . x^r ·/
Libri dimidiu^ est, pag^a 34 . —
Pagellaru^ numeri veri ·/

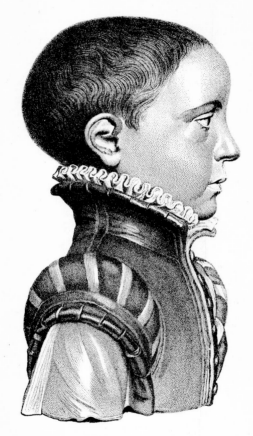

III. FRANCIS BACON AT THE AGE OF TWELVE

'two years younger than Her Majesty's
happy reign. . . .'

Bacon argued that as man fell through his intellectual presumption, knowledge is a dangerous thing, and for this reason 'is to be limited by religion, and to be referred to use and action'. It is to be accepted with caution and distinction because 'it is not easy to discern where the issues and streams thereof will take and fall'.

Science is too dangerous to be pursued merely for itself without reference to its purpose, 'which is the benefit and relief of the state and society of man; for otherwise all manner of knowledge becometh malign'. It carries the 'serpent's sting' (illustrated in our own time by the invention of thermo-nuclear bombs, capable of ending life on earth. An ungoverned science drags man to his second fall, and this time without any reprieve or opportunity for salvation or recovery).

'And therefore it is not the pleasure of curiosity, nor the quiet of resolution, nor the raising of the spirit, nor victory of wit, nor faculty of speech, nor lucre of profession, nor ambition of honour or fame, nor inablement for business, that are the true ends of knowledge; some of these being more worthy than other, though all inferior and degenerate; but it is a restitution and reinvesting (in great part) of man to the sovereignty and power (for whensoever he shall be able to call the creatures by their true names he shall again command them) which he had in his first state of creation. And to speak plainly and clearly, it is a discovery of all operations and possibilities of operations from immortality (if it were possible) to the meanest mechanical practice. And therefore knowledge that tendeth but to satisfaction is but as a courtesan, which is for pleasure and not for fruit or generation. And knowledge that tendeth to profit or profession or glory is but as the golden ball thrown before Atalanta, which while she goeth aside and stoopeth to take up she hindereth the race. And knowledge referred to some particular point of use is but as Harmodius which putteth down one tyrant, and not like Hercules who did perambulate the world to suppress tyrants and giants and monsters in every part. . . .' Here Bacon had the explanation: 'that is, man's miseries and necessities', but he struck it out, feeling perhaps that it was too plain a concession to the unimaginative.

Bacon published the same thoughts in the *Advancement of Learning*, but expressed with a different emphasis. 'The greatest error of all the rest is the mistaking or misplacing of the last or

E

furthest end of knowledge. For men have entered into a desire of learning and knowledge, sometimes upon a natural curiosity and inquisitive appetite; sometimes to entertain their minds with variety and delight; sometimes for ornament and reputation; and sometimes to enable them to victory of wit and contradiction; and most times for lucre and profession; and seldom sincerely to give a true account of their gift of reason, to the benefit and use of men: as if there were sought in knowledge a couch whereupon to rest a searching and restless spirit; or a terrace, for a wandering and variable mind to walk up and down with a fair prospect; or a tower of state, for a proud mind to raise itself upon; or a fort or commanding ground, for strife and contention; or a shop, for profit or sale; and not a rich storehouse, for the glory of the Creator and the relief of man's estate. . . .'

Bacon did not esteem the usefulness of science more than its spiritual significance. He spoke of the 'sword of the spirit'. He was not a *bourgeois*, who believed that science should be developed primarily because it is profitable. Nor was his passion for beautiful things, flowers, jewels, clothes, decorations, music, merely avaricious. These were part of the 'magnificence' which ministered to the 'glory of the Creator' as well as the pride of man.

At his fall, man had been doomed to live in the sweat of his brow. He could therefore help himself only by labour, and this could be mitigated only by invention. It should be noted that his recovery was to depend more on the sweat of his brow than of his body, that is, on the labour and explorations by the mind rather than the muscles. Time would show 'that the new-found world of land was not greater addition to the ancient continent than there remaineth at this day a world of inventions and sciences unknown . . . .'

It appeared that antiquity also believed in the dignity of endowing man's life with new commodities. 'For whereas founders of states, lawgivers, extirpers of tyrants, fathers of the people, were honoured but with the title of Worthies or Demigods, inventors were ever consecrated amongst the Gods themselves.'

The amplification of the power and kingdom of mankind over the world is a divine work, which proceeds without noise or perturbation, unlike the activities of the ambitious, within their own countries, and in the world at large. The humility of mind which labours to spell and so by degrees to read in the volumes of nature, rather than the invocation of a man's own spirit to give him oracles, receives the divine blessing.

Some of the worst impediments to knowledge arise, not from the difficulty of investigation, but of recognizing what should be investigated. The mind fails to perceive the path that should be taken, and in these conditions, 'it is more hard to attempt than to achieve'. The formulation of the problem to be solved in scientific invention and discovery is more difficult than the finding of the solution.

The advance of science has hitherto been hindered by lack of travel and communications. This has prevented men from combining their abilities in the attack on problems. The admiration for speculative philosophies has prevented advance of knowledge by successive effort, as the greatest achievements in that field are commonly by the earliest authors, such as Aristotle, Plato and Democritus. But in the mechanical and experimental sciences, scientists can contribute to an unending succession of discoveries. Hence these sciences continue to grow through many ages, whereas the growth of the speculative sciences does not last longer than one man's life.

As 'the state of knowledge is ever a *Democratie*' those philosophies which are most agreeable to the senses and intellect of people are the most popular and prevailing. For this reason, the philosophies of Aristotle and Plato, which are respectively: subtle and fractious, and expressed in a beautiful and majestic style, have displaced that of Democritus which is closer to reality.

After commenting on the impediment arising from the seductions of comprehensive abstract thought, he noticed that caused by the contrary fault of specialization. He regarded the separation of particular sciences from general knowledge as one of the worst hindrances, for it prevented one science from throwing light on the limitations of another. For this reason, knowledge requires a system of administration in which each science has its own autonomy, but all are related through a general committee of knowledge, on which each science has its representatives, rather in the manner in which the King of Spain administers his great dominions.

The tendency of every man to work by himself, and have his own way or not go at all, has been another impediment. There had never yet been any conjoint or combined effort in starting research, in which men could choose their problems in the light of common discussion and criticism. Men who follow the inclination of their nature, or common example and opinion, tend to 'set themselves in the right way to the wrong place'.

Impelled by 'the natural curiosity and desire to know', they set out on the way 'without foresight or consideration of their journey's end'.

He found that 'even those that have sought knowledge for itself, and not for benefit or ostentation or any practical enablement in the course of their life, have nevertheless propounded to themselves a wrong mark, namely satisfaction (which men call truth) and not operation'.

As in the courts of princes it is much easier to give satisfaction than do the business, so in the sciences it is much easier to satisfy the mind of man than to make new discoveries and inventions. Bacon added a marginal note in his own hand that philosophers were like Scylla, who appeared 'a fair woman upwards in the parts of show, but when you come to the parts of use and generation, Barking Monsters'.

Bacon now takes pains to say that various writers who have emphasized the importance of referring sciences to action and the use of man have quite a different meaning from his. He is not opposed to their precepts for using science to improve practice, as long as it does not damage science. But his aim is to 'increase and multiply the revenues and possessions of man', and not merely to improve the practices already available.

In order to demonstrate 'what is the true end, scope or office of knowledge', which does not consist 'in any plausible, delectable, reverend, or admired discourse, or any satisfactory arguments, but in effecting and working, and in discovery of particulars not revealed before for the better endowment and help of man's life', he proposed to make an inventory of 'the wealth, furniture, or means of man according to his present estate, as far as it is known . . .'. He did not propose this in order to show his own width of knowledge, or make a satire on men's wants and errors, but because new thoughts needed concrete illustrations to make them be perceived. He felt it necessary to show what this new way of using the means available to mankind might produce in the future, and to give 'some awaking note both of the wants in man's present condition and the nature of the supplies to be wished', in case he should die before he was able to reveal this new light, or direction.

Bacon then outlines a part of what was to have been his eleventh chapter. This contains a statement of the problem which led him to his development of inductive logic. It arises out of an analysis of what is necessary to make inventions. This should lead to the discovery of how to make any desired invention 'without the errors and conjectures of art, or the length or difficulties of experience', that is, of trial and error.

Bacon started by trying to make a frontal attack on the problem. If you wanted to make a desired body out of an available raw material, you had to give the raw material all the properties of the desired body. The product would then be indistinguishable from the desired body.

He therefore discussed how an available substance could be given any required property, such as 'whiteness'. The direction on how to do this must possess certainty in operation, and must not be limited to particular means. If the direction is certain it will produce the desired result under all conditions, and if it is free in operation, the presence of the effect will indicate that the direction has been followed. Bacon derived these two rules from Peter Ramus, who in turn considered that they were implied by Aristotle's principles of demonstration in his *Posterior Analytics*. For example, says Bacon, beating water and air together will certainly produce a white froth. But this is a very limited way of producing whiteness, for it is restricted to water and air. The second and more general direction is to beat or powder any colourless transparent body such as water or glass, and intermingle it with air. The third and still more general direction is to remove the restriction to colourless bodies; if beer or amber is beaten or powdered, though they are coloured they produce white froth. The fourth and still more general direction aims at removing the restriction to transparent bodies such as water, glass, beer and amber, which are heavier than air, by using flame. The fifth and more general direction still aims at the removal of the restriction of one of the bodies to air. This can be done by mingling two bodies, each of which is transparent but in an unequal degree, such as oil and water.

But you are still tied to transparent bodies. Bacon now says that he forbears to proceed further with his analysis partly because it would become too long, 'but chiefly because it would open that which in this work' he is determined to reserve; but as he did not now intend to reveal, so he was circumspect not to mislead. He was engaged only in giving an example of a free direction, and not a method of interpretation of nature by which it might be discovered. He would say, without providing the inductive proof, that the sixth direction would be 'that all bodies or parts of bodies which are unequal equally, that is in simple proportions, represent whiteness'.

From this assertion follow a multitude of effects and observations, such as that whiteness and blackness are most incompatible with transparence, blackness stops light, whiteness keeps it, but neither passes it; nor are blackness and whiteness produced by rainbows and prisms; that white does not dye, and black can hardly be dyed, that flowers are generally of fresh colours, and rarely black, etc.

Bacon draws attention to other ways of producing whiteness which require analysis, but this he omits, because he would otherwise have to 'open that which I think good to withdraw'.

Bacon explains his method more fully in the *Novum Organum*, which was published seventeen years later. It will be discussed further, in the course of considering that work. Here it is sufficient to note that his account in *Valerius Terminus* shows that his method arose out of his analysis of the logic which is involved in solving any technical problem. In this, he made use of, and added to, logical procedures derived from Aristotle and Ramus.

Another feature of Bacon's thought is indicated by his discussion in *Valerius Terminus* of how to produce whiteness and colours in bodies. This shows that he considered colour of secondary importance, and determined by other more fundamental properties, such as structure. He supposed that natural philosophy consists of explaining the so-called secondary qualities in terms of the primary. In this his position is the same as that of Galileo.

He said that the test for the truth of a 'direction' was that it should contribute 'a degree or remove nearer to action, operation, or light . . .' that is, the truth of the theory was to be decided by the result of experiment. The nature discovered should 'be more original than the nature supposed', that is, that colour should be explained in terms of structure.

When Bacon wrote *Valerius Terminus* he had not yet decided whether all discoveries should be published, or that the scientist should exercise discretion in publishing discoveries which might be used to the injury of mankind. His editors Ellis and Spedding devote considerable attention to Bacon's attitude to secrecy in science, and differ in their interpretation of it. Ellis, who was a technical expert in the history of philosophy and science regards Bacon's decision in *Valerius Terminus* to conceal the full description of his method, or express it in an obscure manner which could be understood only by a few adepts or a chosen audience, as a relic of scholasticism, whereas Spedding the humane scholar suggests that Bacon was also actuated by social conscience. Ellis remarks that concealment of discoveries in medieval times was regarded as normal, and arose from the current conception of science. Discoveries were then regarded as accidental, or due to access to hidden sources of information, and not to hard work or acuteness. It was like concealed treasure which, if shared with others, lost its value. The love of the marvellous inclined men to believe that wonders had been handed down from antiquity, and new discoveries were given the prestige of mystery by keeping them secret. Men were inclined to keep new discoveries secret to avoid being accused of possessing unlawful knowledge.

Spedding felt that Ellis's explanation was inadequate. He collected many of the passages in Bacon's works where he refers to secrecy, in order to see whether his motive in limiting his audience was 'unwillingness to part with his treasure, or solicitude for the furtherance of his work'. He thought that the first of these motives was incompatible with Bacon's general aim, and that like Milton he wished for a 'fit audience, though few'. He not only wished 'to find the fit, but also to exclude the unfit'.

Ellis's attitude to secrecy was the one generally held by scientists during the nineteenth century. They took it for granted that all scientific knowledge should be published without any consideration of its implications. In the light of our experience in the twentieth century, we can see that Spedding, who was not a scientist but a scholar of exceptional sensitivity and width, had a deeper view.

In *Valerius Terminus* Bacon discusses the impediments in the communication of knowledge. Two are particularly noxious: the building-up of formal systems on the basis of a few observations, and the use of tricks of style which are 'so many characters of imposture'. They conceal the 'true motives and proofs' of their opinions, and avoid 'free confessing' of 'ignorance or doubts'.

It is no easy thing to explain new and unfamiliar ideas, and knowledge is never expounded, even in mathematics, 'in the same order it was invented'. The method of teaching science for practical use is not the same as that of teaching it for purposes of bringing a student to the frontier of knowledge, to prepare him to undertake research. The student must be instructed in the method by which the existing knowledge was discovered, in order to see where it is deficient. In modern terminology, he must study the original papers.

Bacon then says that while the ancient tradition of 'publishing part, and reserving part to a private succession, and of publishing in a manner whereby it shall not be to the capacity nor taste of all, but shall as it were single and adopt his reader, is not to be laid aside, both for the avoiding of abuse in the excluded and the strengthening of affection in the admitted'.

Ellis regards Bacon's opinion in this matter as related to the medieval alchemists' tradition of transmitting secret knowledge from master to disciple. Spedding stresses Bacon's aim as the 'avoidance of abuse in the excluded', that is, the prevention of the misuse of scientific knowledge by the vulgar: the intellectually, morally and socially uninformed. Spedding suggests that Bacon feared that this might arise because the subject was 'too abstruse to be handled successfully except by the fit and few'. To us, the danger appears to rest more in the misuse of science by the morally and socially uninformed.

Bacon retained to the end of his life the view that knowledge of science should be under moral and social control. In *New Atlantis*, one of his latest works, the discoverers of fundamental new scientific knowledge exercise their discretion as to whether it should be generally published.

Bacon refers briefly in *Valerius Terminus* to his views on 'the internal and profound errors and superstitions in the nature of the mind', and the 'four sorts of idols or fictions' which obstruct the understanding in the search for knowledge. He describes them as idols of the Tribe, Palace, Cave, and Theatre. In the *Novum Organum*, he changes the name of the Idols of the Palace into those of the Market-Place, a reflection on the evolution of his social preoccupations from feudalism to capitalism.

He concluded the work with 'an abridgement of divers chapters of the first book of Interpretation of Nature'.

There was to be a chapter on the methods of determining the truth of knowledge. Among those that are not adequate are the 'coherence of a knowledge in itself'. The 'discovery of new works and active directions not known before', and of facts leading to the discovery of new scientific laws which in turn lead to the discovery of new facts, is the only true test of knowledge.

The subtlety of words and the senses is gross in comparison with that of things, consequently theories must always be submitted to the test of experiment.

It is a mistake to aim too much at the production of particular concrete things, because these are 'infinite and transitory'. One should rather search for the 'abstract natures' which determine what properties a concrete thing will have. These 'abstract natures' of which things consist are 'few and permanent', like the alphabet of letters or 'the colours mingled in the painter's shell, wherewith he is able to make infinite variety of faces or shapes'.

Bacon frequently meditated on the notion of the universe as a composition in an alphabet of fundamental natural units. It is similar in type to the notion that the universe is a complex structure made out of combinations of particles of a small number of different kinds. He thought at one time of casting his great work on the development of the sciences into the form of a treatise with the title: *The Alphabet of Nature.*

He was influenced in his belief in the possibility of such an alphabet by the views of Democritus, who had remarked that while the nature of things is rich, being infinite in quantity and variety of individuals, it was limited in combinations and species, which scarcely totalled one thousand. If this were true, then it was very encouraging for science, since, if these thousand basic uniformities could be discovered, a tolerably complete description of nature could probably be made, and reasonably quickly.

F. Gowland Hopkins at the beginning of the twentieth century encouraged biochemists by a similar kind of idea. He suggested that the baffling complexities of living processes and matter are really infinite variations on a few fundamental themes, and not an infinite collection of particulars, all of them different and forever beyond the possibility of scientific description and interpretation.

In the headings for his *Alphabet*, Bacon emphasized that 'natural and artificial are potentialities of being, without or by means of human assistance'. Here again he is breaking down the belief in the fundamental difference between the natural and the artificial, which has been essential for the development of science.

All profound and radical alteration of substances depends on the discovery of these 'abstract natures'. (By these, Bacon means such notions as the theory of heat and atomic constitution.)

Research should aim at the explanation of motions and affinities, and not at the 'dead beginnings or principles of things', because 'there are no such beginnings, and if there were they could not be known'.

The 'voluntary collections' of information and ideas that the mind makes are another obstacle to knowledge. Many of the errors arising from this cause are unjustly charged on the senses. But the information of 'the senses is sufficient, not because they err not, but because the use of the sense in discovering knowledge is for the most part not immediate'. The senses can be used for making a reliable observation which will decide whether or not a theory is true. The information gained in this way is generally more fundamental than that reported directly by the senses.

The mind of man needs a great variety of aids in discerning knowledge, just as the hand of man in manual and mechanical practices needs the aid of a great variety of tools.

Investigators are liable either to devote too much attention to particulars, which is an exercise of 'tedious curiosity', or to fly at once from a few particulars to abstract theories. It is necessary to proceed with 'strength and patience of mind' through the middle stages, in order to arrive at proved theories, for 'chance discovereth new inventions by one and one, but science by knots and clusters'.

Bacon's insistence on the continual checking and re-checking of theory and practice in a slow and steady ascent resembles Clerk Maxwell's comments on the peculiar difficulty of mathematical physics, which involves the wrenching of the mind backwards and forwards between the facts of experiment and the mathematics of symbols.

The facts of natural history must be collected on a more extensive and systematic basis, in order to provide facts for the new method of interpretation or research, which will 'abridge experience' and make discoveries as certainly in a short time as previously by infinite trial-and-error during ages.

One of the greatest impediments to the progress of science has been unfounded despair and diffidence over its difficulty.

The over-estimation of the 'infiniteness of particulars' has un-necessarily depressed the investigator. The new method of in-vestigation is more reliable than any previously used, and in-creases confidence because it 'doth in sort equal men's wits', and leaves 'no great advantage or pre-eminence to the perfect and excellent motions of the spirit'. Any ordinary man can draw a better circle with the aid of a pair of compasses than the most skilful artist by his practised hand alone.

The progress of science has been hindered by social and intel-lectual pride. Men have disdained important information because it was 'vulgar in currency, and base and ignoble in use'. They have despised 'arts mechanical and illiberal, and preferred generalities' because they are not subject to control by 'persons of mean observation' and remind men of their ignorance and not of what they know. Nevertheless, the importance of true general-izations cannot be magnified too much. They are the most funda-mental reflections of the nature of things.

The understanding by its own way of working will, when freed from the various impediments that obstruct it, arrive at the true interpretation of things. Anticipations or guesses at the truth are, on the contrary, successful only by chance.

Bacon concluded his review of the obstructions to the pro-gress of science with a consideration of those arising from reli-gion and social structure.

True religion was no impediment to science, but religion that consists of 'rites and forms of adoration, and not in confessions and beliefs' is adverse to science because it leaves men the liberty to expend their mental energy on the problems of theology, and so neglect the investigation of nature. But 'if men's wits be shut out of that part' it turns them again into the course of dis-covery.

A religion 'that is jealous of the variety of learning, discourse, opinions, sects . . .' fearing that these will shake its foundations, is 'adverse to knowledge'. The Turkish religion is of this type, and Christianity has had this characteristic at various periods. But true Christianity has singular value for the advance of science because it interdicts human reason from investigating the mysteries and principles of faith.

Finally, there are the social conditions which determine the development of science, arising from 'the nature of society and the policies of the state'. These are different in different kinds

of social system, and in different social classes. Every form of
society, and every social class contributes its own peculiar obstacles to the progress of science. 'There is no composition of
estate or society, nor order or quality of persons, which have
not some point of contrariety towards true knowledge.' Monarchies 'incline wits to profit and pleasure, and commonwealths
to glory and vanity. The universities incline wits to sophistry
and affectation, cloisters to fables and unprofitable subtilty;' and
'it is hard to say, whether mixture of contemplations with an
active life, or retiring wholly to contemplations do disable and
hinder the mind more'.

Of all the views propounded in *Valerius Terminus* the most far-
reaching are those on the social relations of science. Bacon conceived science as a means for benefiting mankind. The source of
this attitude is to be found in the social ideas and aims of the
class of which his father Nicholas Bacon was a leader, the new
kind of competent professional administrator, with modest
material ambitions. When Bacon examined science in this perspective, his mind of genius started by investigating how this
instrument, of such obvious benefit to man, might be improved.
When he discovered how primitive the method of scientific research was, and that he himself was able to make improvements
in the method of inductive logic, by which general conclusions
are derived from collections of facts, his mind at once envisaged
the possibilities of a perfected method of research. It could
'accomplish all things possible', and place the whole universe at
the disposal of man.

He naturally extended his inquiry into the reasons why more
progress had not hitherto been made with an instrument of such
signal value to mankind. This led him to analyse the obstructions
to the development of science which lie in the nature of man himself, and in the nature of the social classes and systems in which
he is organized.

He thereby cleared the ground and laid the foundation for
the organized development of science in a rational system. He
became the parent of planned scientific research. By raising the
question of the dependence of the advance of science on the
nature of the social system within which it is pursued, he opened
the path to the social systems, with their planned scientific research, that are becoming more and more characteristic of the
modern world.

7. *Preliminary to Planning*

BACON'S 'census of the sciences' enabled the whole of learning to be seen as one. By holding the main aspects of knowledge in view at the same time it became easier to see where there were obvious gaps, and where advances were most needed and might be most fruitful. It was a necessary preliminary to the planning of research, aimed at the balanced development of every aspect of science, not only with regard to science itself, but to its use for the benefit of mankind.

In the course of his review, carried out in his *Dignity and Advancement of Learning*, he had to formulate briefly and simply the main features of every kind of scientific activity, clarifying his own mind and presenting his readers with a large number of working conceptions. These were not elaborated, but packed into short pregnant phrases. Throughout his review there are numerous formulations and comments which have provided starting-points for his successors.

He divided all human learning into history, poetry and philosophy, which he related respectively to the memory, imagination and reason.

These three main divisions are considered in their general features, and then each is sub-divided into more special parts, making a total of some 150 altogether. A number of sub-headings have been introduced in this chapter as a guide to particularly important topics.

He regards history as concerned with individuals who are circumscribed by place and time, or the conditions of their environment. Poetry is concerned with individuals or entities which are invented in imitation of those who have been seen in history, but in which various aspects are joined together by the imagination in a way that had not actually happened.

In contrast, philosophy is not concerned with individuals, nor does it deal with the impressions immediately derived from them, but with 'abstract notions derived from these impressions'.

All this may be easily seen 'by observing the commencements of the intellectual process. The sense, which is the door of the intellect, is affected by individuals only. The images of those individuals—that is, the impressions which they make on the sense—fix themselves in the memory, and pass into it in the first instance entire as it were, just as they come. These the human mind proceeds to review and ruminate. . . .'

From this activity flows the whole of learning, and there can be no other source. All learning is one, 'for I consider history and experience to be the same thing, as also philosophy and the sciences'.

Bacon's concern with the individual sense-impression as the source of knowledge, and the arts of the advancement of the individual as well as the advancement of science, make him one of the parents of the philosophy worked out by Locke, which has been the main foundation of English thought for three centuries. Though the concept of a science of society underlies his vast scheme for the conquest of nature in the interests of man, he did not work it out in detail. Nevertheless, the two aspects of his thought, the individual and the social, are not to be separated. These twin features give it a dialectical character, which make him as much a forerunner of socialism as of individualism.

The Transformation of Nature

Bacon discussed natural history before civil or human history. He pointed out that it consisted of more than a mere description of nature. The latter view led to the subtle error of supposing that man could not be more than an assistant to influence nature's course in minor points, and 'by no means to change, transmute, or fundamentally alter' her. This had 'bred a premature despair in human enterprises'. The exact contrary was in fact the truth. 'The artificial does not differ from the natural in form or essence.' Man has no power over nature except by rearranging her constituents. The properties of matter are revealed only by submitting it to experiment, just as a man's nature is never fully revealed until he is crossed. 'Man can put natural bodies together, and he can separate them,' and by these means he 'can do everything'.

His abolition of the difference in essence between the natural and the artificial undermined the pessimistic human belief that men would never be able to make the substances produced by living organisms. He thereby indicated the way to the triumphs of synthetic chemistry both in industry and biology, and the general idea of the transformation of nature which is proceeding at so great a pace in our own day.

He noted that in works on agriculture and the manual arts 'familiar and vulgar' experiments were often neglected. These could sometimes throw more light on the interpretation of nature than experiments which seemed more subtle. In fact, it appeared to him that the history of the mechanical arts was 'the most radical and fundamental to natural philosophy; such natural philosophy I mean as shall not vanish in the fumes of subtle or sublime speculations, but such as shall be operative to relieve the inconveniences of man's estate'.

He explained that this part of natural history should not be derived only from the history of the mechanical arts, but should include 'the operative part of the liberal sciences', and also other practices which had not yet grown up into arts. Thus engineering and experimental science should not be considered apart, or in isolation from theoretical physics, for all three interact on each other. New commodities will be discovered by 'transferring the observations of one art to the use of others'. When a man brings together in his mind the results of experiments from different branches of science, the conjunction often suggests new and useful discoveries.

Social Conditions for Scientific Development

Bacon's consideration of civil history led him to observe that no adequate history of learning as yet existed. He wished this to be made in order to reveal the conditions under which learning flourishes, as a guide to future planning of learning. In his discussion he remarked that 'sciences migrate like nations', and thereby foresaw the idea of cultural diffusion which has had an important part in modern anthropological science. He desired that above all events should 'be coupled with their causes', and that the facts should be simply narrated, 'with but slight intermixture of private judgement'.

He did not wish the work to be undertaken because of his own 'exceeding love of learning', but because it would 'very greatly assist the wisdom and skill of learned men in the use and administration of learning'. From the history of learning 'the best system of government' of intellectual and scientific matters might be derived and established. The study of the history of science is more instructive on the government of science than the study of any particular scientist's works, just as the study of the works of St. Ambrose or St. Augustine will not make so wise a bishop as the study of ecclesiastical history.

Civil history, dealing with 'our ancestors, the vicissitudes of things, the foundations of civil policy, and the name and reputation of men' is of pre-eminent dignity and authority. But it is difficult to write because it is hard to bring one's mind into sympathy with the past and see things from the ancient point of view, and discover the details of events, the characters of persons, 'the bottoms of pretences, and the secrets of governments'. The historian's work entails great labour and judgment because in ancient transactions 'the truth is difficult to ascertain, and in modern it is dangerous to tell'. Bacon was in favour of detached objective history, in which prejudice and 'party' spirit, and the inculcation of 'favourite political doctrines' were avoided, and full use was made of the study of all concrete data, such as coins, in addition to literary material.

Expounding Philosophy through the Interpretation of Myths

Bacon paid particular attention to the deficiencies in the study of that part of poetry concerning the interpretation of myths. The full importance of his work in this field has been explained only recently by F. H. Anderson, who has shown that it is 'one of the most significant contributions to philosophy in the history of English thought'. Bacon was inclined to believe that myths contained concealed knowledge, discovered in earlier and more glorious ages before the decay of historical times had begun.

Whether or not he really believed this, Bacon interpreted the ancient myths as if they had concealed his own deepest thoughts on the relations between man and God, and science and theology. They are also found to possess, as he expounds them, his own ideas on the properties of matter, the character of the scientific method of investigation, the processes of nature and the aims of science. He greatly extended this line of thought in his *Wisdom of the Ancients*.

In his review, he gives three examples of such analyses; the myths of Pan, Perseus and Dionysus. He discusses Pan first and finds that he represents and denotes the universe, and his activities are a disguised account of 'the nature of things'. According to one version of the myth, Pan arose from 'the promiscuous intercourse of Penelope with all the suitors'. Bacon identifies matter as Penelope, and says that Plato and Aristotle, who represented matter as 'entirely despoiled, shapeless and indifferent to forms' have described things as begot on 'matter as a common harlot' by 'Forms as suitors'.

Leucippus and Democritus, who in their doctrine of Atoms ascribed shapes and respectability to Matter, had greater penetration and judgment.

Bacon detects in Pan's sheephook a metaphor that denotes the mixture of straight and crooked ways by which nature gains her ends. Nor are the parallels between the ways of nature and of man ever to be forgotten. Just as 'in all wise human governments' rulers can introduce what they desire for the good of the people more easily by indirect than direct ways, so nature may more easily be deceived than forced; 'so ineffectual and self-impeding are all things which are done directly', whereas by the indirect way the end is smoothly gained.

Nevertheless, we hear elsewhere that 'he that dissembles deprives himself of a principal instrument of action, namely, trust and belief'.

In his pamphlet on a *Holy War* against the Turk, Bacon discusses what qualities a statesman should possess. He says it is 'a perplexed business', for 'it is not only in order of nature for him to govern that is the more intelligent, as Aristotle would have it; but there is no less required for government, courage to protect; and above all, honesty and probity of the will, to abstain from injury'.

After considering all history, which 'walks upon the earth' and performs the office of a guide rather than of a light, and poetry which is 'as a dream of learning' and contains something of the divine, Bacon feels it is time to start 'winging' his 'way through the clear air of Philosophy and the Sciences'.

Fundamental Science

Philosophy may be conveniently divided into knowledge of God, Nature and Man, but these three divisions are not as lines which meet in a point but boughs that spring from the trunk of a tree. This trunk corresponds to the one universal science which is the mother of all sciences. He describes this as primary philosophy, and is not sure whether it is in a backward condition, but

F

is inclined to think that it is. Setting aside fanciful metaphors, primary science consists of laws which are not peculiar to any particular science but belong to several. Among these are the rules of logic, and such principles as 'the nature of everything is best seen in its smallest proportions', which led to Democritus's conception of atoms, and the idea of analysis; 'all things are changed and nothing is lost', and the 'quantum of nature is neither diminished nor increased' (which foreshadow the modern ideas of the conservation of mass and energy). He finds in the earth's control through gravitation of all the smaller bodies on its surface a justification for the precedence of principles which are necessary for the preservation of the state over those which are merely of benefit to individuals.

No one has as yet collected any body of such laws, which are excellent for displaying the unity of nature.

Included in this inquiry should be the consideration of why some things exist and others do not, and why some exist in large quantities and others in small. What determines the proportions of things, and why should there be more iron than gold, and grass than roses? No one has sufficiently explained why between species there are individuals which partake of the nature of both. For instance, there are fishes that stick to rocks and cannot move away, and lie between plants and animals; bats which lie between birds and beasts, and flying fishes between birds and fishes.

Here Bacon is asking the questions which have led to the explanation of the relative proportions in which the elements are found in the universe, and the modern theory of the evolution of plants and animals.

If Natural Philosophy teems with deficiencies, Divine Philosophy is in a happier condition. The Scriptures indicate that the world is the work of God. Many have given excellent demonstrations, based on the characteristics of this work, that God must exist and govern the world, that he is all-powerful and a rewarder and avenger.

But it would be most unsafe to derive by induction from nature and human knowledge any conclusions about the mysteries of faith. As there is no deficiency, and indeed 'an excess' of excellent Natural Theology (James I had written extensively on the topic) Bacon hastens to close his brief chapter on this subject, and proceed to consider at length further aspects of the less dangerous topic of Natural Philosophy.

He notes by the way that the sober study of angels and spirits is by no means interdicted, nor that of evil spirits, which is as legitimate as the investigation of poisons in medicine, and necessary so that we shall not be ignorant of the stratagems of the devil.

For Bacon, illnesses of body and mind were equally amenable to scientific investigation. He opposed the ancient prejudice against the scientific investigation of mental disorder which has consigned the mentally ill to so much neglect and suffering. He divided natural philosophy into physics and metaphysics, giving a new meaning to the latter word. The former dealt with that which is most inherent in matter and subject to change, while the latter dealt with that which is more abstracted and fixed. Bacon thereby made metaphysics definitely part of nature and indeed 'much the most excellent part'. The effect of this innovation is to have identified what was regarded as outside physics with the basic principles of science. Thus Bacon implied that there is no such thing as metaphysics but only science.

While engaged in abolishing this favourite idea of Antiquity he is careful to pay his respects to her, and takes the occasion to praise the excellence and wonderful acuteness of Aristotle, but also to observe that he was given to coining new words at pleasure, and waging war on all his philosophical predecessors. Perhaps he had learned his 'humour from his scholar (Alexander the Great had been Aristotle's pupil) whom perhaps he emulated; the one aspiring to conquer all nations, the other to conquer all opinions, and to establish for himself a despotism in thought'. Bacon was deeply impressed by Aristotle's assertiveness. It confirmed him in the belief that a bold front is one of the principles which leads to success in propaganda.

As for physics proper, he regarded astronomy as part of it. This was in a very bad state. In his time it was so mathematical that it could with reason be classified as part of mathematics. It gave a beautiful description of the positions and movements of the stars, but none at all of the inherent causes of their behaviour as physical bodies. He suggested that a theory might be devised which would not only describe their movements, but 'set forth the substance, motion and influence of the heavenly bodies as they really are'.

In these sentences Bacon formulated the great problem to which Isaac Newton gave the answer. He asked that the motions

of the heavens should be explained in terms of the physics of
bodies on the earth, and he forecast that a better understanding
of the stars would provide 'no slight knowledge of some motions
of the lower world as yet undiscovered'. In our own time discoveries about the physics of the stars have thrown light on such
problems as the control of the hydrogen fusion reaction for re-
leasing atomic energy.

Bacon held that each branch of science should be checked in
the light of natural philosophy as a whole. He said: 'the opinion
of Copernicus in astronomy, which astronomy itself cannot correct because it is not repugnant to any of the appearances, yet
natural philosophy doth correct'.

He distrusted mere mathematical description. He believed
that the real description of the celestial bodies must be given in
terms of physics; of 'expansion, contraction, impression, ces-
sion, collection into masses, attraction, repulsion, assimilation,
union and the like . . .'.

In the scientific climate of the nineteenth century, Bacon's
objection to Copernicus was regarded as simply erroneous. But
today it is easier to see that it contained an important caution.

Modern cosmology makes as much use of physics as mathematics,
and has advanced along the lines indicated by Bacon. Newton
founded modern cosmology in terms of physical properties and
forces, while Einstein's discovery of the general theory of relativity arose out of the application of the very principle recommended by Bacon: the consideration of a wide range of phenomena hitherto regarded as unrelated, in the light of natural
philosophy as a whole.

Since the discovery of the general theory of relativity, ideas on
cosmology have become far more fluid. Contemporary theories of
the 'primeval atom' and the 'continuous creation of matter' are
as contrary to conventional scientific ideas as Bacon's objection
to Copernicanism. In view of them, the question whether the
earth is going round the sun, or the sun round the earth, does not
seem so pressing.

Perhaps Copernicus's theory is now of greater value in under-
mining man's conceit in imagining himself the centre of the
universe, than as a description of celestial phenomena.

Bacon regarded astrology as full of superstition, but believed
that it should be reformed rather than rejected altogether. Its
assertions of coincidences should be tested by thorough research,

and if verified, accepted. The possibility of stars asserting influences on the earth should be investigated in terms of physical principles. He was 'certain that the celestial bodies have in them certain influences besides heat and light'. This opinion has been confirmed by the discovery of gravitation and cosmic radio waves. He was inclined to believe that it should be possible to predict comets, meteors, floods, earthquakes, harvests, seditious schisms and transmigrations of peoples.

Research by future experiments, consideration of past experiments, the study of traditions and the explanation of such events in terms of scientific principles, should throw light on all these matters.

In his new Metaphysics, or principles of science, Bacon explains that the Forms, which are what we call scientific laws, are not, as was formerly believed, beyond the power of human discovery. They are the most fundamental part of knowledge, and the difficulty of discovering them is an indication of their importance.

But it must not be supposed that because we have difficulty in discovering them, they do not exist. 'They are ill discoverers who think there is no land where they can see nothing but sea.' Plato, 'a man of sublime wit (and one that surveyed all things as from a lofty cliff) did in his doctrine of ideas descry that Forms were the true objects of knowledge'. But unfortunately he supposed that his Ideas were 'absolutely abstracted from matter', and this led him to mix up his science with theology, by which it became 'infected and polluted'.

In the past, men had withdrawn their thoughts too soon from experience and particulars, and so failed to find the laws in nature. On securing a general idea they had given themselves up to meditating on it, before they had established its true relevance to the phenomena under consideration.

Democritus's Atomism the best Philosophy for Science

The discovery of laws is the main duty of science, for it reveals the utmost possibility of changing and transforming things. Plato had correctly urged scientists to seek these laws, but there had been a lack of perseverance in the hard and painful task of keeping the mind ever in contact with matter and experience.

He found, too, that Plato, Aristotle, Galen and their followers had hindered the advance of science by their preoccupation with

the explanation of the sequence of events in terms of final causes
outside the sequence itself. Thus Plato referred every scientific
phenomenon too precipitately to God. 'The Inquisition of
Final Causes is barren, and like a virgin consecrated to God
produces nothing.' In this famous comment Bacon did not imply
that religious devotions were valueless, but that they were irrelevant to science.

Aristotle was even worse than Plato, for he found the final cause
in nature, and substituted nature for God.

Hence 'the natural philosophy of Democritus and others, who
removed God and Mind from the structure of things' and
assigned the causes of particular things to the necessity of matter,
without any intermixture of final causes, seems to 'have been, as
regards physical causes, much more solid and to have penetrated
further into nature than that of Plato and Aristotle . . .'. Nevertheless, Bacon elsewhere makes his debt to Aristotle quite clear.
'I, that should know best, do freely acknowledge that I had my
light from him; for where he gave me not matter to perfect, at
the least he gave me occasion to invent.'

When Aristotle 'made nature pregnant with final causes' in
such assertions as 'nature does nothing in vain', he had in fact
no further need of God. How much superior was the effect of
Democritus's philosophy of atoms, for while subtle wits approved
of this as an explanation of phenomena, they laughed at the
notion that the fabric of the universe had come together as a
fortuitous concourse of atoms. Such an alternative to God was
obviously ridiculous, so Democritus had performed a great service to theology in making it more than ever clear that God
was necessary. The atomic theory was respectable as well as
apposite.

Thus, the philosophy of Democritus was to be preferred, and
men's thoughts were to be directed towards the Atomic Theory,
both on scientific and theological grounds. In this way, Bacon
contributed to the spade-work on the foundations of the prodigious creation of Atomic Science, which has indeed given man the
power to exterminate life.

A List of Required Inventions

He advocated the extension of the practical mechanics, inventions and building of machines described by Hero, and the
technique of mining and mineralogy described by Agricola, and

said that this kind of practical science ought to be developed more diligently by the moderns.

Those who worked in these fields seem to advance only by acquiring discoveries and improvements as they occurred by accident. They were like sailors who navigate by hugging the shore. But he thought that hardly any fundamental alterations of nature could be discovered, either by accident or by experiment, without the prior discovery of scientific laws. It is difficult to believe that silver could be converted into gold, but if it is possible it can only be found out through the mastery of physics, which can throw light on the causes of the properties of metals, such as density, colour, malleability, hardness, etc.

In our own time gold has been made successfully out of another metal, through our knowledge of the laws of atomic physics.

Like making gold, the retardation of old age and restoration of youth, seemed hardly credible possibilities, but if they were to be discovered they would be derived from the science which is now called biochemistry.

In order that 'human invention may be stimulated', he desired that an inventory of all inventions and practical scientific processes be made, so that 'those who address themselves to the discovery of new inventions may not waste their pains upon things already discovered and extant'.

He suggested that a list should be made of things which in common opinion seemed impossible. Against each of these the existing inventions which seem to come closest to them should be noted. The comparison would help to show in which directions inventions may be possible. For instance, the artificial freezing of water by the mixture of ice and salt revealed a new principle of great importance. It was easy to melt and vapourize things by fire, but hitherto there had been great difficulty in cooling and condensing things. Bacon recognized in the discovery the principle of refrigeration, 'than which nothing is more serviceable to man'.

Bacon regarded mathematics as belonging to what he called metaphysics or the principles of nature. It was the auxiliary or handmaid to every branch of science. But it had come to pass, he knew not how, that mathematics and logic had presumed to domineer over science on the strength of their certainty. Profound though it is, mathematics should be kept in its place. He suggested that there was room for improvement in 'the abridgement of compilation', and in the use of infinite series in physics. Napier's invention of logarithms, the inventions of the calculus, and of modern calculating machines bear him out.

He predicted that as physics 'advances farther and farther every day', it will 'require fresh assistance from mathematics in many things'. 'If men be not idle,' many new branches of applied mathematics will come into existence.

Co-operation in the Conquest of Nature

After his considerations of God and of Nature, he proceeded to consider Man. He announced that he entered this field not as a combatant but as a trumpeter, and hoped accordingly to be able to proceed unhurt between the fiercest and bitterest contestants of rival opinions.

For his was not 'a trumpet which summons and excites men to cut each other to pieces with mutual contradictions, or to quarrel and fight with one another; but rather to make peace between themselves, and turning with united forces against the Nature of Things, to storm and occupy her castles and strongholds, and extend the bounds of human empire, as far as God Almighty in his goodness may permit'.

He had foreseen the policy that would be required by the scientific and technical society of the twentieth century in order to survive.

The supreme knowledge for man, from his personal point of view, was knowledge of himself. But this was a part of the knowledge of nature. While the separation of fields of knowledge is helpful for the purposes of investigation, it should never be forgotten that it is artificial. When sciences are isolated from one another they tend to become barren, and may depart from common sense.

He thought that while the miseries of men had been set forth 'elegantly and copiously', their abilities had not been sufficiently described. He therefore suggested that a treatise on the supreme achievements of man, moral and intellectual, should be compiled, in order to show what humanity is capable of.

Body and Mind

The study of the mutual interaction of body and mind would be fruitful. Useful knowledge of the human body at rest had been gained in anatomy, but knowledge of the body in motion was even more important, and was equally susceptible of investigation. He suggested, too, that the interpretation of dreams could be put on a more scientific basis.

There was no doubt that the imagination could hurt the body, and it was necessary to investigate how far it can mend the body and cure ill-health. As pestilential airs could hurt the body, might not beneficial airs exist, which could 'cure a man in sickness'? This is one of the suggestions which led to the study of 'airs' for curing disease.

Bacon discussed knowledge of the body under the headings of medicine, cosmetics, athletics and the 'Art Voluptuary'.

The most pressing need in this field was for a true and developed natural philosophy 'for the science of medicine to be built upon'. He found that the literature of medicine was exceedingly repetitive. There was a great deal of professing to cure disease, but much less labour on finding out how. The positive advances in medical knowledge were even smaller.

He advocated the development of comparative anatomy, in which the structures of different kinds of animals are compared, as providing a wider comprehension of the relations between organs and diseases.

The lack of an anatomy of living bodies was a defect, even though 'it is a thing hateful and inhuman'. But it was nevertheless true that many anatomical features not present in dead bodies were visible in live ones. Consequently, he recommended the use of vivisection.

'Wherefore that utility may be considered as well as humanity, the anatomy of the living subject is not to be relinquished altogether, nor referred (as it was by Celsus) to the casual practices of surgery; since it may be well discharged by the dissection of beasts alive, which, notwithstanding the dissimilitude of their parts to human, may, with the help of a little judgment, sufficiently satisfy this inquiry.'

He was opposed to naming diseases as 'incurable', as this was made an excuse for not investigating them. He suggested the compilation of a list of so-called incurable diseases, in order to draw attention to them as problems to be solved.

The Science of Old Age

He was particularly interested in the Prolongation of Life, a subject which he considered had been grossly neglected. It was necessary not only to live long, but healthily, with a vigorous body and mind.

In our own day, with the improvements in sanitation, nutrition and medicine, the proportion of old people is growing rapidly. The prolongation of their lives in a state of vigour, through which they can be both happy and useful, is a problem of increasing importance. As a consequence, it is becoming a subject of properly equipped and endowed research, and is now called gerontology. Bacon foresaw this new science, which would have been particularly close to his heart.

He regarded cosmetics as a science ministering to cleanliness, decency and modesty. In so far as it contributed to these it was to be esteemed, but he had no use for 'that adulterate decoration, which makes use of dyes and pigments'.

Athletics was to be cultivated in so far as it conduces to 'the procuring of any kind of ability of which the human body is capable; whether of ability or endurance'.

Scarcely anyone had looked into the science underlying record performances, such as the holding of the breath by divers. He thought that it was due to training, or 'continual custom from boyhood'.

Bacon was not sure of the social as distinct from the scientific value of the ability to break records, 'for the Olympic Games are over long since; and besides in such things mediocrity is enough for use, excellency in them serving for the most part only for mercenary ostentation'.

Sight and sound are the noblest of the senses, leading to painting, architecture, decoration and music, and requiring mathematics for their analysis. The other senses are more 'allied to luxury than magnificence'.

It had been well observed that military arts flourish in the rise of states, literary arts when at their peak, and voluptuary arts when in decline. 'And I fear that this our age of the world, as being somewhat on the descent of the wheel, inclines to arts voluptuary.'

The Human Mind

After reviewing the sciences of the human body, Bacon considered the Human Soul. It had two parts, the rational and the irrational. The first was divine, and presided over by religion. The second man had in common with the brutes, and was sub-

ject to scientific investigation. It was a material thing, by which
the motions of the body and the senses were operated. It passed
along the nerves and muscles, enabling the body to perform its
various actions. How this occurred was little understood. He
indicated that the mode of operation of the muscular and nervous
systems should be made a subject of research. He noted that all
natural bodies had 'a kind of choice in receiving what is agreeable, and avoiding what is hostile'.

Living tissue responds to a stimulus. But this sort of perception is not necessarily revealed in sensation. For instance, the
digestion, the heart and many other organs 'are like so many
workshops' each performing its own work, with substances supplied to them, yet all these reflex actions proceed without sensation.

Bacon helped to formulate the conception of nervous and
reflex action developed by Descartes, which became the inspiration of modern research in this field, such as that of Sherrington
and Pavlov.

After his discussion of what should be done in the realm of
the irrational soul, or the muscular and nervous physiology which
man shares with the animals, Bacon considered the condition of
the knowledges with which the rational soul, that is, the human
mind, is concerned. These are Logic and Ethics. Logic is the
mode of operation of the reason, the application of which leads
to indications of what can be done, while ethics comprises the
principles of operation of the will which produces action.

In both provinces, execution is carried out through the imagination. The images raised in it through the messages from the
senses are examined by the reason, which judges and selects what
shall be done in the light of them, and the imagination is then
called upon to put these decisions into action.

In matters of faith and religion the imagination raises itself
above the reason. It is possible, too, for the imagination to be so
inflamed by eloquence that it 'becomes ungovernable, and not
only sets reason at nought, but offers violence to it, partly by
blinding, partly by incensing it'.

Logic was 'less delightful to the taste and palate of most
minds'. Its 'dry light' parched most men's 'soft and watery
natures'. But to speak truly, 'rational knowledges are the keys
of all other arts'.

The logical arts are four in number, dealing respectively with invention, criticism, memory and tradition. He found that concerned with invention altogether wanting. As America would never have been discovered unless the magnetic compass had been discovered first, so it could not be regarded as strange that no further progress has been made in the discovery and advancement of the arts, 'when the art itself of discovery and invention has as yet been passed over'.

Traditional logic says nothing and takes no thought of arts and sciences. Indeed, those 'who have written about the first inventors of things or the origins of sciences have celebrated chance rather than art, and represented brute beasts, quadrupeds, birds, fishes, serpents, as the doctors of sciences, rather than men . . .'.

It was for this reason that the Egyptians, who invented so many of the useful arts, filled their temples with statues of beasts rather than men. The Greeks, who did attribute the first inventions to men, nevertheless did not ascribe them to thought but to accident. This is illustrated by the story of Prometheus, who did not discover fire through the study of such a phenomenon as the striking of sparks from flint, but came upon it by accident at the foot of Jupiter's chair, and stole it.

So it seemed that 'hitherto men are rather beholden to a wild goat for surgery, to a nightingale for music, to the ibis for clysters, to the pot lid that flew off for artillery, and in a word to chance, or anything else rather than to Logic'.

The pot lid that flew off is reminiscent of the nursery story of how James Watt came to recognize the power that resides in steam. Both of them go back to the ancient belief that invention arises from accident or chance. Bacon's dissatisfaction with this belief, and his demand for systematic invention based on science is one of his most valuable contributions.

The Science of Invention

Men had hitherto made little use of reason, and no use at all of systematic research and experiment in the discovery of inventions.

The kind of induction which logicians had proposed for the discovery of inventions was quite incompetent. Anyone who studies how the mind proceeds in scientific discovery will find that 'she does of herself by nature manage and act an induction much better than logicians describe it'.

The logicians' induction merely enumerated a number of particulars, from which a probable conjecture was drawn. The particulars were not submitted to a test to determine whether they could provide evidence on the point at issue, and that their selection was relevant. They used them merely as starting-points, from which they could hurry on to the deduction of their theories and dogmas, and as 'serjeants or whifflers to drive back the crowd and make way for their opinions, and never called them into council from the first, for the purpose of legitimate and mature deliberation concerning the truth of things'.

The deductive method of reasoning may be legitimately used in the 'popular sciences, such as ethics, politics, laws', and in divinity also, 'because it has pleased God in His goodness to accommodate Himself to the capacity of man; but in physics, where the point is not to master an adversary in argument, but to command nature in operation, truth slips wholly out of our hands, because the subtlety of nature is so much greater than the subtlety of words . . .'.

The failure to derive the correct starting material from the examination of the original data of experience, or the raw material of science, prevented deductions from this defective starting material from arriving at valid conclusions.

This was the reason why so many of the most gifted philosophers had become sceptics, and had concluded that man could never achieve any certain knowledge, or any knowledge other than of appearances.

The sceptics laid the blame on the deceptiveness of the senses. Assuming that these could provide no sound basic information, they 'pulled up the sciences by the very roots'.

But 'the senses, though they often deceive us or fail us, may nevertheless, with diligent assistance, suffice for knowledge'. This may be obtained through instruments which magnify the powers of the senses, such as telescopes and thermometers, but far more through experiments which enable the sense to perceive effects which would otherwise be too subtle for it.

He found that the methods in use for drawing correct conclusions from the perception of the senses were very deficient. He said this not to discourage men and disable the intellect, but to stir them 'to provide the intellect with proper helps for overcoming the difficulties and obscurities of nature'. He therefore was labouring with all his might 'to make the mind of man by help of art a match for the nature of things; to discover an art of indication and direction, whereby all other arts with their axioms and works may be detected and brought to light'.

He had to record that so far, this art did not exist. Meanwhile, through the sagacity developed from scientific knowledge and experimental experience, which is more like 'a kind of hunting by scent than a science', it is possible to produce a shower of inventions both useful and new. If these results from the different sciences are brought 'within the knowledge of one man, or of a few who may sharpen one another in conference', they may shed light on each other and lead to further discoveries of an entirely new character.

Information Services

After reviewing the state of experimentation as a means of increasing knowledge and invention, Bacon drew attention to what are now called information services, and the methods of using them. They are a kind of mixture of 'logic with the proper matter of each science'.

The discovery of what is already known is essential, otherwise the scientist, however gifted, will have no materials at the frontier of knowledge to work upon. 'The scope and end of this invention is readiness and present use of our knowledge rather than addition or simplification thereof'. To save the scientist's time, 'the place where a thing is to be looked for may be marked, and as it were indexed'.

Meditation on the information acquired from this index will help to suggest the questions which should be asked, for 'a faculty of wise interrogating is half a knowledge'. As Plato had said: 'whosoever seeks a thing, knows that which he seeks in a general notion, else how shall he know it when he has found it?'

Scientists should be trained in how to use libraries, and select and read with advantage 'those authors, books, and parts of books', which may best help them in finding what they require. He gave an example of how students of mechanics should assemble material for the investigation of mass, weight and gravity.

Finally, the methods of discovering relevant scientific information, like those of scientific discovery itself, should be continually improved. For men can be 'assured that the solid and true arts of invention grow and increase as inventions themselves increase . . .'.

Limitations of Personality, or the Personal Equation

After considering the method by which the mind makes discoveries, it is necessary to examine the fallacies to which it is susceptible, in order to take precautions against them.

Very careful consideration should be given to the general notions from which any investigation is to start. If this is not done, the investigation is liable to end in disputes about words. Words and verbal descriptions which do not adequately describe the notion under discussion lead to the worst confusions, which are the greatest hindrances to advances in knowledge. They are the 'sophisms of sophisms'. Here Bacon drew attention to the basic idea which has led to modern Semantics, which deals with the science of words and symbols, and their relation to philosophy.

The mind suffers in its operations from four limitations. There is the limitation arising from the nature of man in general. There is the limitation arising from the individual nature of each man. There is that arising from the use of words and the other means of communication of information from one man to another. Finally, there is the limitation which is imposed on the mind through its being possessed by false theories, which prevents it from recognizing the true meaning of the facts before it.

Bacon adopted social symbols for indicating these four causes of fallacy. He called them idols, and respectively Idols of the Tribe, of the Cave, of the Market-Place and of the Theatre.

The fourth kind, arising from the belief in wrong theories, can be entirely removed by the acquisition of correct theories, but it is impossible wholly to eliminate the other three.

Examples of the first kind are the tendency of the mind to prefer confirmation of an accepted theory, and to assume uniformities in nature which do not exist, such as the belief that all heavenly bodies move in perfect circles.

The limitation of the second kind arises from the peculiar nature of each man's mind and body, his customs and education, and the particular experiences that have befallen him.

But the most serious is of the third kind, which arises from 'the tacit agreement of men concerning the imposition of words and names'.

Words are generally invented for common use, and are consequently adapted to such broad lines of definition as can be easily understood. When an attempt is made to define them more acurately by acute intellectual examination and diligent observation, it is found that the words, inherently unsuited to these processes, rebel.

Communications Theory

Here Bacon is a forerunner of information or communications theory, which has been stimulated in recent years by the development of telephony, automation and other modern techniques.

He pointed out 'that whatever can be divided into differences sufficiently numerous to explain the variety of notions (provided those differences be perceptible to the sense) may be made a vehicle to convey the thoughts of one man to another'. From this principle, all methods of communication of knowledge are derived.

The Social Status of Science

After discussing the technique of discovering and communicating knowledge, Bacon considered the state of knowledge of the mind itself, as an apparatus. He found that the moral philosophers had given excellent descriptions of the proper aims of the mind, but not of how the mind should be trained and improved to attain them.

He believed that this neglect had arisen from the tendency of men to despise 'ordinary and common matters which are neither subtle enough for disputation, nor illustrious enough for ornament'. But in order to tackle the subject, he said he would not scruple to throw aside the dignity of his name and wit, in his endeavour to advance human interests, 'Being one that should properly perhaps be an architect in philosophy and the sciences', he would on occasion advisedly 'turn common labourer, hodman, anything that is wanted', taking upon himself 'the burden and execution of many things which must needs be done, and which others through an inborn pride shrink from and decline'.

Here Bacon helped to raise and establish the social status of routine research, which has been essential for the modern development of science.

He started by asking whether the mind is seen at its best in the contemplative or the active life, and decided strongly in favour of the active life. For this brought the mind in contact with things as well as moral principles. The contemplative life tends to concentrate on personal interests, while the active is concerned

with public interests. To fail in virtuous efforts on behalf of the
public is a much greater source of happiness than to obtain
everything that we wish for ourselves. The truly virtuous man
cannot withdraw from affairs, for 'men must know that in this
theatre of man's life it is reserved only for God and Angels to
be lookers-on'.

The first step in the inquiry of how to improve the working
of the mind is to investigate what is, and what is not, within its
power. It is necessary to ascertain the nature of a mind, just as
one must ascertain the nature of a soil, before one can cultivate
it. The various types of personality should be enumerated, so
that the treatment appropriate for each particular type could be
worked out.

The assessment of character is one of the few things in which
the common discourse of men is wiser than books. But many
useful examples could be found in the poets and historians.
Machiavelli was particularly valuable because he described what
men do and not what they ought to do. It is impossible for the
virtuous man to deal with the wicked unless he understands all
the recesses of his malice.

He recommended Julius Caesar as an instructive example, for
he had written much, and much had been written about him,
and he was thoroughly known. He thought him, apart from his
ambition, the most highly endowed personality of the 'uncon-
verted world'.

Bacon wrote a brief biography of Caesar. It is one of the most
perfect, if not the most perfect, of brief biographies ever composed. He depicted Caesar as a master propagandist who used
this art to secure a base for the acquisition of military power, as
a means to absolute power: a startlingly modern figure.

Psychoanalysis

Portraits of individuals were not, however, enough. Characters should be analysed into their separate traits, so that all
the traits which can exist in the human mind should be identified
and recorded. Any particular character would then be a combination of a certain number of these basic traits. The nature of
separate traits should be investigated, and the connexion between traits, and their influence on one another, should be ascertained.

In this way, says Bacon, 'we may have a scientific and accurate
G

dissection of minds and characters; and the secret dispositions of particular men may be revealed; and that from the knowledge thereof better rules may be procured for treatment of the mind.'

He says that not only must these innate dispositions be analysed and recorded, but also those 'imposed in the mind by sex, by age, by region, by health and sickness, by beauty and deformity . . . and again, those which are caused by fortune, as sovereignty, nobility, obscure birth, riches, want, magistracy, privateness, prosperity, adversity, and the like'.

Unless all these differences and varieties were ascertained, it would not be possible to apply the treatment appropriate to the particular mind, and one would be in danger of making the mistake of the empirical doctors, who give the 'same medicines to all patients of every constitution'.

The diseases of the mind are most adequately portrayed by the poets and historians, who 'are the best doctors of this knowledge'. They show how the affections are excited, pacified and controlled, 'how they disclose themselves, though repressed and concealed', how they interact, and 'fight and encounter one with another . . .'.

Bacon uses the notion of psychological repressions and conflicts, and says that the latter is 'of special use on moral and civil matters', for, by setting affection against affection, one may be used to master another. 'For as in the government of states, it is sometimes necessary to bridle one faction with another, so it is in the internal government of the mind.'

In his recommendation of the poets as psychologists, he may have had Shakespeare in mind, for he would have seen *Hamlet* and *Macbeth*, with their classical depictions of the operations of repressed complexes.

After considering the innate traits, which are outside the individual's own control, Bacon discussed those agents, such as custom, exercise, habit, education, friendship, etc., which have a great influence on the mind, but are within the individual's control.

With a knowledge both of the innate and the controllable traits of mind, the individual is in a position to follow an appropriate course for mental health and happiness. He can best achieve this by choosing a virtuous aim in life, such as may be 'within his compass to attain'. By embarking on such a course, all the

traits of his mind will work together with the maximum harmony.
And as there seems to be a relation between the good of the mind
and the good of the body, improved physical health will accompany a tranquil and happy mind.

Bacon concluded his contribution to the foundation of modern
psychology with the remark that if anyone judged that he had
done nothing more than 'collect into an art or science that which
has been omitted by other writers as matter of common sense and
experience, and sufficiently clear and self-evident, he is welcome
to his opinion', but he should remember that he was in pursuit of
utility and truth, not beauty.

'*Commanding Attention and Winning Disciples*'

His programme for research in the arts of private and public
affairs was significant. He excluded the science of government or
politics, making the excuse that James I, to whom he had addressed this review, had been brought up in this science since
he was in the cradle, had already been on the English throne for
eighteen years, and was in no need of instruction.

He therefore restricted himself to an outline of the art of
managing one's own life, or the science of self-advancement. He
thought that personal was more difficult than public morality,
because 'civil knowledge requires only an external goodness, for
that suffices for society'.

The quality which recommends a man most to those in
authority is swiftness in the dispatch of business. All other virtues may, under some circumstance, give offence. Men of honour, for example, are liable to be unmanageable.

The first principle in the art of getting on is to study the people
with whom one must deal. Their natures, desires, ends, customs,
means of support, friends, enemies, the party to which they
belong, should be learned by 'carefully procuring good information' of them. It is necessary to study also the actions in which
they are engaged, for 'men change with actions'.

Knowledge of men can be gained in six ways; from their expressions, words, actions, dispositions, ends, and 'by the reports
of others'.

Diligent study of a man's countenance nearly always reveals
something of his secret aims, for it is very difficult to control
the expression completely over a long period.

Words are 'full of trickery and deceit', but even the most

politic man is liable to give himself away if caused to speak suddenly or in anger.

Deeds are 'the most assured pledges which the human mind
can give', but these also must be received with circumspection,
as they may have been performed as blinds to secure confidence.

The surest key to men's minds is obtained by 'searching and
thoroughly understanding' their natures, characters, intentions
and ends.

As for knowing men from the reports of others, a few words
will suffice: 'Men's weaknesses and faults are best known from
their enemies, their virtues and abilities from their friends, their
customs and times from their servants, their opinions and
thoughts from their familiar friends, with whom they discourse
most. General fame is light, and the judgment of superiors is
not much to be trusted; for to them men are more masked. "The
truest character comes from a man's own household";' as Cicero
remarked.

Knowledge of oneself is even more important than that of
others. It is not only a rule of universal wisdom, but has a special
place in politics. One should take an accurate and impartial view
of one's own abilities and limitations, and act so that the former
are slightly over-estimated, and the latter slightly under-
estimated.

The first consideration is to observe whether one's disposition and abilities are consonant with the times, and if they are
not, to lead a more reserved and retired life. One should choose a
profession for which one's abilities are suited, and one in which
there is the minimum number of competitors. As Caesar said, on
invading Gaul, he preferred to be first in a village rather than
second in Rome. One should choose one's friends according to
one's own nature, and be careful not to model one's conduct on
that of others with very different temperaments.

After knowing others and oneself, one should learn how to
show oneself to advantage, without arrogance or causing disgust.
Bacon frequently quoted Machiavelli on men's motives, but he
was careful to dissociate himself from his principle of private
conduct: 'that virtue itself a man should not trouble himself to
attain, but only the appearance thereof to the world because the
credit and reputation of virtue is a help, but the use of it is an
impediment'. He recommended only Good Arts and not Evil
Arts of self-advancement.

As a formulator of the common proverbial philosophy of modern individualism he was a forerunner of Benjamin Franklin, Samuel Smiles and Dale Carnegie.

Bacon says that, so far as he knows, the only book written in antiquity about this kind of 'particular business' is Cicero's *On Canvassing* for the Consulship. Fowler in 1878 agreed with Spedding's conjecture that Bacon in these passages, and in his drafts on different methods of presentation, was experimenting 'in the art of commanding attention and winning disciples'. Bacon contributed to the modern art of public relations.

There is a connexion between his inductive cast of mind, preferring particulars to generalities, his atomism both in physical science and psychology, and his individualism in sociology.

Yet in his thought about the organization and utilization of science, he was collectivist. The ambivalence of his mind is very marked. He was in the habit of investigating simultaneously both sides of every question. Consequently, in his works, equally strong statements in support of contradictory views can frequently be found. He was fond of classifying them in parallel columns.

Antithetical or dialectical modes of thought pervade his philosophy. His most profound aphorisms resolve the contradiction of opposites. His whole life, as well as his thought, was a dialectical struggle, between the active and the contemplative, the personal and the social, the noble and the ignoble.

Social Organization

Bacon did not give a systematic exposition of his views on social organization, but the principles he held are disclosed in the social aims that he recommended to the individual person as wise. Great riches had no real use, except for distributon. Only those riches should be sought that can be got justly, used soberly, distributed cheerfully and left contentedly. Yet one should 'have no abstract nor friarly contempt of them'. He did not conceive great riches as capital for carrying out big constructive enterprises.

The stability of states was ensured by removing poverty. This was obtained by promoting trade and the 'well-balancing of trade', the encouragement of manufactures, the removal of unemployment, the repressing of waste and extravagance, the improvement of the land and agricultural technique, pricecontrol, and moderation of taxes. The population should not be so large as to strain the country's resources. A large population that works hard for modest wages provides a stronger state than a smaller one which spends more and earns less.

If the nobility increased excessively in proportion to the common people the strength of the state was reduced. The same result ensued from too many clergy, 'for they bring nothing to the stock', and also when 'more are bred scholars than preferments can take off', that is, when there are more educated men than suitable jobs for them.

But above all things, good policy should ensure that the wealth of the state is not concentrated in a few hands. 'For otherwise a state may have a great stock, and yet starve. And money is like muck, not good except it be spread.'

When Bacon found himself without the means to secure the place in the ruling class to which he had been born and brought up, he set about extolling the dignity of the middle and professional class into which he had been forced. 'Every man is a debtor to his profession,' he said, trying to put the best face on it. He assembled reasons why persons of the middle rank should be specially esteemed, and announced that he aspired to nothing more than a life of useful activity in the rank between a gentleman and a labourer. Indeed, men of the middle rank, such as yeomen, were the heart of the state. Yeomen made the best soldiers, for they had farms sufficiently large to keep them in 'convenient plenty and no servile condition'. They were physically strong and mentally independent, and it was advantageous to the state that the ploughs and instruments of agriculture should be in the hands of owners or at least tenants, and not in those of 'mere hirelings'. In his exclusion from a position in government, he remembered the virtues of the class from which his ancestors had sprung. He was in favour of an even distribution of property.

Bacon described himself as 'between nobility and people', working towards the welfare state.

The only justification for aspiring to power and place is that they are necessary for carrying out good works. For plans for benefiting men are little better than good dreams without the means of realizing them. But 'the rising into place is laborious; and by pains men come to greater pains; and it is sometimes base; and by indignities men come to dignities. The standing is slippery and the regress is either a downfall, or at least an eclipse, which is a melancholy thing . . . ', as he wrote in the second edition of his *Essays* in 1612; a prophetic forecast of his own experience. It suggests that Bacon was unsure of himself and aware of unresolved conflicts in his mind.

Universal Justice

After his brief remarks on politics, he enters with more enthusiasm on the deficiencies in the science of the law. All who have written on law have either been philosophers or lawyers. The former had been concerned with precepts generally not applicable in practice, while the latter had been concerned entirely with particular laws, such as the laws of their own country. But, says Bacon, surely those who are best qualified to discuss the general principles of law, or Universal Justice, are statesmen, 'who best understand the condition of civil society, welfare of the people, natural equity, customs of nations, and different forms of government; and who may therefore determine laws by the rules and principles both of natural equity and policy'.

He proposed the invention of comparative law, by which the fundamental principles of justice common to all good laws could be derived from a comparison of the laws of the various nations and codes. He called these 'laws of laws'. The quality of any existing or proposed law could be determined by comparison with these fundamental principles.

He proceeded, in ninety-seven aphorisms, to found the subject. The end of laws is 'the happiness of the citizens', though in the interpretation of law the people is 'the teacher of all errors'.

Besides providing principles which influenced the drafting of the Code Napoleon, and the reformation of English law in the nineteenth century, this profound work illustrates Bacon's conception of the rôle of statesmanship in the realm of learning. The statesman could perform functions above the powers of specialists within learning itself. This applied to natural as well as legal science. Only the statesman experienced in affairs and conversant with the main branches of science can draft a social policy which will provide for the proper development both of science and society in themselves and in their inherent inter-relations.

The Separation of Science and Religion

Bacon concluded his review of existing knowledge with a consideration of religion. He said that 'Sacred Theology ought to be derived from the word and oracles of God, and not from the light of nature, or the dictates of reason.'

Nevertheless, reason may be utilized in a secondary capacity to explore the consequences of the principles enumerated in revelation. Religion differs from natural knowledge, in that in the latter, principles as well as consequences are amenable to examination by reason. In this respect, religion is like 'games, as chess or the like, that the first rules and laws are merely positive, and at will; and that they must be received as they are, and not disputed; but how to play a skilful and winning game is scientific and rational'.

He thought that a temperate and careful treatise on the proper use of human reason in theology would be of especial use and benefit, for it would 'act as an opiate', which would not only lull 'curious speculations', but also in some degree 'assuage the fury of controversies, wherewith the church is troubled'.

Bacon regarded himself as a sincere Christian, but his theology was of a kind which raised the minimum number of obstacles to the pursuit of social and scientific aims.

A Message to Posterity

On re-examining the 'small globe of the intellectual world' he had just completed, it seemed to him that it was 'not unlike those sounds and preludes which musicians make while they are tuning their instruments, and which produce indeed a harsh and unpleasing sound to the ear, but tend to make the music sweeter afterwards'.

He hoped that the strings would in the future be touched by a better hand. He saw a promise of this in the condition of the times, in which there seemed to be a third revival of learning, following on the Greek and Roman. The numerous able men, the art of printing which brought books within the reach of all men, the exploration of the world in every part, 'whereby multitudes of experiments unknown to the ancients have been disclosed, and an immense mass added to Natural History', provided the means and the material. Opportunity was given by the greater leisure now available to the greatest minds, by the peace which Britain, Spain, Italy, France and many other countries enjoyed, the 'exhaustion of all that can be thought or said on religious questions', which had diverted so much energy and attention from the development of natural knowledge. He believed that the new period of learning would far surpass those of the past, 'if only men will wisely and honestly know their own strength and their own weakness; and take from one another the light of invention and not the fire of contradiction; and esteem the inquisition of truth as a noble enterprise, and not a pleasure or an armament; and employ wealth and magnificence on things of worth and excellence, not on things vulgar and of popular estimation'.

For his part, he would not have been true to his aim if he had not added as much as he could to the inventions of others, being however no less willing that his own inventions should be 'surpassed by posterity'. He hoped that in those things in which he had erred, he had not prejudiced the discovery of the truth by misleading arguments. He recognized that a whole age might perhaps be required to prove his words, and 'many ages to perfect them'. But it was enough for him to have 'sown a seed for posterity'.

8. *How it is to be Done*

THE importance of the second part of the *Novum Organum* is not that it gives a demonstration of how discoveries are to be made, but that in it several of the logical processes involved in discovery, and used intuitively, are brought out and consciously explained for the first time. In doing this, Bacon made important contributions to inductive logic. The process of scientific discovery is still far from being completely analysed, but Bacon's contribution constitutes a mighty fragment of the whole process which may one day be worked out. There is still much disagreement about his contributions to scientific method. Some of his ablest admirers, who rate his technical contributions to inductive logic very highly, doubt whether he made any original contributions to scientific method as it is at present practised.

It is possible that Bacon's work on scientific method will prove to be even more significant for the future than it has been up to the present. Following the opinion of Robert Hooke, the seeds of a future machinery of scientific discovery may be found in them.

But for the majority of readers the *Novum Organum*, or the new method containing 'true directions concerning the interpretation of nature' is not an appropriate title for Bacon's chief book. They would find Nature, Aims and Possibilities of Science more relevant, and they would regard the second part dealing with method as subsidiary.

The matter did not appear to Bacon in this light, because the idea of an improved method of discovery occurred to him first. He regarded it as the more fundamental. It was only after he was convinced that an improved method could be discovered that he thought it worth while working out what the implications of the 'discovery of discovery' would be for the human race.

Bacon conceived the basic features of his project in early youth, and developed them throughout his life. He worked on the same notions over and over again, expressing them with variations and extensions, in different forms and styles, according to his current preoccupations. His persistent attention to them enabled him to explore their numerous perspectives and nuances. Rawley said that he had seen at least twelve drafts of the *Novum Organum*. Bacon's thoughts grew and developed from embryonic forms conceived in his youth. They were clarified during this process of growth. As he was trying to express growing notions, not set ideas whose growth was complete, it is not generally possible to select any particular statement of one of his basic notions, and say that it is the best.

The same notions underlie *Valerius Terminus*, the *Dignity and Advancement of Learning*, the *Novum Organum* and his other works, so that all of these overlap. The treatment of the same topics in these various works each has its peculiar bloom and significance, and in some cases it is necessary to see how he has dealt with the same notion in different works, especially in the three mentioned.

Because Bacon's notions were always developing they are not susceptible of final expression. Like living organisms they retain their inherent characteristics, but are never repeated in quite the same form. This living quality in his notions is one of the sources of the permanent viability and suggestiveness of his thought.

As his notions were alive they were able to take root and grow in other men's minds. Their power arises not from their precision but their capacity for growth.

Descartes followed Bacon in devoting his chief work to Method. He and others carried forward and clarified notions that Bacon had formulated, and turned them into effective instruments of research. But the gain in clarity was at the expense of Bacon's ultimately more fertile universality.

Bacon's notions cannot, like mathematics, be reduced to a few general principles but must, to some extent, be described in their various manifestations, as a naturalist describes the multitude of living things because summaries of their general features leave so much out.

Bacon bequeathed the *Novum Organum* to mankind, with the statement that, having reasoned with himself in the following manner, he judged that it would be for 'the interest of the present and future generations that they should be acquainted with his thoughts'.

He was convinced that the human intellect raises its own difficulties, through failing to make use of the aids to its operation that are at hand. He thought that every effort should be made to try to find these, through the interaction between the mind and nature, 'which is more precious than anything on earth, or at least than anything that is of the earth'.

The mind will make little progress if it is left entirely to go its own way, because the primary notions of things that it imbibes from experience contain false elements and are over-hastily abstracted. Unless these defects are removed by the natural force of the understanding, or by the application of due scientific method and logic, we raise our knowledge on an inadequate basis and it is like a magnificent building without a foundation.

While men are engaged in admiring the mind's false powers, its true powers are passed over. But if the mind is furnished with the proper aids, and men are content to wait on nature and not try to overrule her, these true powers can be brought within reach.

Bacon did not suppose that knowledge was based on simple unanalysed experience. This could provide true knowledge only after it had been duly sifted, and errors arising from the nature of the senses and the understanding had been removed.

As knowledge had hitherto been reared on inadequate foundations, he supposed that there was nothing else to be done than to attempt to reconstruct, according to a better plan, the whole edifice of sciences, arts and human knowledge, on a proper foundation. This seems to be an infinite labour and beyond the powers of man, but when it is considered, it is found to be not so forbidding.

So, in spite of the solitary nature of the enterprise, and knowing how difficult it was to make it seem worth while, he was not to be deterred from entering on the one path by which the human mind could attain true knowledge. For it was better to make a modest beginning which would lead to something, than to follow impressive courses which end nowhere.

As the discovery which he had made might not occur to anyone else for a long time, and he had not observed any predecessor following the same line, he thought he should publish an account immediately, though incomplete. This haste was not inspired by ambition or the desire for priority, but in order to promote the work and leave on record an outline, in case of his death; and as a memorial of his 'honest mind and inclination towards the benefit of the human race'.

Bacon followed his manifesto to the future with a dedication to James I, in which he apologized for having taken so much time from his Majesty's business in order to pursue philosophical inquiries. He suggested, however, that his work might contribute to the memory of James and the honour of his age.

He said that his notions, whether worth anything or not, were certainly new, though copied from nature and the human mind. He felt that they were the 'child of time rather than of wit', and were extraordinary only in that such deep suspicions should have entered any man's mind about things which had been established for so long. That this discovery had fallen to him had been a kind of luck, which he ascribed to God's goodness, and the felicity of James's times. As he had been 'an honest and affectionate servant' of the King in his life, so after his death he might be the means, through kindling the new light in philosophy, of making the 'age famous to posterity'.

Bacon followed this far-from-skilful flattery of so vain a man and intellectual as James I with an appeal to him to order the collecting of a Natural and Experimental History, unencumbered with book-learning, according to a plan which Bacon would lay down, in order to provide at last, after so many ages, a solid foundation for philosophy and the sciences.

He had 'provided the machine, but the stuff must be gathered from the facts of nature'.

The dedication of the *Novum Organum* provides one of the many pieces of evidence that Bacon's devotion to philosophy and science took precedence over his other passions. It follows that our judgment of Bacon must primarily depend on our assessment of his services to philosophy and science.

In his preface Bacon said that the progress of philosophy and science had been held up by those who presumed to pronounce on everything, and by the sceptics who contended that knowledge is impossible. He considered that some of the arguments of the latter were not to be despised, but that the better course had been taken by the early Greek philosophers, who held views between these two extremes. They were frequently complaining of the difficulty of discovering any truth about nature, but they evidently believed in trying rather than arguing. They depended entirely, however, on the force of their understanding, and tried to find the truth by sheer hard thinking, without the aid of any special method.

Bacon's preference for the early Greek philosophers is in accordance with modern scientific thought, and is one of the qualities which have enabled him to be a formulator of the attitude to experience and nature which has made modern science possible.

He said that the new method he had invented was easy to explain though hard to practise. He proposed to establish progressive stages in reaching certainty. He started from the evidence of the senses subject to a due process of correction, but he mostly rejected the mental operation which usually follows the sensation. He proposed instead to apply the mind to the original simple sensation according to a new procedure. Those who had attributed so much importance to logic had no doubt also felt that the mind required the help and support of a special procedure, to enable it to escape from some of its own limitations. But they had introduced the procedure of logic, after the mind had already accepted, through the unanalysed experience and exercise of daily life, unsound ideas and principles. Thus logic had been employed at too late a stage to reveal the errors in the basic data from which the thinking had started, and had 'had the effect of fixing errors rather than disclosing truth'.

Consequently, in his opinion, it was necessary to start the

whole work of the understanding over again from the beginning, not leaving the mind to follow its own course, but guiding its operation at every step by a due procedure, as if the business were being done by machinery. Just as mechanics who are set to work with their naked hands, without the help or force of machines, cannot accomplish much even with collective efforts, so natural philosophers cannot accomplish much by the naked force of the understanding without the aid of appropriate method and intellectual machinery.

Mechanics who attempted to shift a gigantic obelisk with their naked hands would be foolish. If, when baffled, they made a selection of extra strong men to attack the task, they would be still more foolish. But if, after the defeat of the extra strong men they then began to train muscular champions for the purpose by athletic methods, they would be mad.

So it is just as mistaken for scientists to suppose that they can make great discoveries merely from the force of the number of scientists engaged in research, or by their collective and co-operative effort, or through sheer acuteness of individual minds, without appropriate scientific method and equipment.

The strengthening of the understanding through the development of logic, which, says Bacon, is 'a kind of athletic art', does not lead to the application of anything more than the naked intellect, even if strengthened by the exercise of logic. But, as in work done by the hand, neither the full strength of each can be exerted individually, nor the strength of all united in collective action, without the aid of tools and machinery in the shape of scientific instruments and method.

Bacon said that as his method was new, it did not impinge on the reputation of the ancient philosophers. No inviduous comparison in ability or wit could arise between him and them, whose reputation remained undimmed. He appeared merely as a guide to point out a new road, 'an office of small authority, and depending more upon a kind of luck than upon any ability or excellency'.

Einstein has expressed a similar view about his own function in the development of physical science. He came to maturity at a time when the difficulties of principle in the theories of Clerk Maxwell and Newton were ripe for solution, which he succeeded in finding. The greatness of the opportunity made the greatness of the achievement possible.

Bacon indicated that he did not wish to interfere with the received philosophy, which he felt was useful for professors' lectures and the ordinary business of life. His new philosophy would not be much concerned with the elegance and perfection of manners, the conduct of committees and the management of persons. It did not flatter the understanding by conforming to preconceived notions, and it would not be appreciated by the vulgar except through its utility and effects.

He suggested that there should be two streams of philosophical endeavour, one for the teaching and the other for the discovery of new knowledge. Most philosophers would have to engage in the former, owing to lack of leisure or mental power to pursue the latter. He invited those who preferred the work of research to join with him in leaving teaching and the outer aspects of things to others, while they in course of time should find a way into the inner structure of nature.

Bacon conceived the development of science as a planned collective activity of many men equipped with a new method and instruments which enhanced their powers of discovery both as individuals and in united action.

He also called for the presentation of scientific knowledge 'in a manner not harsh or unpleasant'. They were to expound their views and write in a good style. 'Words are the footsteps of reason,' and they are to be put down carefully, one after the other, each with an individual completeness, bearing a great and stately weight, and yet forming a dignified harmony. That is the style in which science should be written, and at which he aimed. The style of scientific literature was to be equal to the importance of the discoveries and contributions to fundamental knowledge.

Like his philosophy, Bacon's style was atomic. Each word has its own individuality, though linked with the others. His sentences are like harmonies sounded by striking the separate notes on a piano, not the fused infinitely varying melodies from a violin.

The atomicity of Bacon's ideas goes deep. He said in his *Description of the Intellectual Globe* that nature could not have a definite structure without proceeding in jumps. 'To a deeper searcher of nature it will plainly appear that nature is accustomed to proceed for some distance by degrees, and then suddenly by jumps, and to take these processes in turn. Otherwise, if a man examined it well, no structure of things or organic figure could be formed, if the proceeding were always by imperceptible degrees. . . .'

A similar argument for the quantum theory of the atom was advanced by Niels Bohr in his *Faraday Lecture*. Without the quantum, or atom of energy, matter would be infinitely varying, and nature would be a featureless chaos. Thus Bacon's mode of thought is consonant with the quantum theory, the most characteristic theory of modern science.

Yet another reflection of Bacon's atomistic mode of thought is seen in his choice of the aphorism as the medium for the expression of his philosophy. He pointed out that this had been used by the early Greek philosophers, and helped them to avoid the temptation of building up philosophical systems, like those of Plato and Aristotle, which have an imposing but ill-founded unity. Man's knowledge is far too scrappy and incomplete to be organized into a system, without straining the argument at many points in order to cover the subject.

The aphorism corresponds far more realistically to man's actual very partial knowledge. It consists of 'short and scattered sentences, not linked together by an artificial method', and does not pretend to embrace an entire art. It is therefore, in Bacon's view, more suited to natural philosophy, where knowledge is so incomplete, and in many directions has scarcely begun. In his view, one should always be on one's guard with respect to grand and comprehensive systematizing in natural philosophy. At the same time, while exercising so much caution against systematization in ideas, Bacon insists with equal emphasis on the systematization of the method and plan of research; another example of his dialectical mode of thought, being simultaneously against and for systematization.

Finally, he asked his readers not to make snap judgments on his work, and to suspend their decision until they had acquired some familiarity with his method, and followed the steps in his investigations. Then, after having mastered the material, the reader might, with due consideration, make his own judgment on its value.

9. *Dialectic*

BACON said he chose the aphoristic mode of expression because 'aphorisms, not to be ridiculous must be made out of the pith and heart of sciences', and he had not the time to develop his notions at length.

The aphorism is a form that only the strongest minds can use. This was exemplified by Whewell, who wrote his *Philosophy of the Inductive Sciences* explicitly on Baconian lines, introducing his subject in aphorisms. Whewell was an able man, but his aphorisms look ridiculous beside Bacon's. They lack the dialectical quality of combining opposites, which make Bacon's so suggestive.

Novum Organum is mainly concerned with the natural sciences. This concentration fitted the requirements of the new industrialists, who were making increasing use of science for improving traditional productive processes. It has caused Bacon to be identified as the scientific leader of the new industrialists. Indeed, in his latest works, he repeatedly appeals to the idea of the application of science for profit.

But this narrowing of interest was a deviation from his profoundest aim, which was the creation of the kingdom of man, and the mastery of the universe.

He described the two parts of the *Novum Organum* with a subtitle, indicating that they concern 'The Interpretation of Nature and the Kingdom of Man'. It is significant that only 'The Interpretation of Nature' appears in the title of *Valerius Terminus*, but that seventeen years later, 'the Kingdom of Man' was added. This indicates Bacon's concern in the intervening period with the social significance of his work. He felt it necessary to draw attention to this specifically.

Bacon opens the first part with several of his most famous aphorisms. The first is that 'Man, being the servant and interpreter of Nature, can do and understand so much and so much only as he has observed in fact or in thought of the course of nature: beyond this he neither knows anything nor can do anything.' In his

H

third he says: 'Human knowledge and human power meet in one; for where the cause is not known the effect cannot be produced. Nature to be commanded must be obeyed; and that which in contemplation is as the cause is in operation as the rule.'

Bacon's dialectical thinking is strikingly demonstrated in these aphorisms. Nature, the external world, exists, and the mind exists, but he represents them as an interacting duality, whose parts cannot be separated from each other, and are to be understood and mastered only through their mutual effects.

In this he was a follower of Heraclitus, and a forerunner of Hegel, and of Marx and Engels. Engels said that the laws of man's social activity, 'which have hitherto confronted him as external, dominating laws of nature, will (after the revolution) be applied by man with complete understanding, and hence will be dominated by man'. The understanding of the laws of nature and society makes it possible for man to obey these laws, and in this way he can achieve freedom. 'It is humanity's leap from the realm of necessity into the realm of freedom.'

Stalin said that 'Marxism regards laws of science—whether they be laws of natural science or laws of political economy— as the reflection of objective processes which take place independently of the will of man. Man may discover these laws, get to know them, study them, reckon with them in his activities and utilize them in the interests of society, but he cannot change or abolish them.' He illustrated how knowledge has enabled man to influence phenomena which were hitherto beyond control, by the development of hydro-electric engineering, with the construction of dams and canals for controlling the overflow of big rivers and floods, which had commonly been regarded as inavertible calamities against which man was powerless.

Not only has man learned how to curb the destructive forces of nature, but he has discovered how to harness the forces of nature to social uses, and to utilize water for the irrigation of fields, and the explosive power of the atom to the generation of power. By what Engels calls the 'appreciation of necessity', the need to submit to the laws of nature and society, and to follow them, man achieves freedom, and he can use his freedom, when achieved, to organize society consciously 'on a planned basis'.

As the Chinese put it in 1958: 'The clarion calling for a technological revolution has sounded and the earth-shaking battle has begun. We shall stir up the minerals which have slumbered underground for hundreds of millions of years. We shall control the waters, conquer the calamities of wind and weather and humble nature to our service. Factory chimneys shall arise in all cities, great and small, throughout the land, all places where productive labour is carried on shall hear the music of machinery and electricity will send its light and power to the remotest village. We shall scale the highest peaks of world scientific technique, wipe out poverty, eliminate backwardness and bring our people a life of the greatest happiness.'

Germs of these notions are to be seen in the foundation of Bacon's thought, and it is not surprising that Marx and Engels said that Bacon's philosophy 'occludes within itself the germs of a many-sided development'. The similarity between the thought of Bacon and the modern formulators and operators of planned social development ally him more closely with them than with any other group of social philosophers and statesmen.

Bacon specifically stated that his new method was to be applied to social science as well as natural science, but in fact he spent most of his effort on developing a natural philosophy which would be a stimulating soil for natural science. In his second aphorism he said that 'neither the naked hand nor the understanding left to itself can effect much. It is by instruments and helps that the work is done, which are as much wanted for the understanding as for the hand'. Then, in his fourth, he said that all that man can do towards the effecting of works 'is to put together or put as-under natural bodies. The rest is done by nature working within.' Here he expressed the principle which underlies the operations of chemistry, and especially the synthesis of new materials.

Though the number of the productions of mind and hand seem very numerous, they had all been derived from the comparatively small number of scientific facts already known. These had been discovered more by chance than by science, which so far con-sisted of the nice ordering of things already known, rather than methods for inventing new things and discovering new know-ledge. This situation had arisen from the tendency to admire and extol the powers of the human mind, instead of discovering ways of helping it to function effectively. As nature is far more subtle than the human mind, speculations and meditations can in no wise catch up with it.

The sciences then in existence did not help towards achieving new works, nor did the method of logical analysis then available

help in the discovery of new sciences. Existing logic was primarily
deductive. It aimed at deriving the consequences from known
principles. But it was of no use in finding these principles, which
were usually wrong. It had the effect of deriving the consequences
from wrong principles, and therefore multiplied error. If principles were over-hastily abstracted from the facts, the whole
superstructure derived by deduction would be wrong. Hence
'our only hope therefore lies in a true induction'.

The scientific discoveries so far made lay close to the surface of
popular experience. But deeper discoveries could be made only by
an improved method of intellectual operation. The method in
fashion consisted of flying immediately from the briefest examination of the facts of experience to the most abstract conceptions,
whereas a surer method was required. This should proceed from
the evidence of the senses and particulars, by a gradual and unbroken ascent, so that it arrives at the most general laws last of
all.

The understanding, if left to itself, has a tendency to proceed
in this cautious way, especially if it is not hindered by received
and preconceived ideas, but it is generally too weak to continue in
it without the support of an improved method.

This uninstructed understanding is apt to glance at experiments and particulars in passing, but the new method rises by
gradual steps, establishing the soundness of each before rising
to a higher degree of knowledge.

The mind can to some extent fly to the truth from the facts of
a limited experience. It can in this way anticipate the truth.
But the arrival at truth by means of a methodical process provides far more certain knowledge, and can be described as, not an
anticipation or speculation, but a genuine interpretation of
nature and the external world, which is founded in reality.

Anticipation or sagacious speculations have some use, for if
men all went mad simultaneously in the same way, and all
arrived at the same wrong idea, they would at least be in general
agreement among themselves.

Anticipations are much more suited than interpretations for
winning assent, because they are swiftly arrived at, flatter the
mind, and appeal to the imagination. Interpretations are at the
first view much less attractive, because they are derived from a
far wider range of facts. They do not suddenly strike the understanding, as they are the product of a far more deliberate and

complicated method. As they are deeper and more original, they are generally out of tune with fashionable ideas, and seem harsh.

If 'all the wits of all the ages should meet together' and combine their efforts, no great progress would be made by anticipations, because the errors in the first principles concocted by them out of experience would never be expunged. While these remain, no excellence of mind can make up for them.

His own method, in the first stage of its application, has something in common with the doctrines of the sceptics who assert that nothing can be known. He also believes that the method of investigation at present in use cannot lead to the discovery of much. But his own method in its later stages diverges as far as possible from the conclusions of the sceptics. They destroy the authority of the senses and the understanding, whereas he does his utmost to provide aids for them.

10. *Limitations of the Mind arising from Social Being*

WHAT are the directions in which the mind requires aids, and what is the nature of these limitations of the mind which have to be overcome or mitigated? The limitations are of four kinds. Their recognition, and the conscious allowance for them, is as important for the correct operation of the new method of induction as is the refutation of sophisms in the use of common logic.

The first are those which arise from the character of human nature itself, for 'all perceptions as well of the sense as of the mind are according to the measure of the individual and according to the measure of the universe'.

It is necessary to disentangle those parts of the conceptions of things which arise from the nature of the human mind and not from the things as they are in nature. Bacon calls this kind of false notion, which arises from general characteristics of the human mind, 'Idols of the Tribe'.

For example, the human mind is apt to find more regularity and order in nature than actually exists. This is one of the causes of the prejudice that the planets move in perfect circles. Then, when the mind has adopted an opinion, it is inclined to draw in all other things which support it, by a process which is now called rationalization. Again, it is inclined to be more impressed with data in support of its opinions, whereas data to the contrary are more important in establishing a true interpretation. The mind is also inclined to be most impressed by striking facts which appeal to the imagination, and it is inclined to jump to conclusions too quickly. The mind is no dry light and is coloured by the affections. 'What a man had rather be true he more readily believes.' He is inclined to construct sciences as he would wish them to be, and not as they should be.

The greatest weakness of the understanding arises, however, from the dullness of the senses. The things that strike the senses outweigh those that are not observed, though these may be more important. The inability to see the sub-visible constitution of bodies is the greatest obstacle to their transformation, and hence to the production of useful works. Nor can this limitation be more than partially remedied by scientific instruments, such as the microscope. For this purpose, properly devised experiments which decide 'the point in nature', or whether or not any proposed scientific explanation is correct, are far more powerful. The aim should be, not to resolve nature into abstractions, but to dissect her into parts. The scientist should search for the configurations of matter, its simple actions, and 'law of action or motion'.

The second kind of false notions arise from the particular nature of human individuals, determined by their heredity and environment, their education, the books they have read, and the ideas they have absorbed from those whom they esteem as authorities.

Examples of this kind are theories to which scientists are particularly attached because they are their authors and inventors. They make them fit their preconceived ideas. Aristotle made his science fit his logic, while Gilbert constructed an entire system of philosophy out of magnetism, which he had investigated so brilliantly. Then there are minds that are particularly acute at perceiving the distinctions between things, while another sort has a talent for noting resemblances. The former is apt to catch at minor subtleties, while the latter grasps at grand but illusory ideas. In short, one must guard against this second kind of false notions by being particularly suspicious of one's favourite ideas.

False notions arising from these sources he describes as Idols of the Cave, or the dens of ideas into which individuals are apt to withdraw themselves.

Then there are the false notions that men collect from those with whom they associate, such as the characteristic errors and prejudices in the ideas of the class of persons to which they belong. These he calls Idols of the Market Place.

Particularly serious examples of them are the errors arising from the socially necessary use of ill-chosen words in establishing languages. These false notions arising from bad choice of words are the most troublesome of all. The mind is apt to fall into sterile discussions of the word instead of the things it represents. This is all the easier, because words are usually created in common parlance, and are not sufficiently precise for philosophical purposes. Consequently, they lead to inconclusive arguments. It is therefore desirable that scientists should adopt the mathematician's method of starting with precise definitions. Often words are applied to things which do not exist, such as the Prime Mover, and other fictions. Discussion of these is a waste of time.

Inappropriate names for substances hinder the progress of chemistry by falsely suggesting that the substances have properties which they do not possess. The inadequate definition of words denoting principles, such as heat, or density, or weight, conceal their true nature and are a serious obstacle to the progress of science.

In this connexion, Einstein has pointed out that his general theory of relativity was deduced from an analysis of a simple fact known since the time of Galileo and Newton, that weight and inertia, which are quite distinct things, are both found to be measured by mass. It is of the utmost importance that the words used by scientists do not conceal such implications, but help to bring them out.

Another simple observation which conceals deep implications is the darkness of the night sky. As early as 1826, Ölbers pointed out that if the universe were infinite in size and the stars were distributed through it evenly, then, no matter in which direction one looked, one would see a point of light, so that the whole sky would appear bright. Bondi has remarked that one can deduce from Olbers's paradox that the universe is expanding: the night sky is dark because the distant stars are receding, and hence reducing the amount of light reaching the earth.

The theory of the expanding universe could have been deduced over a hundred years ago, if astronomers had been able to penetrate the implications of the night sky described as 'dark'. The word 'dark' suggests that there is nothing, and nothing to explain.

Finally, there is a fourth kind of false notions, derived from the acceptance of philosophical dogmas and erroneous demonstrations. He calls these Idols of the Theatre, because in his judgment 'all the received systems are but so many stage-plays, representing worlds of their own creation after an unreal and scenic fashion'. Unfortunately, when an acute mind has embraced a wrong system, it multiplies errors with all the greater facility.

His aim is to reduce dependence on acuteness of mind by providing a better method of scientific discovery, which 'places all wits and understandings nearly on a level'.

In his discussions of the Idols of the Market Place, and of the Theatre, Bacon recognizes the influence of social conditions on scientific thought. It is implicit in his choice of terminology. He uses social conceptions to explain the philosophy of science. 'The state of knowledge is ever a Democratie.' He evidently regarded his scientific method as, in some degree, an egalitarian instrument. In politics he was non-egalitarian.

One of his criticisms of the philosophical systems is that they appeal to the 'ambition of the understanding', and are insufficiently based on the laboriously ascertained and humdrum facts of nature. 'In the plays of this philosophical theatre you may observe the same thing which is found in the theatre of the poets, that stories invented for the stage are more compact and elegant, and more as one would wish them to be, than true stories out of history.'

The arrogance of the intellect prompts men to lay down the law about knowledge, some asserting positively what they believe to be perfect truths, while others say with equal dogmatism that nothing can be known. The latter are not so harmful, but they undermine confidence, and 'when the human mind has once despaired of finding truth, its interest in all things grows fainter . . .'.

It relapses into amusement, roaming without much earnestness from subject to subject, no longer expecting to discover anything worth while.

But the human senses and the understanding, weak as they are, are not to be robbed of their authority, but are to be assisted with suitable aids, which will enable the various false notions that afflict the mind to be allowed for. By their means the mind will be thoroughly 'freed and cleansed'. It will then be in a condition to make modest, but steady, progress in understanding nature. But this cannot be effectively started without due humility of mind. 'The entrance into the kingdom of man, founded on the sciences,' is gained on much the same conditions as entrance into the kingdom of heaven, which is permitted only to those who approach it in the spirit of a little child.

He supposed that men might always produce philosophical systems, as the Greeks had done in such profusion, but he gave social reasons why they produced more in some ages than in others. There had been fewer in recent times, because of the preoccupation with religion, and because civil governments, 'especially monarchies, have been averse to such novelties, even in matters speculative; so that men labour therein to the peril and harming of their fortunes—not only unrewarded, but exposed also to contempt and envy . . .'.

Bacon had perceived that the progress of science depends on the character of the social system within which it is cultivated. His onslaughts on philosophical systematizing reveal the strength of his determination to avoid it, and why he pursued with an almost insensitive obstinacy the rough and jagged method of aphorisms and inductions from particulars. He was far more concerned in establishing sound foundations, even if fragmentary, than completing an even and polished structure, most of whose vital parts would subsequently be found to be deficient.

His severest criticism was of the mixture of science and theology, and especially of those who attempted to base a natural philosophy on the first chapter of Genesis and the Book of Job, which he compared with 'seeking for the dead among the living'. The mixture of the human and the divine not only produced a fantastic philosophy, but also a heretical religion.

In his famous criticisms of the Idols, or false notions of the mind, Bacon's activity as a statesman of science can be seen in full power. Having established that science is of decisive importance to the future of the human race, he sets about clearing the ground for building and utilizing it. His mind knocks down the rotten old shanties in the out-of-date citadels of the intellect, it tears down the forest of decaying mental scrub, and cuts through the rough and rocky virgin lands of knowledge, like a powerful bulldozer clearing a site for one of the immense engineering constructions of modern times.

He says that 'arts and sciences should be like mines, where the noise of new works and further advances is heard on every side'. His own style is vibrant with the clamour of forthcoming scientific and technical ages.

11. *The Statesman of Science*

AFTER analysing the false notions which afflict the human mind, Bacon discussed the condition of science and the causes of its backwardness. To do this, he reviewed its history, incidentally conceiving a proper use for the history of science. He showed what its functions should be in a correctly organized system of science and learning, and treated it as an independent subject of research. He remarked that most of the science then existing had come from the Greeks. The Romans and Arabians had in the main made additions of only secondary importance. Thus existing science suffered from the characteristics of Greek thought, which was 'professorial and much given to disputations'. It was a 'kind of wisdom most adverse to the inquisition of truth'. He quoted with approval the Egyptian criticism that the Greeks 'were always boys, without antiquity of knowledge or knowledge of antiquity'. Science, as a Greek creation, had an unpromising origin and birthplace.

The Greeks were a new people, who 'had no history, worthy to be called history'. Their knowledge of the surface of the earth was very limited. Both in time and space their experience was restricted, which is one of the worst conditions for science. The travels of Democritus, Plato and Pythagoras were no better than suburban excursions compared with the voyages of Columbus and Magellan. The new discoveries had infinitely extended men's knowledge of the world, and provided a far more promising basis for the development of science than the limited experience available to the Greeks. In the light of this, one could confidently forecast that a new development of science was about to occur which would far surpass that of the Greeks.

The most certain measure of the value of any science is the fruits it produces in works. When Greek science is assessed in this way, one must acknowledge that it has led to extraordinarily few useful works.

Bacon utilizes the conception of the continuous progress and growth of a science as a measure of its value. He incidentally makes use of the idea of progress, with which his thought is deeply impregnated.

He calculated that science flourished among the Greeks for only about two hundred years, and for about the same period among the Romans. The science of his own day was also only about two hundred years old. So out of the two thousand five hundred years of history known to his age, only about six hundred had been fruitful for science. Bacon's respect for pre-Greek achievements and opinion, and his quantitative approach to history, have an extremely modern ring.

Why had the growth of science been restricted to such short periods? He supposed that in the unfruitful nineteen hundred years science had failed to grow because its roots in nature and experience had been cut. 'For what is founded in nature grows and increases; while what is founded on opinion varies but increases not.' One can see that in the mechanical arts, which are founded on nature and experience, the contrary has happened. 'As long as they are popular,' they thrive and grow continuously, as if they had a breath of life. They are at first crude, then made convenient, and finally elegant, but at all times they continue to advance.

Bacon expresses astonishment that these historical and social views on science had not been brought forward before, and that it should have fallen to him to do so. By recognizing and understanding those things which had hindered science in the past, one could take steps to remove or attenuate them, and thus free science for a swifter development. He recommended the study of the philosophy and history of science in order to discover how to release science from its shackles and enable it to spurt forward with multiplied success.

He wondered how all these thoughts could have entered any man's mind, and esteemed it a happy accident that they had happened to arise in his. He did not ascribe it to any special talent, but to 'a birth of Time rather than of Wit'.

Bacon gave social reasons for the retardation of science in the unfruitful periods. After the adoption of the Christian religion, most of the ablest men applied themselves to theology, which then had the highest awards to offer. Even in the best Roman period, the ablest men applied themselves to moral philosophy, and even more to public affairs, 'the magnitude of the Roman Empire requiring the services of a great number of persons'.

Bacon said that even in his own times, it was very rare for a man to devote all his efforts to science, unless he happened to be a monk in a cell, or a gentleman in a country house, who could do as he liked. Scientists could pursue their investigations only in the spare time left after professional work, such as doctoring, or teaching boys.

Nor could the sciences progress unless natural philosophy be applied to them, and they in their turn be applied to natural philosophy. Only through this dialectical interaction could both advance with due speed. Astronomy, optics, engineering, medicine remained superficial because they lacked the profound new ideas which could only be derived from the natural philosophical consideration of 'motions, rays, sounds, texture and configuration of bodies, affections, and intellectual perceptions . . .'.

Besides the absence of full-time jobs for scientists, the lack of a proper aim for science has hindered its progress. If the goal has not been rightly placed, the race towards it cannot be run aright. 'Now the true and lawful goal of the sciences is none other than this: that human life be endowed with new discoveries and powers.' But unfortunately the majority of scientists have no feeling for this and 'are merely hireling and professorial'. Occasionally an able and ambitious man makes an invention, but usually only at his own expense. The majority have no concern with research and are interested only in what they can use in their lectures, or which will impress others. Even the rare man who courts science 'with honest affection and for her own sake', is generally more concerned with amusing ideas (what the Germans call *spielerei*) than a severe search after truth. And when he is primarily concerned with the search for truth, he applies himself to the rigid proof of existing knowledge, rather than the discovery of new scientific facts and laws which can lead to new works.

It is not surprising that the progress of science should be disappointing if the aim has not been properly chosen. But it is really astonishing that no one has applied himself to the development of the method of discovery, laying down a sure road of progress from the data of the senses, by which the understanding can arrive at substantial laws. The existing method of discovery most commonly used consists of reading what previous workers have done on the subject, and then meditating on it. The scientist, by 'much agitation and working of the wit solicits and as it were evokes his own spirit to give him oracles; which method', Bacon says, 'has no foundation at all, but rests only upon opinions . . .'.

The fact that men have used poor methods of discovery is a cause for hope, since the adoption of a better one will certainly accelerate the progress of discovery.

Together with the other handicaps under which science labours is lack of social status. There is an ancient opinion that 'the dignity of the human mind is impaired by long and close intercourse with experiments and particulars, subject to sense and bound in matter, especially as they are laborious to search, ignoble to mediate, harsh to deliver, illiberal to practice, infinite in number, and minute in subtlety'.

In fact, science and especially experimental science, has hitherto been regarded as dirty, untidy, low-class and difficult, and consequently has been 'rejected with disdain'.

Yet another hindrance has been the reverence for antiquity, and belief that nothing of the same order can be done in one's own times. This arises from a misunderstanding. The true antiquity is not the ancient past, but our own day, which has all the advantage of thousands of years of experience and research which has subsequently been done. We are so much richer than our forebears in scientific data and knowledge that we are in a far better position than they were to advance. This is a further ground for hope.

Indeed, says Bacon, 'it would be disgraceful if, while the regions of the material globe—that is, of the earth, of the sea, and of the stars—have been in our times laid widely open and revealed, the intellectual globe should remain shut up within the limits of old discoveries'.

If the discovery of the New World and the contemporary advances of science could give such encouragement to Bacon, what encouragement ought not we to gain from the exploration of the atom, and of outer space, in our own day? Shall we not be doubly disgraced if, under the inspiration of these triumphs, we fail to solve the ordinary problems of daily life which concern the mass of mankind?

Reverence for the great philosophers and scientists of the past should not lead to an excessive regard for authority. It is rightly said that truth is the daughter of time, not of authority. In fact, time is 'the author of authors', and ultimately of all authority. Bacon's thought was profoundly historical. One should have confidence in the steady advance of science and scientists as a body, most of whose members will not at any moment be making resounding discoveries, but will be doing useful, if inconspicuous work.

As too much respect for authority inhibits the understanding, so too much admiration for existing science and inventions inhibits new discoveries. Bacon remarked that the best inventions then existing, such as clocks, depended on only one or two scientific principles. It was to be expected that the discovery of other scientific principles would lead to a great increase in useful appliances and applications. He noted, too, that the majority of the most important existing discoveries, such as agriculture, cooking and brewing, were made before written history, and are 'older than philosophy and intellectual arts'. One might almost say that useful invention had ended when the rational philosophies began.

The examination of existing literature, like that of existing inventions, showed an extraordinary poverty of new ideas. Most of it was a mass of endless repetitions.

Yet there was much complacency over the richness of existing science and literature, and this had removed the spur to discovery and creation of new riches of knowledge. It was not 'strange if opinion of plenty has been the cause of want'.

One of the hindrances to recent research had been excessive claims by discoverers, caused by motives ranging from vanity to imposture. These had damaged the reputation of contemporary science, and repelled honest and talented men who might otherwise have engaged in it.

Even worse were the effects of littleness of spirit. Some

scientists emphasized the difficulty of research, in order to excuse failures in discovery and exaggerate the value of what they had already done. They did not welcome new facts which upset the attractive symmetry of their existing views.

They advocated theories which make discovery impossible, such as the assertion that the heat of the sun and of fire differ in kind. If that were so, then discoveries relating to the one could not bear on the other. Such views unfairly circumscribe the possibilities of human endeavour, destroy hope, and remove the spur to research.

Even when they conduct research properly, they are apt to concentrate on one thing, such as the magnet, or the system of the heavens. But 'it is most unskilful to investigate the nature of anything in the thing itself'. It cannot be done satisfactorily except within the setting of the whole of knowledge.

Here Bacon is giving his view on the danger of specialization, and the reason why he could only give qualified approval even to such investigators as Gilbert and Galileo. It is a view that has been unpopular and misunderstood for three centuries, but can now be seen to contain important truth. Today we are aware that the greatest triumphs of the specialist geniuses can produce a culture which is out of balance and unstable, unless they are duly related to knowledge as a whole, and fitted within a system under rational human control.

Bacon repeatedly refers to the ill-effects of mixing science and religion. He castigated the fathers of the Church, who denied that the earth is round, and 'the simpleness of certain divines', who feared that the investigation of nature would undermine religion, especially among the unlearned. He thought this notion utterly wrong and savouring of 'carnal wisdom'. In his view, natural philosophy was, after the word of God, the most approved nourishment for faith; for the former 'displays the will of God, the other His power'. Meanwhile, that science should be retarded was not surprising, if religion, 'which has most power over men's minds', had been directed against it.

The way in which science and learning were administered and governed was a further obstacle to progress. The curricula in the schools and universities were restricted to the works of certain authors, and anyone who put forward new ideas was arraigned as a turbulent person and a dangerous innovator. In this atmosphere it was almost impossible for a man to think of anything out of the common way.

But, says Bacon, there is a profound difference between innovation in science and in politics. 'In matters of state even a change for the better is mistrusted, because it unsettles what is established'. The establishment is founded on authority and opinion; unlike scientific truth, which is based on proof and demonstration.

Besides the faults in the government and administration of science, there is an absence of rewards to encourage endeavour. Those who are best able to advance science are not usually the same as those who are in a position to bestow rewards and honours. Science is best advanced by persons of great intellectual ability and learning, whereas the politicians and the people, who have the power to award great prizes, rarely understand it, and therefore do not see the value of spending money on it.

Nor is there even the encouragement which comes from popular applause, because scientific matters are generally above the heads of the public. 'And it is nothing strange if a thing not held in honour does not prosper.'

However, 'by far the greatest obstacle to the progress of science, and to the undertaking of new tasks and provinces therein, is found in this—that men despair and think things impossible.' In this the wisest men, who are most conversant with the obscurities of nature and the limitations of human ability, often do the greatest harm. They are apt to believe that what has not been done in thousands of years is beyond human power, and that assertions to the contrary are a sign of lack of judgment.

It is therefore doubly necessary to meet their objections thoroughly and with patience, and even to take the principles of statesmanship into counsel, 'whose rule is to distrust, and to take the less favourable view of human affairs'. After due consideration, and making every allowance for the difficulties of nature and the weakness of man, he nevertheless felt justified in preparing men's minds for the conquest of nature. Not to do so would leave men with a meaner opinion of themselves than they need have. It would make them sad, and feel the unhappiness of their condition more keenly.

He therefore considered it proper that he should publish his conjectures which suggest that mankind's voyage into the future need not be so hopeless as it imagines.

Just as Columbus's reasons for believing that new continents existed, which were generally rejected before his wonderful voyage, so his own reasons for believing in the possibility of a new world of science may seem extravagant now, but might also prove to be 'the causes and beginnings of great events'.

After comparing the significance of his work with that of Columbus, Bacon now compared it with that of Alexander the Great. He quoted Livy's remark that Alexander 'had done no more than take courage to despise vain apprehensions', and said that he supposed that a like judgment might be passed on himself in future ages. It might be said that he had done 'no great things, but simply made less account of things that were accounted great'. In the meanwhile there was no hope for the human race except in a 'new birth of science', raised up regularly from experience. In other words, the future of the human race depended on the planned development of science, 'which no one (I think) will say has yet been done or thought of'.

The great scientific events of the twentieth century have amply confirmed the justice of Bacon's comparison of his own achievements with those of Columbus and Alexander. His part in promulgating the new scientific exploration of the world of nature and the conquest of the universe has proved to be of even more significance for humanity than the feats of the greatest navigators and conquerors.

He suggested that any who felt like desponding should look at him 'being of all men of my time the most busied in affairs of state, and a man of health not very strong (whereby much time is lost)' following a course in which he was a pioneer and not sharing counsels with anyone, and yet by resolutely entering on the true road and submitting his mind to things, had advanced the development of science, he supposed, some little way.

Now consider what could be done by men abounding in leisure, banding themselves together for this work, and pursuing it for ages. Science is not an activity which can be advanced only by passing through one man's intellect. It is best advanced by setting men to work in various directions, and then combining the results of their labours. Men will learn their strength only when instead of everybody doing the same thing, one man undertakes one thing, and other men undertake others. The full power of scientific research will be realized only through planning and co-operation.

Having reviewed the obstacles to the progress of knowledge, he concludes that 'even if the breath of hope which blows on us

I

from that New Continent were fainter than it is and harder to perceive; yet the trial (if we would not bear a spirit altogether abject) must by all means be made'.

If we do not try we throw away the chance of doing immense good, and if we fail we lose only a little human labour. But in view of what has been said, it is evident 'that there is hope enough and to spare, not only to make a bold man try, but also to make a sober-minded and wise man believe'.

The tremendous development of science which has followed this superlative expression of inspiration more than three hundred years ago is a splendid illustration of Bacon's intellectual penetration and social spirit.

His words are as wonderfully apposite to our age as his own, for even if the breath from outer space and the inside of the atom were fainter than it is and harder to perceive, we shall bear a spirit altogether abject if we do not explore to the uttermost, and master for the good of humanity, the new powers to be derived from the interplanetary regions and the atomic nucleus.

Bacon specifically stated that he did not propose to found a school or a new sect in philosophy, and he did not believe that one's abstract ideas on the nature of things had much bearing on the fortunes of mankind. His purpose was to try to lay the foundations and extend the limits 'of the power and greatness of man'.

He did not believe that the time had yet come to attempt to propound a new universal philosophy. All that he aimed to do was to sow the seeds of the great undertaking, which would be carried out in future ages.

Nor did he aim at the hasty production of practical works. By all means let those proceed who wanted to get on with them, but for his part, he staked all on 'the victory of art over nature', to be gained by the application of his new method of research. This would lead to the discovery of scientific laws, and from these would be derived not only isolated useful products, but whole clusters of new inventions and practical applications.

His method was to the intellect what a scientific instrument, such as a pair of compasses, is to the hand. It enables a man of moderate ability to work more exactly than a highly talented man without its help. 'For my way of discovering sciences goes far to level men's wits, and leaves but little to individual excellence.'

While emphasizing in this passage that method, or systematic and planned procedure, in research enables men of moderate abilities to do useful work, he had already remarked that the biggest advances come from the greatest minds. He recognized the rôles both of method and of talent in promoting discovery.

Bacon was also at pains to explain that while he was always urging men to seek how to produce useful works, he did not regard utility and magnitude of works as superior to the contemplation of truth. In fact, he believed the very opposite. His aim was to discover truth, but the best proof that truth has been discovered is that it should lead to works. This superior truth which he sought is the building in the human understanding of 'a true model of the world, such as it is in fact, not such as a man's own reason would have it be; a thing which cannot be done without a very diligent dissection and anatomy of the world'.

Bacon takes the existence of the external world absolutely for granted. In this he is a materialist. His ascriptions of the process of discovery to an interaction between mind and matter, and between method and genius, provide further examples of his dialectical thinking.

He is at pains to state that his method applies just as much to ethics and politics as it does to the natural sciences. But discoveries in the sciences have an advantage over political achievements because they benefit the whole race of man, whereas the latter usually apply only to a particular nation. This is the reason why, in former ages, the ancients awarded divine honours to the authors of inventions, but 'to those who did good service in the state (such as founders of cities and empires, legislators, saviours of their country from long endured evils, quellers of tyrannies, and the like) they decreed no higher honours than heroic'.

There are three grades of human ambition; to extend one's power in one's own country, which is vulgar and degenerate; to labour to extend the power of one's country, which is more dignified but no less covetous; and finally to 'endeavour to establish and extend the power and dominion of the human race itself over the universe', which is a nobler and more wholesome ambition than the other two. 'Now the empire of man over things depends wholly on the arts and the sciences. For we cannot command nature except by obeying her.'

12. *The New Method*

WHILE Bacon outlined his policy for science in the first part of the *Novum Organum*, he provided what he considered to be the instrument for carrying it out in the second. This was his new method of discovery, which he described in considerable detail, and illustrated by a striking example. He applied it to the phenomenon of heat, evidently one of the most important principles in nature, especially for effecting changes in things, and thus leading to new and useful works.

His choice of this principle shows his profound scientific judgment, and ability to recognize what was of the most fundamental importance, for the coming sciences of chemistry and physics, the industrial revolution and the modern conception of energy were, to a large extent, to arise out of the utilization and understanding of heat.

By the application of his method he reached the conclusion that 'Heat itself, its essence and quiddity, is Motion and nothing else.' By his new method he discovered the Dynamical Theory of Heat.

'Heat is a mode of expansion,' he says, 'not uniformly of the whole body together, but in its ultimate particles; and at the same time checked, repelled and beaten back, so that the particles acquire a motion alternative, perpetually quivering, striving and struggling, and irritated by repercussion, whence springs the fury of fire and heat.' As Tyndall remarked, Bacon here is groping towards the wave-theory of radiation.

After every deduction has been made for the imperfections of his proofs, these are formidable achievements. They are strong evidence that his method, even if imperfect, contains very effective elements.

Bacon follows and extends the argument started in *Valerius Terminus*. He discusses what a scientist has to do when he wishes to create something new, such as making gold out of silver. This consists of giving a body a new nature, and belongs to 'the work and aim of Human Power'. The way in which the new nature is produced depends on the scientific laws of the new nature which is desired. The discovery of these scientific laws, which show how the new nature can be obtained, is 'the work and aim of Human Knowledge'.

Knowledge is the key to power, and 'what in operation is most useful, that in knowledge is most true'.

The discovery of the fundamental nature of 'the thing in itself', those laws and 'determinations of absolute actuality', which govern and constitute the manifestations of principles such 'as heat, light and weight in every kind of matter and subject which is susceptible of them', reveal 'the unity of nature in substances the most unlike', and lead to the possibility of performing operations 'such as neither the vicissitudes of nature, nor industry in experimenting, nor accident itself, would ever have brought into act, and which would never have occurred to the thought of man'.

Two kinds of laws govern the transformation of bodies. The first deals with a body regarded as a collection of properties, such as yellowness, heaviness, ductility, etc., in gold. Anyone who can transform a substance to have all these properties, can make something which is indistinguishable from gold. The second kind of law deals with the changes by which, for example, gold is extracted from its ores. It is concerned with the drawing out of the gold, which is *latent*.

Any radical operations on nature depend on laws of these kinds. And any knowledge of things which cannot be experimented with, such as the heavenly bodies, depends also on the laws appertaining to the mechanics of rotation, attraction, etc.

Besides having the correct properties, a body which has been transformed into a desired substance must have a correct configuration, or structure. Distillation may show, for example, that a liquid consists of two other liquids. But one must be careful with the use of fire or other agents for investigating configurations; they are liable to destroy the substance. Consequently, one must evoke Minerva instead of Vulcan, and investigate these bodies not only by heating, but also 'by reasoning and true induction' (the mind being a kind of divine fire), that is, by discovering the scientific laws by which they are governed, and not trusting merely to trial-and-error experiments.

By this method one will arrive, for example, not at hypothetical atoms, but at 'real particles, such as really exist'. The inquiries will have the best result 'when they begin with physics and end with mathematics'. His directions for the interpretation of nature have two main divisions; how to deduce laws from experience, and how to deduce and derive new experiments from such laws.

To do this, one must start with a collection of data, or natural history. Then the data should be arranged in order. When this has been done, they should be considered by the intellect, guided by 'true and legitimate induction'.

For example, to discover the law of heat, 'the thing in itself', he assembled all the known instances in which heat is manifested, even 'though occurring in substances the most unlike'.

Then he made a list of known instances of the absence of heat, not in all phenomena because the list would be endless, but in those akin to the phenomena in which heat is present.

This was followed by a list of instances in which the various 'degrees' of heat were noted.

The three lists were then reviewed, in order to find 'a nature as is always present or absent with the given nature, and always increases and decreases with it'. All those instances where the given nature, heat, is not found, are rejected. Similarly, instances where heat is absent, or increases when heat decreases, or decreases when heat increases, are also rejected. 'This is quickly said; but the way to come at it is winding and intricate.'

For example, one can say that as hot iron can communicate its heat to other bodies and yet lose none of its weight, heat cannot consist of 'the communication or admixture of the substance of another hot body'.

As similar effects are caused by heat and cold, heat cannot be a motion of the body as a whole.

As heat is produced by the attrition of bodies, or friction, heat cannot exist 'in the nature of things positively, and not as the effect of any antecedent nature'.

Bacon says that the process of exclusion contains the foundation of induction, but this is not completed until it produces affirmative conclusions. How can the process of exclusion be made more accurate? He cannot render 'the human understanding a match for things and nature' without improving the method of induction.

But before applying this perfected induction, he considers it permissible for the understanding to attempt to leap to an affirmative conclusion from the three lists as they stand, because 'truth will sooner come out of error than from confusion'.

Heat 'in itself', or the law of heat, will be perceptible in every instance where it exists. But in some instances it will be conspicuously present. Bacon called these 'striking instances'. For example, flame is a 'striking instance' of heat.

It was in this way that Bacon came to introduce the familiar phrase 'striking instance' into the English language. It was one of his contributions to the quickening of the process of induction. By concentrating on 'striking instances' one could often afford to ignore a great deal of trivial data.

He showed in the first place that every instance of heat contains motion. Further examination showed that the motion was not of the whole, but of the constituent particles. Hence the true definition of heat is that it 'is a motion, expansive, restrained, and acting in its strife upon the smaller particles of bodies'. He immediately deduced from this that if an expanding motion is repressed, and turned back on itself, heat will be generated. This is the explanation of why the air in a closed pump becomes hot when suddenly compressed.

Bacon now proceeded to make an analysis of the different kinds of instances in which a principle such as heat, light or attraction might appear. He distinguished no less than twenty-seven. For example, there are Solitary Instances, in which heat is exhibited in a subject which has nothing in common with any other subject exhibiting heat. These 'make the way short, and accelerate and strengthen the process of exclusion; so that a few of them are as good as many'.

Here again, in introducing 'solitary instances', Bacon gave the English language a new phrase.

An example of a solitary instance in respect of resemblance is a colour produced by a prism, and by a flower. Neither has anything in common except the colour. 'From which we easily gather that colour is nothing more than a modification of the image of light received upon the object.'

Then he discussed Migratory Instances, 'in which the nature in question is in the process of being produced when it did not previously exist'.

These instances not only accelerate and strengthen the process of exclusion, but narrow the range within which the law being sought for is to be found. They are of particular importance as guides to practical operations.

An example of this kind of instance is seen when whiteness is produced by pounding glass or agitating water into froth. The discovery that whiteness can be produced from transparent bodies without any further addition, except pounding into particles and mixing with air gives, he says, considerable information about the nature of this quality.

Then there are Clandestine Instances, which exhibit the nature under investigation in its lowest degree of power. They are the opposites of Solitary Instances. For example, if the consistency, as opposed to the fluidity, of bodies is considered, it is found that the two notions are only rough and relative to the senses, for it turns out that 'there is inherent in all bodies a disposition to shun and escape discontinuation', that is, attractive forces are at work, which hold bodies together, and account for such properties as adhesion and capillarity.

The fifth kind of instance is Constitutive, and is a particular species of the given general nature. Suppose this is Memory. If we try to recollect something without any previous notion of what it is, our minds wander as it were in infinite space. We need a help, or particular kind of memory, by which this infinity is cut off. The help is a constitutive instance, and may consist of a place or a person, a knot in a handkerchief, etc. There are six kinds of such aids; the reduction of the memory of an intellectual to that of a concrete thing; the impression of the mind during strong excitement or while it is free from any other consideration; the multiplication of points by which the mind can seize what it wishes to remember, as in the remembering of poetry which is assisted by the repetition of the metre; and expectation beforehand, which makes us remember better something we have waited for, and not come across casually.

The sixth kind is the Parallel or Conformable Instance. This is specially valuable for revealing resemblances between the configurations of different parts of the universe, and between the different kinds of living organisms.

The consideration of this kind of instance prompted Bacon to compare the structures and organs of animals and plants. This work of his provided a strong stimulus to the type of investigation which led to the discovery of the Theory of Evolution. He said that hitherto men had devoted far too much attention to the oddities of animals and plants, which were largely accidental, and not to their resemblances, 'for these it is that detect the unity of nature, and lay a foundation for the constitution of sciences'.

While the recognition of conformable instances guided men towards the theory of evolution, Bacon's method of exclusions contains a hint of the process by which evolution has come about. According to it, truth is the result of the exclusion of everything that does not apply to the subject under consideration, and is a kind of 'survival of the fittest'. When Darwin started his note-book in 1837 on the problem on the origin of species, one of his first entries is that he would proceed on 'true Baconian principles', collecting facts without preconceived theory. He had Bacon's notions in mind at the beginning of his work.

Scarcely less remarkable is Bacon's anticipation of Wegener's theory of continental drift. He says that 'the very configuration of the world itself in its greater parts presents Confirmable Instances which are not to be neglected. Take for example Africa and the region of Peru with the continent stretching to the Straits of Magellan, in each of which tracts there are similar isthmuses and similar promontories, which can hardly be by accident.'

He mentions, too, that the mathematical postulate that if two things are equal to the same thing they are equal to one another is parallel to the syllogism in logic, which states that if two propositions agree with a middle term, then they agree with one another. Here he is anticipating mathematical logic.

Such were some of the conclusions he derived from merely one of his twenty-seven kinds of instances.

After Conformable Instances, he considered their opposite, which he called Singular Instances, again contributing a phrase to the English language. These draw attention to the differences between things which otherwise have much in common. They are particularly valuable for sharpening the attention, and to 'cure the understanding depraved by custom and the common course of things'.

The next kind of Instance is the Deviating. It differs from the Singular, as dealing with individuals rather than species. They are useful in practice, for it is very difficult to produce new species, but less difficult to vary known species.

After this comes the Bordering Instance. This exhibits bodies which seem to be composed of two species, or to lie between them. They are of excellent use for indicating 'the causes of the number and quality of species in the universe'. Notable examples are flying fishes, bats, and the ape, 'between man and beast'.

Then there are the Instances of Power. These are the most consummate examples in any art or human industry. They show what can be done, and excite and inspire the understanding to achievement. Care, however, should be taken to prevent them from depressing the spirits, because they may seem impossible to surpass or equal.

In discussing this instance, Bacon refers to the remarkable properties of paper, an artificial material which is cohesive and tenacious, and unlike all 'concreted juices', such as glass, earthenware etc., which are brittle. It owes its properties to its fibrous structure, and 'imitates and almost rivals the skin or membrane of an animal, the leaf of a vegetable, etc'. The best artificial materials are those which either imitate nature most closely, or 'on the contrary overrule and turn her back'.

It may well be that these remarks inspired Robert Hooke's suggestion that synthetic fibres should be made as an alternative to natural fibres, an achievement realized in our own times by the invention of rayon, nylon, etc.

Instances of Alliance are those in which two natures, supposed to be heterogeneous, are found to be modifications of a common nature. An example is the heat of the sun and of fire. These were supposed to be of an entirely different character, the sun's heat causing growth and creation, whereas fire destroys. But if a branch of a vine is bent so as to come into a room in which there is constantly a fire, its grapes ripen a month sooner, as if they had been in the sun. This is an Instance of Alliance showing that the sun's heat and the fire's heat can have similar effects. It prompts the investigation of why the two kinds of heat should usually appear so dissimilar, even though they partake of a common nature.

Instances of the Fingerpost distinguish between possible causes of a phenomenon. For instance, a body may have weight because all bodies have a tendency to move towards the centre of the earth, or because 'they are attracted by the mass and body of the earth itself'. If the latter is the case, the body will move fastest when it is nearest to the earth. 'If they were removed to such a distance from the earth that the earth's virtue could not act upon them, they would remain suspended like the earth itself, and not fall at all.' (Like artificial satellites.) Bacon then suggests the following Instance of the Fingerpost, or crucial instance, to decide between the two possible causes.

'Take a clock moved by leaden weights, and another moved by the compression of an iron spring; let them be exactly adjusted, that one go no faster or slower than the other; then place the clock moving by weights on the top of a very high steeple, keeping the other down below; and observe carefully whether the clock goes more slowly than it did on account of the diminished virtue of its weights. Repeat the experiment in the bottom of a mine. . . .' If the clock goes more slowly on the steeple, and faster in the mine, 'we may take the attraction of the mass of the earth as the cause of weight'.

This is a remarkable anticipation of the kind of experiment made by Carlini on Mont Cenis, and Airy at the bottom of the Harton coal mine, on the change in time of swing of a pendulum when removed from the surface of the earth to a place above or below it.

The Crucial Instance, which is the most famous of all his instances that have passed into the English language, expresses the principle of the crucial experiment for deciding between two theories.

He distinguished Instances of Divorce as simply notifying 'the separability of one nature from another. He used it to analyse the notions of magnetic and gravitational attraction, and the transmission of light, and succeeded in formulating some pregnant thoughts on action at a distance, and action through a medium, which have contributed to the evolution of the idea of field theories for explaining the properties of matter and radiation.

He described scientific instruments as providing Instances of the Door, in which the senses by which information enters the understanding are aided. As sight is by far the most important sense for this purpose, the microscope and telescope are particularly important. He was critical of the early microscope because it revealed only minute bodies, and not the details of large bodies; and of the telescope because the few discoveries made by it were indeed noble, but 'many others things equally worthy of investigation are not discovered by the same means'.

Bacon was always looking for principles and instruments of the widest generality, which was one of the causes of his qualified praise for various great discoverers. It has often been suggested that this attitude of Bacon showed that he did not fully understand their achievements, or that he grudged them. The most important explanation is, however, that he was aware of the limitations of the scientific method they used, and he was engaged in contributing to the creation of a method of greater generality and power.

Bacon called instances in which things that are not directly perceptible are made manifest through things that are, as Summoning. For example, weighing is a very powerful means of following changes of materials that cannot be seen. In conjunction with the principle, than which nothing is more true in nature, 'that the absolute quantum or sum-total of matter remains unchanged', weighing was utilized by Black and Lavoisier to revolutionize chemistry.

Weight is a measure of the quantity of matter. Bacon ascertained by weighing that the density of solids and liquids varied only over a range of about 21 to 1; 'so limited is nature', he commented, 'or at any rate that part of it with which we have principally to do'. This comment is like that of Eddington on his remarkable discovery that the masses of visible stars vary only over the range of about 100 to 1.

Bacon also measured by experiment the ratio between the densities of alcohol liquid and vapour, and found it at least 100 to 1.

Other examples of Summoning Instances are the use of thermometers to measure temperature changes too small to be detected by touch, and the aggregation of motion to reveal one that is too slow to be observed directly, as in the hands of a clock. Bacon remarks that 'motion that is too quick has not hitherto been competently measured; and yet the investigation of nature requires that this be done in some cases'.

Instances of the Road reveal changes which escape observation though perceptible by the senses. For example, in studying the growth of seeds or eggs, men are inclined to concentrate on the beginning and end of the process, and leave the process itself unobserved. This can, however, be investigated by planting many seeds and hatching many eggs, so that one of each can be examined on each successive day, and thus reveal the development of the process as a whole.

Then there are Awakening or Dissecting Instances, which remind the understanding of 'the wonderful and exquisite subtlety of nature', and so inspire investigation. Notable among these is the passage of light and magnetism through matter, and yet without confusion: 'all (I say) at once without impeding one another, just as if they had their own roads and passages set apart, and none ever struck or ran against other'.

After discussing the kinds of instances which are of aid in making more effective use of the senses, Bacon concluded his list with seven kinds of Practical Instances, of particular importance in the performance of works and operations.

These are concerned with measurement, for 'the chief cause of failure in operation (especially after natures have been diligently investigated) is the ill-determination and measurement of the forces and actions of bodies'. These are subject to distance, time, concentration of quantity and strength, and cannot be utilized efficiently unless the law of their dependence on these has been ascertained accurately.

The forces of electrical, magnetic, gravitational and capillary attraction should be measured. It is certain that all these powers are fixed and finite in the nature of things and have a limit 'which depends either on the mass or quantity of matter in the bodies acted on . . .'.

Then there are motions of expansion and contraction. He experimented on air and on water. He filled a hollow lead sphere with water and sealed it, in order to find the effects of compression on water. The sphere was hammered and then pressed, until a fine dew of water exuded through the lead. He calculated how much the water had been compressed from the degree of deformation of the sphere.

Under Instances of the Course, he discussed the application of the measurement of time for elucidating changes in nature. The fact that the bullet from a gun flies too fast to be seen, suggested to him 'a strange doubt; viz. whether the face of a clear and starlight sky be seen at the instant at which it really exists, and not a little later; and whether there be not, as regards our sight of heavenly bodies, a real time and an apparent time, just like the real place and apparent place which is taken account of by astronomers in the correction for parallaxes. So incredible did it appear to me that the images or rays of heavenly bodies could be conveyed at once to the sight through such an immense space, and did not rather take a perceptible time in travelling to us. . . .'

Bacon had anticipated that the stars we actually see are as they were when their light set out to us millions, and perhaps thousand of millions, of years ago, and that light travels at a finite speed.

Instances of Quantity reveal the rôle of quantity in actions. For example, changes in liquids often depend on the quantity present. Here Bacon is groping towards the law of mass action in chemistry.

Instances of Strife throw light on the conflict of motions and forces, 'for the motions and efforts of bodies are compounded, decomposed, and complicated, no less than the bodies themselves'.

He discussed nineteen kinds of motion. Among these is Excitation. It is particularly conspicuous in heat and cold. In heating a body, heat does not diffuse itself by communication of the original heat, 'but simply by exciting the parts of the body to that motion which is the Form of Heat . . .'. For this reason, solids are heated less quickly than gas, because their parts are less quickly put in motion.

He pointed out that self-multiplication of motions, as occurs in the growth of organisms, also occurs in inanimate bodies, such as flames. He noted the self-multiplying character of motions which are now described as chain reactions. In these the cause is 'small, as compared with the work and effect produced'.

Intimating Instances should be collected, for indicating things that would be useful to man. 'Mere Power and mere Knowledge exalt human nature, but do not bless it.' It is necessary to compile 'a Human Chart, or Chart of Things to be wished for', because the formation of judicious wishes is as much a part of knowledge as to ask judicious questions.

Bacon concluded the second book with the remark that in his method he was handling logic, not philosophy. Since his logic was not aimed at laying hold of abstract motions, but at the dissection of nature, and the discovery of the properties and laws of action of matter, it was necessarily illustrated by scientific speculations and experiments.

An analysis and assessment of Bacon's contribution to scientific method and inductive logic has been made by Tadeusz Kotarbinski, an eminent member of the Polish school which is in the forefront of modern world studies in the philosophy of logic. He remarks that Bacon was trying to discover how a given external feature of a body can be explained in terms of internal structure or movement of the parts.

The method by which this can be done is the one used by the chemist in deriving the chemical formula for a body with given external properties. 'Bacon was indeed a kind of chemist,' says Kotarbinski. The method he sought is also the one which is required for the localization of functions in the brain associated with motor or psychic functions. It is required, too, for the discovery of chromosome structures corresponding to given external features of living organisms. In his method, despite its shortcomings, he hit upon the essential things: the comparison of facts; elimination of hypotheses not based on fact, and of hypotheses which, while based on fact, were contradicted by other facts; the demonstration of co-existence through the coincidence of quantitative changes, etc. 'Perhaps Bacon has not taught anybody a method, but he found out and described essential features of the inductive method.'

His chief technical merit may be that he made an important advance in the analysis of the inductive method. He was followed in that path by Herschel, Mill, and others. Indeed, Mill's contributions were implicit in Bacon's doctrine, and in respect of the utilization of quantitative changes for discovering the existence of influencing factors, 'Mill represents a step backwards as compared with Bacon, who considered that kind of speculation not merely a substitute used in case of necessity, but on the contrary the most fruitful method.' Following Kotarbinski's graphic comparison, if the modern mature theory propounded by Nicod, v. Wright, Greniewski and others may be regarded as the *imago*, then John Stuart Mill's theory may be regarded as the *larva*, and Bacon's theory the *caterpillar* stage in the development of induction.

While Bacon's genius as a statesman of science is manifest, his technical contributions to the analysis and development of inductive logic are also very considerable.

Bacon said that he intended in subsequent books to extend the exposition of his developments in the inductive method and the principles of latent processes and configurations. After these had been done, he would be able to 'hand over to men their fortunes'. Their understandings would then be emancipated, and mankind would come of age. They would be able to mitigate their condition even in this life. By virtue of the charter 'In the sweat of thy face shalt thou eat bread,' men will through various labours, but not disputations or idle magical ceremonies, at length and in some measure subdue creation 'to the supplying of man with bread'.

13. *Natural Histories*

WITH the publication of the *Novum Organum* in 1620, Bacon reached the peak of his career. He was the King's first minister, and he had established his place as one of the major thinkers in history by his works.

A few months later, he was condemned and disgraced. His confident grandeur vanished, and was replaced by varying moods. Sometimes he felt at peace with destiny and wrote nobly, as in the *New Atlantis*, but more often he was soliciting James and Buckingham with indefatigable importunity for financial aid. All through the last five years after his catastrophe his concern for his life-long project, now for the relief of man's 'sorrows and necessities', never ceased. Under the blow the quality and tone of his work generally declined, but his industry, if anything, increased. He hurried on with the third part of his great project, the collection of facts about nature, which were required as the raw material on which his new method was to operate. Facts of every kind, whether dignified or not, were to be recorded in a neutral, objective spirit.

Bacon then gave some interesting advice on the state of mind in which these facts, which constitute 'the volume of Creation', were to be studied. They were to be examined 'with minds washed clean from opinions'. Such 'purification of the understanding' will enable one to approach the facts of nature without prejudice.

The first of his collections of natural facts summarized what was known about the winds. With the help of secretaries, relevant information, including speculations from the ancients and old wives' tales, was collected from available books, reinforced by verbal reports from practical men such as sailors. He divided the winds into four kinds and discussed their origin, and the effects of the features of the earth on them, such as mountain snows, and human activities such as the cultivation of the land. If forests were cleared and the land tilled, would the winds be affected? He asked whether 'perpetual discharges of cannon' would produce winds, as we today discuss the influence of hydrogen bombs on the weather. He suggested that the possibilities of causing and calming winds should be investigated. The existence of winds at different heights should be studied through observations on mountains, or on the drift of clouds. By the latter method, five different layers of winds had been detected. The directions of winds at different places at the same time were to be noted, and the relation of their directions to the aspect of the sun was to be investigated. Records should be compiled in order to see whether the direction of winds follow a cycle. In particular, the statement that the weather recurs in a thirty-five-year cycle should be investigated.

This suggestion immediately recalls modern research on the meteorological influence of the thirty-three-year sunspot cycle. Humboldt saw in Bacon's suggestions on the relation between the direction of winds and the variations of temperature, rainfall and evaporation from the sea, the beginning of the modern theories of the circulatory currents in the earth's atmosphere.

Bacon dwelt on the immense practical importance of knowledge of the winds. The steadiness of the winds blowing from the Atlantic onto Portugal had been one of the facts which had made Columbus believe that land existed in the west. The winds are as wings to men, which do not enable them to 'fly through the air but over the sea', by which means 'a vast gate of commerce is opened, and the whole world is rendered accessible'. Bacon expounds the phenomena of meteorology in the terms of economics, for the winds are traders in vapours, 'which they collect into crowds for importation or exportation to and from different countries, receiving winds in return by way of exchange'. This is one of the earliest examples of the illustration of the conservation of natural forces by analogy with the notion of economic exchange.

He referred to the sun's heat as one of the physical causes of winds. It could expand the air by as much as 'one-third of its volume', which was 'no trifling difference'. He investigated the artificial production of winds by exploring the air-currents

K

set up inside a closed tower by a bowl of hot coals. The currents were detected by means of a mass of feathers tied to the end of a long thread. When a small hole was made in a window in the tower, the warm air streamed out like a wind.

Bacon called this collection of new facts gained by experiment the compilation of Designed History, in contrast to the simple enumeration of phenomena observed in nature, which constitutes Natural History.

He said that research should be conducted to see how winds could be better utilized to meet 'human requirements'. For instance, the design of sails and windmills should be investigated experimentally. Bacon gave first place to research on the better exploitation of the winds as a source of locomotion and power.

He made model windmills with paper sails, which he drove by artificial winds generated by a pair of bellows, in order to try to improve the design. He made different shapes and numbers of sails, and added vanes to them, and studied how they behaved, and whether they produced more rotary force. He said that he carried out this work as much to see whether present practice would be confirmed as efficient, as to discover any possible improvements.

These experiments were not very skilfully performed and contained errors, but they show that Bacon had conceived experimental aerodynamics, and engineering development research.

He said that research on the winds would lead to better weather forecasting, which was important not only to sailors in the shipping trade, but also for forecasting harvests and the spread of epidemics.

Scientists were to 'see if there be anything which, on being communicated in a small quantity to the air, can excite and multiply the motion of dilation or contraction in the body of the air. For if this could be done, the raising and calming of the winds would naturally follow.' Here Bacon has a notion for controlling winds analogous to the modern idea of 'seeding' for causing rain.

He sketched out a plan for a history of the Sympathy and Antipathy of Things, which he did not succeed in carrying out. It was to deal with what we would call attraction, repulsion, and affinity. He said that 'strife and friendship in nature are the spurs of motions and the keys of works'. From these agencies are derived the attraction and repulsion of bodies, the mixture and separation of parts, and the possibility of giving matter the fundamental qualities which enable nature to use it to accomplish her great constructive achievements.

The possibility of the existence and form of the earth, the stars, the universe, living things, arise from the fundamental properties of matter. A knowledge of these fundamental properties enables man to imitate the achievements of nature, and to make for himself products hitherto made by her.

14. *The Principle of Conservation*

BACON intended to review existing knowledge on motion, force and gravitation in a history of Heavy and Light, but he did not go beyond writing a brief introduction for such a work. He said in this that none of the moderns had contributed anything to the subject, apart from a few mechanical inventions. But Gilbert had raised the question of magnetic force 'not unscientifically' though he had ascribed too many things to magnetism and had as it were 'himself become a magnet'.

He had better fortune in completing a review of what would now be called the Properties of Matter, under the title of a history of Dense and Rare. His method of treatment, as in all his writing on science, was 'more adapted to inform the judgment than to instruct practice'.

He gives a description of density, specific gravity, distillation, refrigeration, the expansion of gases, liquids and solids, and solution of solids in liquids, in a clear matter-of-fact style completely free from fancies, like that of a textbook on elementary science.

Bacon's description of the solution of iron in nitric acid has a very familiar ring: 'Take one penny weight of iron in plates to nine penny-weights of aqua-fortis; without fire the iron rises in large bubbles, not only within the body of the water but above it, so as to boil over the rim of the glass, at the same time emitting a thick and copious saffron-coloured fume; and this too with a very great internal tumult, and a very violent heat, greater than the hand can bear.' He proceeds with observations and experiments, evidently made by himself, and presents them methodically.

In this way he has helped to create the modern manner of writing textbooks and research papers, with concise and orderly presentation, distinguishing clearly between theory, data, results of experiments, interpretations and conclusions.

His experiments were sensible rather than brilliant. He was not a great scientist in the conventional sense. He showed a remarkable grasp of the importance of general method, but he had not the elegant technique of the born experimenter.

He advocated a systematic review of the whole of nature, rather than pausing to dig deep at any particular point. He wanted to have descriptions of the main features recorded in writing, because 'invention always proceeds by writing, and not by memory (for that would be something ludicrous in such a variety of instances); so that it may afterwards be perfected by the light of true induction'.

Towards this end, he gave descriptions of such phenomena as boiling in various kinds of liquids, and the comparatively small changes of volume which occur in a liquid when a solid is dissolved in it. He started by indicating that in the general subject of the properties of matter, only one fundamental principle had as yet been correctly recognized, that 'the sum of matter in the universe is always the same; and there is no operation either from nothing or to nothing'. When bodies were transmuted there was no creating of something out of nothing, nor is anything annihilated.

Bacon said that it would be good and useful in many respects if nature were made to give an account of how much was turned into gas, and how much remained behind, when a liquid is distilled. He was applying an idea taken from commerce to the description of exchanges in nature. 'This may be done if before distillation you weigh both the body that is to be distilled and the vessels in which the distillation is to be performed, and after distillation you weigh the liquid and the lees, and then the vessels again.' The deficiency of weight in these three weighings compared with the weight of the whole body will show how much has been turned into gas.

He investigated the effect of nitric acid on mercury, lead, silver, copper, tin and iron; using weighed portions of both acid and metal, so that he was able to determine the different weights of acid required for the solution of the respective metals.

His quantitative conception is illustrated by an extensive investigation of the densities of substances. He said that the proportions of matter in things are the basis of natural philosophy. These proportions were to be discovered by measuring the densities of substances, which revealed the quantity of matter in them.

He gave a table of the results of his experimental determinations of the densities of seventy-eight substances, ranging from gold and iron to strong beer and petroleum which, he tells us, he had carried out many years before.

He had two identical hollow cubical vessels made of thin silver, which were however a little deeper than wide. He made a small cube of gold which would slip neatly into either of these vessels, leaving a little rim round the top, because of the extra depth.

He made a mark on the inside of one of the vessels at a height above the bottom which was equal to the length of an edge of the cube. By filling the vessel up to this mark he was able to obtain cubes of liquids and powders which were of the same size as the gold cube. He was then able to compare the masses of all the various cubes by weighing with a balance. He found that the densest material that he measured was gold, and the lightest, fir wood. According to his figures gold was thirty-two times as dense as fir wood.

He commented that the range of density of solids and liquids of the earth appeared to be remarkably narrow, and he at once drew an important philosophical conclusion from it. 'We may observe with satisfaction how finite and comprehensible the nature of things is in tangible bodies. For the Table brings nature as it were within the grasp. Let no one wander off therefore, or indulge in fancies and dreams.' But 'of things in the interior of the earth however I say nothing, seeing that they are not subject either to sense or experiment. These, it may be, being far removed and completely separated from the heat of the heavenly bodies, are more dense than any known bodies.'

He explained that one could deduce from his table of densities whether a particular kind of heavy stone or metal would float in mercury, 'and this not with a view to marvels and imposture, but to the investigation of the nature of mixtures'.

He investigated the density of gases by weighing a quantity

of a volatile liquid, and then turning it into a gas or vapour by external heating, and finding how large a volume it occupied at about atmospheric pressure.

'I took therefore a small glass phial, which would hold about an ounce. Into this phial I poured half an ounce of spirit of wine; for that being the lightest liquid approaches nearest to a pneumatic (gaseous) nature. I then took a very large bladder which would hold eight pints (or a gallon as we call it in English). The bladder was not an old one; therefore it was neither dry nor stiff, but fresh and soft. . . .'

Bacon describes how he forced out all the air as well as he could, until the sides stuck together. Then he gently rubbed the outside with oil to fill up the pores. Then he placed the mouth of the phial within the bladder and tied it tight with a wax thread. He put the whole over hot coals in a bowl. In a short time part of the spirit of wine was converted into vapour which expanded the bladder very tightly. Then he pricked the bladder so that the vapour might escape rather than condense inside. He quickly removed the glass phial and measured the amount of liquid left in it. From this he was able to calculate the amount vaporized. It was about one-fortieth of a pint, and when vaporized it had occupied about one gallon of volume.

From this he concluded that the lightest liquids or tangible bodies are at least a hundred times as dense as the densest gas.

He suggested that the degree to which gases can be rarefied should be investigated, 'in order that we may be better able to judge of the variety of the air in the higher regions, and thence of the ether itself'.

He proposed that a strong iron vessel should be completely filled with water, tightly closed, and then alternately heated and cooled several times. He thought that the 'grosser parts of the water' would be forced by the heat 'into a new configuration (less simple and uniform), until it either acquires some colour, or smell, or taste, or oiliness, or any other remarkable alteration (such as is found in composite bodies), no doubt a great thing would be achieved opening the way to many others'.

He had the idea of polymerization, by which the simple constituents in substances are caused to coagulate into more complicated ones, and had even imagined the production of oily substances from water. The Fischer-Tropsch process in which oil is synthesized from steam and coke, is reminiscent of this conception. Modern plastics such as polythene are made from colourless liquids and gases by high pressure.

He said that close distillation in which heat operates on the substance 'without separating or consuming the parts, may effect and produce wonderful transformations'. He thought that while it would never transform water completely into oil, another more 'tensible' raw material might be transformed by it into fat. This 'would be a thing of immense utility, as all alimentation principally consists in fat'.

Here Bacon is foreseeing the synthesis of edible fats, an achievement which has only just started in our own time.

He commented on the importance of allowing sufficient time for the completion of a chemical reaction. A moderate heat acting over a long period often had a result similar to that of a great heat over a short period. For instance, the rusting of a metal over a long period produced a result rather like that obtained by strong heating over a short period. As he put it, 'age by itself is only a stage or measure of motion'.

Another idea towards which he was groping was the use of biological processes for obtaining non-biological products, a method used today on a huge industrial scale, in the production, for example, of chemical solvents from agricultural wastes. He suggested that 'medicines be sometimes tried and exercised on lifeless bodies'. Though most of them would have no effect at all, as he supposed that their action would depend on the presence of a living spirit, yet there could be 'no question but some of them will operate on some lifeless bodies'. They would, however, have to be in a stronger power 'to operate on a dead body than on a live one'.

Bacon's systematic reviewing of natural phenomena encouraged the advancement of science simultaneously on all fronts. He did not stop to concentrate his effort on any particular phenomenon, so he was able to obtain a balanced view of a whole aspect of nature. This had a profound influence on the founder members of the Royal Society. Besides adopting his comprehensive approach, they followed his ideal of style, which Tenison described as 'not so much neat and polite, as clear, masculine and apt'. The early volumes of the *Philosophical Transactions* consist mainly of comprehensive reviews of natural phenomena, written in plain and unexalted language.

It is only through this approach that the whole of nature can be described without undue emphasis on particular aspects, and the material provided for a balanced development of pure and applied science.

Within a century of Bacon's death, the first comprehensive approach had given way to concentration on particular aspects. One of the causes for this specialization was the needs of capitalism, the growth of which after Bacon's time concentrated scientific attention not systematically over the whole of nature, but mainly on those aspects which promised immediate profits. So, for about two centuries, Bacon's comprehensive view fell into the background.

The great but uneven development of science that now occurred had, by the beginning of the twentieth century, begun to endanger human society and life. In our own day, these dangers have threatened the existence of the human race and all life on our planet.

We are consequently becoming more concerned with the balanced or planned development of science which Bacon advocated, and are not so absorbed in pursuing a relatively few but very profitable aspects, such as the development of power and the discovery of new resources. We view with more sympathy Bacon's effort to bring the whole of nature into one focus, and are less disturbed by the limitations of his ability as a personal experimenter and discoverer in particular fields, and his many failures to escape from the scientific ignorance of his time. Our problem is not how to make discoveries, but how to manage them, and see them all in relation and as a whole, so that we can safely control and utilize them in a stable as well as an advancing scientific society.

15. *The Prolongation and Renewal of Life*

THE problem of prolonging life, and preserving the faculties in as good vigour as possible in old age, which is the subject-matter of the modern science of gerontology, was an aspect of Bacon's project in which he was particularly interested, and on which he often wrote. But he composed his *History of Life and Death* earlier than he had intended, perhaps with the secondary aim of securing more attention from James I, not only for his project, but also for himself after his fall. James was ageing prematurely, and it might be calculated that any suggestions for how this decay could be resisted would secure his personal interest.

Bacon swiftly composed the work, though this hope, as always, was disappointed. He comforted himself with the observation that it would be a work of God's favour, 'if in our pilgrimage through the wilderness of this world, these our shoes and garments (I mean our frail bodies) are as little worn out as possible'. The idea seems inconsequent. He says that though those who aspire to eternity set little value on earthly life, yet they should not despise performing works of charity, such as keeping men well and fit.

He said that the subject should be introduced through a study of the longevity of inanimate, vegetable and animal bodies. This should be conducted under seven headings. The length and shortness of men's lives should be investigated in relation to the environment, such as the times, countries, climates and places in which they were born and lived.

Their heredity, and their bodily constitution should be studied.

The time of birth should be investigated, to see whether this has any significance, but all astrological fancies were to be excluded.

Diet, manner of life, amount of exercise, and the air in which they live, were to be investigated; and the relation of longevity to profession, way of life, and qualities of mind.

Medicines supposed to prolong life should be inquired into, and notes made of those constitutional features in healthy people which are correlated with longevity. The signs that death is near should be excluded, for these belong to the sphere of medicine.

Bacon started from the consideration that anything which can be repaired gradually is potentially eternal. In the time of growth and youth all parts of animals are repaired entirely, and indeed are increased in quantity and quality. If the process of repairing did not fail, they would be eternal. In age repairing takes place very unequally, so that healthy parts are adjacent to dead or dying parts. According to one of his favourite similes, the human body begins to suffer the torture inflicted on Mezentius, in which the living die in the embraces of the dead.

Consequently, the parts that are still easily repaired, such as the blood, flesh and fat, are forced to decay by those parts that are repaired less easily, such as nerves, bones and bowels. 'The workshop of the body with its machines and organs' are made 'incapable of performing the work of repair.'

There are therefore two main subjects of inquiry, the consumption and wearing-away of the tissues, and their repair. The first he thought had to do with the external air, and the second with the 'whole process of alimentation'. He was groping towards the notions of oxidation and metabolism.

He said that whatever the external air did to living, it also did to inanimate bodies. We should say that the processes of respiration in living bodies and combustion in inanimate bodies are similar in principle.

Inanimate bodies could, however, exist for a long time without repair, whereas animal bodies without food and repair 'collapse and die out like fire'. He thought, therefore, that the human body should be studied firstly as an inanimate body not repaired by nourishment, and secondly as a living thing which is nourished.

His conception of the problem was modern in his statistical outlook and his insistence on applying the same naturalistic method of investigation impartially to inanimate and living processes.

Bacon made a review of the length of life of inanimate things, such as metals and stones. Metals generally lasted so long that men could not observe their duration, but, except in the case of gold, they gradually rusted. Stones and precious stones lasted longer, but even they showed signs of change with age. He supposed that the dissolution of inanimate things was due to the action of a spirit inside them. They could be made durable by detaining or fixing this spirit. The primitive animistic idea of 'spirit' had evolved in Bacon about half-way towards the modern idea of the reactions in living processes. He sometimes implies that the 'spirit' is a subtle chemical substance.

Plants varied very much in length of life, but some trees lived for eight hundred years. He noted that the trunk could be made longer-lived by pruning the branches. He assembled the facts then known on the methods of preserving grain and fruits. The former was kept fresh for thirty years in cellars in East Germany, while an apple or chestnut which happened to fall into the snow on mountains, might be found months later 'as fresh and fair as if it had been gathered the day before'.

Investigation of the processes by which plant and animal products are cured and preserved might suggest how ageing could be retarded. The process of hardening, dessication and wrinkling of tissues should be studied for the same reason.

He thought that the decay of the blood might be arrested by new kinds of drugs yet to be discovered. 'I fully believe, that if something could be infused in very small portions into the whole substance of blood . . . it would stop not only all putrefaction' but would 'be very effectual in prolonging life'. The modern anti-bacterial and anti-biotic drugs are a great advance in this direction.

Recent research on the cause of wrinkling in skin has led to the discovery that the blood contains a substance which inhibits the action of the ferment elastase which breaks down the elastic tissue of the body, and that ageing may be due in part to the decrease of the amount of this inhibitor in the blood. This is in line with Bacon's idea. It may be that the inhibitory substance will be extracted from animal tissue or synthesized in the laboratory, and then given to persons suffering from hardening of the arteries, or from clots obstructing the flow of their blood, as in thrombosis.

He collected information on the length of life of forty-nine species of animals. He noted that birds seem to be relatively long-lived. He attributed this among other factors to their being carried by the air, which reduced exertion of the limbs. He also thought it might be affected by the smallness of their heads. He believed that the head was the principal seat of the spirit which caused consumption of the flesh and putrefaction. Birds had less of this consuming spirit than other animals with relatively larger heads. Men with very large heads were generally short-lived.

Bacon's science is a mixture of the common science of his day, with some original observations and rough experiments, and shrewd realistic comments. He aimed at handling the conventional scientific theories in an orderly and coolly critical way. He had no outstanding talent for discovering new scientific facts, but he was able by his detached critical views to propound broad scientific ideas in front of his time.

He remarked that 'it is strange how men, like owls, see sharply in the darkness of their own notions, but in the daylight of experience wink and are blinded'.

In his review of the effects of nutrition on ageing, he suggested that methods of feeding the body, other than through the mouth, should be investigated. These could be used to evade the weakness of digestion which afflicts old men. He vaguely suggested feeding through the intestines and by injections, and he gave much attention to the possibilities of feeding through bathing and anointing the body.

He thought that too near a connexion between the kind of nourishment and the thing nourished was not good. For instance, it is bad to sow a field with grain which has been harvested from it. But the provision of nutriment that is close in composition to the thing nourished is good. A seed of an onion put in the earth will not grow so well as when it is grafted onto the root of another onion which is then set in the ground.

Bacon believed that the process of grafting, which produces rejuvenation phenomena, should be investigated, in order to see whether it would throw light on how ageing in human tissues might be combated. He mentioned that people with ugly noses had been supplied with new ones made from other parts of the body, which proved 'the consent of flesh to flesh'. He was aware of the possibility of plastic surgery.

He collected information on the living of parts of bodies after the organism as a whole is dead. In this connexion he quotes an observation of his own. 'I remember to have seen the heart of a man who had his bowels torn out (the punishment with us for high treason), which on being cast according to custom into the fire, leapt up at first about a foot and a half high, and then by degrees to a less height, for the space, as I remember, of seven or eight minutes.'

After discussing nutrition, he reviewed the length of life of men and women mentioned in history, who have lived beyond the age of eighty. To each he appended a brief biographical notice of two or three lines, including such points as in his judgment had 'some bearing on longevity (which is in no slight degree influenced by fortune and habits)'.

We hear that Xenophanes of Colophon 'wandered no less in his mind than in his body', so that besides travelling for seventy-seven years, he changed his name to Xenomanes, and was 'doubtless a man of vast conception, breathing nothing but infinity'.

Democritus lived to 109. 'He was a great philosopher, and a true student of nature, if ever Greek was; a great traveller in countries, but a greater still in the works of nature; a diligent experimenter; and (as Aristotle objects) a follower of similitudes rather than an observer of the laws of argument.'

Plato lived to eighty; 'a man of great spirit, but loving quiet, in contemplation sublime and imaginative, but yet rather composed than merry and of a majestic carriage'.

The stage of the theatre or of the world, seemed to be good for ladies. Galeria Copiola was brought back to the stage ninety-nine years after her first appearance, on the dedication of a theatre by Pompey the Great. 'Not now as an actress, but as a wonder. And this is not all; for she was exhibited again at the votive games in honour of Augustus.'

Livia, the wife of Augustus and mother of Tiberius, lived until she was ninety. If Augustus regarded his own life as a play (he asked his friends to give him a round of applause as soon as he had expired), then Livia also could claim to be an excellent actress in the affairs of life, as a wife, mother, and head of a household.

Hippocrates of Cos was reputed to have lived 104 years. The length of his life 'approved and credited his own art. He was a man of wisdom as well as learning, much given to experiments and observations, not striving after words and methods, but picking out the very nerves of science and setting them forth.'

Even in England, men of eighty were to be found in nearly every village. He had heard that in May-day games in Herefordshire a few years ago, eight men, whose total age exceeded 800 years, had performed a morris dance.

Moses's saying that the normal length of life is seventy years, and in exceptional cases eighty, appears to have remained true, in spite of being in conflict with the immense ages attributed to biblical characters. In the light of the latter, one might have expected that there would have been a gradual shortening of life during subsequent ages, but this had not been so. Bacon suggested that the periods of great longevity were terminated by the Flood, and other great natural disasters might have similar effects.

He discussed the possible effects of climate and geography, and thought that islands and plains might be more conducive than continental countries and mountains and valleys to long life.

Observation showed that to some extent, long life was hereditary. He thought that longevity was inherited more from the mother's than the father's side.

Bacon describes physiological types which, according to him, are inclined to longevity.

It is illustrative of his character that in this work, which contains many significant notions and comments, he should instance paleness in youth, dark complexion and freckled skin, 'a deep wrinkled brow' and 'rough and bristly hair' (all features of James I) as indicative of longevity. Stiff curly hair (like that of Charles I) and thick curls (like those of Buckingham) were also a good sign. He describes other features as conducive to longevity which have been identified. Here Bacon's arts coincided with those of the fortune-teller.

He believed that 'a well-regulated diet contributes most to the prolongation of life', but he put in saving clauses which were probably meant to excuse the excesses and habits of James, Charles and Buckingham. The first of these was his remark that 'The duties of life are preferable to life itself,' an unexceptionable sentiment, which would enable James to plead his kingly duties as a reason for ignoring self-control.

However, he concludes that saints and hermits live longest. After them are scholars, whose life is passed in leisure, and meditations which have no relations with affairs. They are free from anxiety, pass their days in what they like doing best, and in the company of youth, 'which is more cheerful'. The tenets of the scholars have a bearing on their longevity. For the best effects they should contain 'A touch of superstition,' such as the Pythagorean or Platonic. Wrangling philosophies shorten life.

Finally, an out-of-doors life is advised, 'not indolent but active, living generally on fresh and home-made food, and free from care and envy.'

Bacon devotes a lot of space to the art of cooking. He shows himself remarkably knowledgeable on the subject, but he assumes the resources of a royal or ducal, or at least a chancellor's kitchen, which exceed even those of Mrs. Beaton.

We hear that wheaten bread 'which has more of the bran in it is more solid than that made of fine flour', which would agree with our war-time regulations in favour of high-extraction wholemeal flour. He recommends maize and asparagus, thorough beating of various kinds of meat and fish in order to make them tender before cooking, and is in favour of sauces in general. They should be light with heavy food, and 'fat' with light food.

He recommends salads, especially watercress, which should be 'young, not old' and taken fresh. Roots of chicory, spinach and beet, 'stripped of their pith and boiled in water till they are tender, with a third part of white wine, and used as common salads with oil and vinegar, are to be recommended'. They are strengthening for the liver.

He was much in favour of warm beverages. He remarks elsewhere that he 'ever had opinion that some comforting drink at four o'clock' was beneficial, for at that hour he was apt to suffer from a 'languishing'.

Bacon studied in detail the effects of his diets, anointings, purgings and medicines upon himself. He recommended odours as comforting to the heart, preferring those from flowers growing in the garden rather than those from cut flowers. 'Violets, pinks and gilly-flowers, bean-blossoms, lime-flowers, the dust or flowers of vines, clary, the yellow wall-flower, musk roses (for other roses when growing give out little smell), strawberry plants, especially when dying, sweet briar, especially in early spring, wild mint, and lavender flowers; and in hot countries, oranges, citrons, myrtle, and laurel.' One should walk or sit among the 'breaths' of these plants.

Bacon concluded that longevity is best ensured by the sensible management of every aspect of life. It was more a matter of regimen and diet, than of medicines.

16. *The Dissemination of Scientific Knowledge*

Bacon's last work was his general treatise on natural history, entitled *Sylva Sylvarum*, which Spedding translates as a 'collection of collections'. It was published two years after Bacon's death, from a manuscript which had been virtually completed by the author. Though Bacon said it was to be regarded as belonging to the third part of his project, it is, as science, one of the less distinguished of Bacon's works. He was conscious of this, for Rawley in his introduction says that he had often heard Bacon say that he would have served the glory of his own name better if he had not published it. He was aware that much of it would appear 'vulgar and trivial, mean and sordid, curious and fruitless'. The excuse for proceeding with, and publishing it, was that if Bacon himself did not start the humblest labouring tasks on behalf of the *Great Instauration*, no one else would. Its style has not the poise of his earlier works. Like most of his writing after his fall, it has a wistful quality.

Sylva Sylvarum is of more interest in its bearing on the circumstances of Bacon's life than as an original contribution to science. Today we would regard it as a piece of popularization, a straightforward exposition of accepted science, with comments on the information, expounded in the light of the author's own experience.

Bacon probably wrote it not only as a contribution to the project, but also to make money. It was not the only piece of writing which he did in his last days partly or wholly to raise money to pay his creditors. It had a considerable success. It became popular reading in the seventeenth century, and went through several editions.

When examined in this perspective, Bacon's motive for writing the *Sylva Sylvarum* becomes more intelligible. It is a substantial book composed in ten chapters each containing one hundred paragraphs. Most of it consists of summaries of information from Aristotle, Pliny, Porta, Cardan and Sandys, to which are added occasional original observations and comments. The topics range through common physical and chemical phenomena, botany, physiology, medicine, agriculture, gardening, cooking, building, music, aesthetics, and psychology.

He includes many brief resumés of subjects he has treated more thoroughly in other works. As it stands, it is a compendium of science which, in Bacon's opinion, every gentleman and owner of an estate should know.

As in other of his last works, Bacon's thoughts seem to have gone back to his youth. After the blow of his fall, he sought refuge in the ideas with which he was surrounded in his childhood. The *Sylva Sylvarum* has echoes of the kind of book which was consulted by his grandfather, the landlord's steward, on how to manage the estate and household, but with the subject-matter transformed by passing through Bacon's scientific and philosophical mind. Bacon reviews every topic, from gravitation to witchcraft, with the practical realism of a responsible steward managing an estate of the intellect. In this work, the influence of the ideas of the social class of Bacon's ancestors, and their attitude to things, comes out strongly, and shows one of the chief origins of his realistic materialism in science.

He approaches the commonplaces of brewing and the fantastic assertions of thought-readers with a uniform cool impartiality. He takes care that his observations and experiments should either be 'of use or of discovery: for we hate impostures, and despise curiosities'. But he is always positive in his consideration of popular beliefs and old wives' tales, 'lest our incredulity may prejudice any profitable operations in this kind'. He repeatedly draws attention to possibilities of making profits out of better scientific knowledge; for instance, by vernalization or pre-treatment of seed, to promote germination and shorten growing time, so that produce can be sent to the market early, when prices are high. Early peas would be particularly profitable. In our time, the development of vernalization by Lysenko has caused worldwide discussion.

Another profitable invention would be a process for preserving oranges, lemons and pomegranates in a fresh condition until the summer, by which time their price would have 'mightily increased'. He would have particularly appreciated our 'deep

L

freeze'. His remarks on homely topics resemble the sayings of Benjamin Franklin's *Poor Richard*, and his less inspired comments are sometimes like the common-sensical sayings of Sancho Panza.

We hear, for example, that 'earthen bottles filled with hot water do provoke, in bed, a sweat more daintily than brick-bats hot'. Massage is good for thin people. 'Gentle frication of emaciated bodies drawth forth the nourishment, by making the parts hungry, and heating them; whereby they call forth nourishment the better.'

Occasionally he rises to his best style. He devotes a good deal of space to the description of the phenomena of sound. He discusses its analogies with light, and the dependence of the qualities of music on its physical properties. When he writes on music, his style usually becomes musical, as when he remarks that 'tunes and airs, even in their own nature, have in themselves some affinity with the affections'.

One of his more interesting suggestions is the possibility of silencers for guns. He does not like the idea because 'it may cause secret murders'. But he conceives that it should be possible, because the noise arises from the impact of the gases from the fired gun on the air. Hence, 'if it were possible to bring to pass that there should be no air pent at the mouth of the piece, the bullet might fly with small or no noise'. Such silencers, which allow the burnt gases in the gun to escape gradually, are now used by gangsters on their tommy-guns, and were developed during the Second World War for silencing artillery.

In his discussion of the origin of the pleasing effects of harmony, he compares effects on the hearing with those on sight. Colour corresponds to tone, while harmony corresponds to order. 'Globes, Pyramids, cones, cylinders . . .' are pleasing, whereas 'unequal figures are but deformities'.

He returns to one of his favourite subjects with reflections on the possibility of making food out of inorganic substances. One of the greatest natural achievements is the making of oil out of water, which, he says, is a greater feat than turning silver into gold. He gives four instances in nature in which water is turned into oil or fat. The first is by the effect of the sun on a mixture of earth and water, whereby plants are produced. He says that if an analogous method by which non-edible materials could be turned into food, it would be exceedingly profitable.

In his discussion of the nutritive value of different foods he remarks that 'children in dairy countries do wax more tall than when they feed more upon bread and flesh', a conclusion confirmed in our own day by Lord Boyd Orr and the nutritionists.

He suggested that the production of new crop plants by experimental methods might be very profitable. But the crossing of different species of plants had not yet been achieved. It would be 'one of the most notable experiments . . . to find it out. Grafting doth it not.' He thought that a species might be transmuted into a new one by feeding it with nutrients which are 'as contrary as may be to the nature of the herb'. This is reminiscent of the modern method of producing new species by treatment with poisons such as colchicine.

He makes an interesting observation on the problem of diseases of corn. He says that these, especially mildew, such as York's Woald, cannot be remedied; though he had himself seen that it had been reduced when small fields had been enclosed into larger fields, an example of the technical advantages of enclosure.

He is particularly at home in introducing remarks on superstition and witchcraft with a profile of the Pythagorean philosophy. This, he said, was full of superstition. It planted a 'monstrous imagination' which was afterwards watered and nourished by the school of Plato. 'It was, that the world was one entire perfect living creature; . . . Having established this foundation, they built on it what they would.' As any effect at one place in a living creature is immediately spread through the whole of the body, it follows that, since the world is a living creature, 'no distance of place, nor want or indisposition of matter, could hinder magical operations'. We might for example here in Europe have an awareness of things being done in China, and we might be able to cause any effect 'without and against matter'. This could be done without the co-operation of angels or spirits and only through the unity and harmony of nature. Some went further, 'and held that the spirit of man (whom they call the microcosm)' could influence the spirit of the world by an intense effort of the imagination, and thus command nature. Paracelsus, and 'some darksome authors of magic' asserted that the imagination had the 'power of miracle-working faith. With these vast and bottomless follies men have been (in part) entertained'.

But these matters were to be inquired into with all sobriety, to separate anything that was clean and natural from super-stition and magic. One had to be careful not to deny any opera-tions by the transmission of spirits and the force of imagination because they sometimes fail, or to accept them because they appeared often to succeed. He began his consideration of the phenomena with a naturalistic approach, comparing such trans-missions with the spread of infectious disease.

If they worked at all, they worked most upon weak minds, such as those of women, the sick, the superstitious and children. It was noticeable that they had least effect on kings and magistrates, who seemed to have an immunity to them, as some have to ordinary infectious disease. Witches and sorcerers have little effect on people whose minds are occupied with weighty thoughts.

In many cases, the result is merely due to the effects of a per-son's own imagination upon himself. If he has a charm, such as a ring, which he believes will help him, he will work with more con-fidence and all the harder, and who does not know what wonder-ful results can be gained by industry and perseverance?

One should be cautious in accepting evidence against witches, or confessions from them, for they are commonly imaginative persons who believe that they have accomplished effects which in fact they have not.

In order to investigate the effects of the force of the imagina-tion, a man must experiment on others and not on himself. The strength of a belief can be fortified by experience, by reason and by authority. By far the most potent of these is authority. Belief based merely on experience and reason is liable to be uncertain.

Authority comes from belief in an art or system of ideas, or in a man. The latter kind of authority is by far the more active.

Where one man has authority over a second, the latter 'must be ignorant, and not learned, or full of thoughts; and such are (for the most part) all witches and superstitious persons; whose beliefs, tied to their teachers and traditions, are no whit con-trolled either by reason or experience; and upon the same reason, in magic, they use (for the most part) boys and young people, whose spirits easiliest take belief and imagination'. Bacon pro-vides here an explanation of the psychology of Hitlerism.

He discussed such phenomena as the picking out of a playing card, which has previously been thought of by another person. These were to be investigated with extreme caution, and he found their investigation by his method of induction 'wonderful hard', because no experiment can be made without having a belief first. But one cannot command oneself to believe what one will, 'so no trial can be made'.

He concluded that if effects at a distance occurred, they were probably conveyed from man to man, 'as fame is', and if a witch injured some person at a distance it was probably through the intermediation of other persons.

If anyone complained that he ought to have made more experiments in this obscure subject, he had to say that 'the truth is, that these effects of imagination upon other bodies have so little credit with us', that he would leave them to be tried when he had the leisure for them, and in the meantime proceed with more important matters. He said that the general root of all superstition is that men are apt to note 'when things hit, and not when they miss'.

Bacon's preoccupation with the ideas of his childhood and youth during the last months of his life are illustrated by two stories which he relates in his *Natural History*. He mentions in connexion with the possible bearing of dreams on the future, that when he was in Paris he had a dream, two or three days before his father's death, in which his 'father's house in the country was plastered all over with black mortar'.

The other story concerned the popular belief that warts can be removed by rubbing them with a thing which is subsequently destroyed. The destruction by the thing is supposed, by sympathetic magic, to destroy the warts.

He remembered that when he was in Paris at about the age of sixteen, a wart which he had had since his childhood, was sudenly accompanied by many others, so that within a month, he had more than a hundred on his hands. 'The English Ambassador's lady, who was a woman far from superstition, told me one day, she would help me away with my warts. . . .' She got a piece of lard, rubbed his warts with it, and then nailed the lard beside her window, in the sun, facing south. Within five weeks all the warts had disappeared. Bacon was not much surprised that the rash of new warts had gone, because they had come quickly, but he was so impressed by the disappearance also of the ancient solitary wart, that he could still remember the incident in his latest years. These strong memories of Paris suggest that the years he spent there in his youth made a deep impression on him.

There is a good deal of repetition in the *Natural History*. Its defects of composition and style seem to have been increased by the use of dictation, putting down things that occurred to him, even when they had been discussed before. In this it resembles some modern books which exhibit similar faults, arising from the use of tape-machines, instead of the pen.

In his last scientific work the spirit of science for profit is vocal. It was a decline from his earlier work, which advocated the development and application of science for the benefit of all mankind, but it was more appropriate to the spirit in which science was actually developed during the next three centuries. From our own time forwards, science will be developed and utilized more and more in Bacon's greater style, for it is the only one which is adequate to the needs of the human situation.

PART II

For Himself

17. *Bacon's Origin*

SIR NICHOLAS BACON, the father of Francis Bacon, was one of the most significant figures of his day. He was born about 1510, a boy of humble parentage, who had been sent to Cambridge because of his ability. There he made friends with other able youths, who were inspired by the ferment of learning which flourished in Cambridge under the impulse of the Reformation. Nicholas visited Paris for a short time after leaving Cambridge, and then studied law at Gray's Inn. Already at the age of twenty-seven, he was appointed to an important legal position, before he had practised his profession. In 1539, on the dissolution of the monasteries, he drew up a scheme for 'a seminary for ministers of state', in which young men of high ability were to be educated in civil law, Latin and French. Some should be attached to ambassadors abroad to learn diplomatic technique, some were to write the histories of foreign transactions, and some of public trials at home.

He subsequently sent his son Francis to be attached to the English Ambassador to France, which shows that he intended him to become a statesman. Nicholas Bacon was solicitor to the University of Cambridge while William Cecil, who was eleven years his junior was a student there. It is said that their great friendship started in Cambridge.

When Elizabeth came to the throne, Archbishop Heath, the Lord Chancellor, refused to carry out her measures. His powers were taken from him and given to Sir Nicholas Bacon, with the hitherto not very important position of Lord Keeper of the Seal. He did not receive the title of Lord Chancellor, perhaps at his own request, for in Birch's words: 'as he was one of the most learned, most pious, and wisest of men of the nation, so he retained in all his greatness a modesty equal to his other virtues, and which rarely accompanies such a distinction of fortune and merit'. One effect of this change was to transfer the position of first minister from churchmen, by whom it had long been held, to civilians. Sir Nicholas, with his civilian and educational

153

interests, advanced the administrative techniques of government. Thus his appointment was an important step towards the modern secularized business state.

He was a zealous protestant, and opponent of Mary Queen of Scots. He had six children by his first wife, none of whom were remarkable, and two sons, Anthony and Francis, by his second wife, Anne Cook, daughter of the tutor of Edward VI, and sister of William Cecil's wife. The two brothers-in-law, as Lord Keeper and Lord Treasurer, presently became the 'twin props of the nation'. Anne Bacon was learned in Latin and Greek, and an ardent Calvinist. She was passionately attached to her sons. She was still admonishing them, in transports of maternal affection, even when they were deep in affairs of state, on their religion, morals and material welfare. She became more and more fanatical and eccentric, and finally, demented. She died in 1610, at about the age of eighty. Bishop Goodman wrote that 'she was but little better than frantic in her age'. A strain of abnormality seems to run through the Cooks, for her sister's son, Robert Cecil, was a hunchback. Nicholas Bacon and William Cecil were normal, able and healthy men from the country.

The younger of Anne Bacon's two sons, Francis, born at York House in the Strand on January 22nd, 1561, resembled her in appearance. Francis was his father's favourite son, but also he was a mother's son and he was ultimately buried beside her. In considering Francis Bacon's characteristics, it is helpful to remember the high gifts but mental aberrations of his mother. His mind had tendencies which could not be regarded as completely and conventionally normal.

The portrait of Sir Nicholas Bacon reveals a very formidable personality, of a character quite different from what is recorded of him. In the picture he looks gross, brutal and cunning. History reports that he was very stout, but 'infinitely witty', as well as wise and modest. He persisted in living in a small house, which drew comment from Queen Elizabeth when she visited him. 'My Lord, what a little house have you gotten.' Sir Nicholas replied: 'Madam, my house is well, but it is you that have made me too great for my house.'

Francis met Queen Elizabeth when he was a boy of twelve. She asked him how old he was, and he replied: 'Two years younger than her Majesty's happy reign.' She was 'much taken' with this method of informing her that he was twelve. She took to conversing with him and delighted to prove him with questions, and referred to him as 'my young Lord Keeper'.

Nicholas Bacon acquired estates in the dissolution of the monasteries. He was descended from farmers and shepherds, and was interested in improving his lands. The surnames of both of Francis's parents: Bacon and Cook, echoed the world from which both were descended, and reveal one of the sources of his practical outlook. Sir Nicholas believed in progressive plumbing, for he arranged that every room in his house at Gorhambury should be served with a pipe, bringing water from a pond a mile away. He was witty even in his death. One day in February 1579, in about his sixty-ninth year, when he had grown very stout, he was sitting in a chair, while his barber was rubbing and combing his head. The weather had turned warm after a hard frost, and the room was very hot. 'The window was open to let in a fresh wind. The Lord Keeper fell asleep, and awakened all distempered and in great sweat. Saith he to his barber, Why did you let me sleep? Why, my Lord, saith he, I durst not wake your Lordship. Why then saith my Lord, you have killed me with kindness. So removed into his bed chamber and within a few days died.'

Sir Nicholas long bore great responsibilities in very difficult times, and yet history always reports well of him. He was evidently a man of extraordinary self-control. Perhaps this helps to explain his picture, for that appears to be the portrait of a frightening character. Here again may be a clue to some of Francis Bacon's characteristics. His father, like his mother, also had a fundamentally peculiar nature, but was more successful than his son in keeping it completely under control, and presenting a balanced, normal personality.

When Sir Nicholas died, he had already made provision for all his children, with the exception of the youngest. He had begun to collect an estate for Francis, but did not live to complete it. Thus Francis Bacon was reared in the highest social circle of the day, and acquired the ambitions natural to one of his ability in his situation. But at the age of eighteen, he suddenly found himself fatherless and without adequate income. Environment and education had bred in him the greatest ambitions, but had left him without means. This circumstance was one of the causes which broke down his resistance to one of the weaker tendencies of his nature, and precipitated him into life-long importunity, begging, borrowing and finally acceptance of bribes.

With Shakespeare he could have said:

> *Oh for my sake do you with fortune chide,*
> *The guilty goddess of my harmful deeds,*
> *That did not better for my life provide,*
> *Than public means, which public manners breeds . . .*

The Calvinist and protestant atmosphere of Bacon's home helped to create his profound faith in works, and hence provided one of the chief motives of his constructive philosophy for the development and application of science.

Bacon did not marry until he was forty-six, and then, it seems, more for convenience than affection. His wife Alice Barnham was very much his junior, younger than twenty and possibly only fifteen. She was an alderman's daughter, with a useful dowry. Little is heard of her in Bacon's life, and ultimately Bacon cut her out of his will, except for her rights, shortly before his death. She subsequently married one of her gentlemen ushers.

Bacon's essay *Of Marriage* exhibits a notable coolness of feeling. Perhaps his deep attachment to his mother interfered with his other heterosexual affections.

Lady Bacon wrote to her elder son Anthony in 1593: 'surely though I pity your brother, yet so long as he pitieth not himself but keepeth that bloody Percy, as I told him then, yea as a coach companion and bed companion,—a proud profane costly fellow, whose being about him I verily fear the Lord God doth mislike and doth less bless your brother in credit and otherwise in his health,—surely I am utterly discouraged and make a conscience further to undo myself to maintain such wretches as he is. . . .'

Bacon's life in bachelor rooms, attended by extravagant young male servants suggests that he was not much inclined towards domestic and family life.

Sir Nicholas sent Francis to the house of his brother-in-law Lord Burghley for his boyhood education. Francis there found himself necessarily taking second place to Burghley's son, Robert Cecil, who was deformed and two years Bacon's junior.

In his later years, Bacon sharply criticized education in great households. He wrote in *De Augmentis*: 'I am, clearly, in favour of a collegiate education for boys and young men; not in private houses, nor merely under schoolmasters. For in colleges there is greater emulation of the youths amongst themselves; there is also the sight and countenance of grave men, which tends to modesty, and forms their young minds from the very first after that mode, and in short there are very many advantages in a collegiate education. . . .' No doubt this was partly a reflection of his own experience.

After three years at Trinity College, Cambridge, he was sent abroad, at the age of sixteen, as a member of the staff of Sir Amias Paulet, the English Ambassador to France. At the French Court, he learned the French language, diplomacy, and courtly manners. He was there for nearly three years, during a period of intense political and international activity. He earned the approval of the ambassador by his assiduous work, but his philosophical studies were probably more important to him. The criticisms of Aristotle by Peter Ramus were being excitedly discussed. Ramus had presented for his doctorate at the Sorbonne the thesis 'that all of Aristotle's propositions are wrong', and had made suggestions for the improvement of Aristotle's method in logic. Bacon's own developments in inductive logic started from the suggestions of Ramus.

His concern with scientific matters while he was in France is indicated by his account of remarkable echoes and natural phenomena observed during visits to Blois, Tours and Poitiers. It is probable, too, that during this period he read Montaigne's *Essays*, and conceived the idea of writing his own works in that kind.

The impression he made at this time is revealed by Nicholas Hilliard, who painted a miniature of him in 1578 when he was seventeen. Hilliard wrote round the picture of his face in Latin: 'if only one could paint his mind'.

A few months later Bacon dreamed that he saw his father's house plastered over with black mortar. Shortly afterwards news came that Sir Nicholas was dead. Francis returned to England now eighteen, bearing a dispatch from the ambassador to the Queen, in which Sir Amias had written that Francis was 'of great hope, and endued with may good and singular parts' and 'if God gave him life, would prove a very able and sufficient subject to do her Highness good and acceptable service'.

Sir Nicholas had brought up his son with the intention that he should be a statesman. If he had lived, he would have arranged for him to receive appropriate appointments and promotion. The intention that he should become a statesman was deeply impressed on Bacon, and remained with him all his life. He felt it a filial duty which he must fulfil, and it was one of the causes which prevented him from abandoning the pursuit of a statesman's life, in spite of his preference for the contemplative life.

Bacon was of average height, slight in figure, and had dark brown hair and greenish eyes. He was physically sensitive, being liable to sickness, and was easily upset. His torrential intelligence inclined him to speak in a rush of words, but he rigorously schooled himself in self-control, until he became one of the most deliberate and effective speakers in English history. While his intellect was profoundly penetrating, there were areas of ordinary awareness in which he was blankly lacking. He often failed to notice simple things in human intercourse which were obvious to most people. On those things which he did perceive, he usually saw farther and more clearly than others.

18. *Formative Years*

Bacon received a permanent religious impress from his learned and passionately protestant mother. But in the course of time his religious beliefs became more formal, and sometimes perfunctory. When he was under great stress they returned to him with the simple and passionate belief of his infancy.

After his fall, he translated certain of the Psalms into English verse. Among them was the 137th, which, begins:

'By the waters of Babylon we sat down, and wept when we remembered Sion. As for our harps we hanged them up upon the trees that are therein. For they that led us away captive required of us then a song, and melody in our heaviness . . .'
Bacon's version begins:

> *When as we sat all sad and desolate,*
> *By Babylon upon the river's side,*
> *Eas'd from the tasks which in our captive state*
> *We were enforced daily to abide,*
> *Our harps we had brought with us to the field,*
> *Some solace to our heavy souls to yield . . .*

His translations were made during a paroxysm of self-condemnation. They are rendered in clumsy and most untalented verse, and are the best proof that he was not Shakespeare. He dedicated them to the poet George Herbert, as a 'poor exercise of my sickness'.

Besides these translations, Bacon also composed a number of special prayers. Like the technique in the verse translations, the attitude of mind in his prayers was also infantile. In his religious works he seemed always inclined to return to his mother's knee.

The second of his formative impressions, the dignity of the statesman's life and the necessity to aspire to it, sometimes exceeded his intellectual aspirations in emotional volume, though not in depth. It pushed all other interests on one side, and occupied the whole of his consciousness for considerable periods. But in spite of this, his conception of a new method of discovery which would greatly exalt human life, power and happiness, remained his deepest and most steadfast motive.

Bacon and his brother were admitted to Gray's Inn when they were boys, under the privileges of sons of judges, with the intention of continuing their education. But when his father suddenly died, and he found himself with only one-fifth of his expected fortune, Bacon went into residence, at the age of nineteen, to learn law as a profession. He had already thought of some special legal work that he might perform for the Queen, and he asked his uncle Lord Burghley to propose to her that she should employ him to carry it out.

Bacon worked hard, and his mother joined him in listening to lectures on the law. He looked after the legal affairs of his brother Anthony, who was touring Europe and studying the condition of various countries. A secretary of Walsingham, Queen Elizabeth's Secretary of State and head of her secret service, arrived one day at Bacon's rooms in Gray's Inn, with a message from Anthony. Bacon refused to see him, on the ground that he was too busy. It was at the period when he was drafting his *Greatest Birth of Time*, the first outline of his project for the restoration of man to his state before the fall. He may also have been cautious about receiving one of Walsingham's agents.

From his earliest manhood he was involved in pursuing professional, philosophical and political ends simultaneously. This comprehensive approach to life was the main cause both of his achievements and his failures.

He entered the House of Commons in 1584, being elected for
Melcombe, in the Parliament called to furnish the Government
with special powers to combat the attempts at assassinating
Queen Elizabeth. These had the aim of putting Mary Queen of
Scots on the throne, and turning England back from Protestant-
ism to Catholicism.

Protestants of every shade, from the conservative bishops to
the radical preachers, rallied to Elizabeth, who was armed with
virtually dictatorial powers. Loyal citizens were permitted to kill
the Queen's enemies at sight.

Though the Queen was equally supported by the various sections of the Protestants, she did not deal equally with them. She
favoured the bishops, and appointed the authoritarian John
Whitgift, who had been Bacon's teacher at Cambridge, archbishop of Canterbury, to enforce conservative discipline in the
Church, even against her own ardent supporters, the radical
preachers. Bacon's mother was deeply affected by these developments. She was a follower of Cartwright, the leader of the radical
protestants. He was the professor who had raised theological tur-
moil in Cambridge during the period when Bacon was a student.

Bacon was doubtful of the government's religious policy, probably under the influence of his mother's views. A long letter of
advice to the Queen, written at the time and attributed to Bacon,
discusses how her enemies could be weakened by skilful policy
rather than force. The author 'was bold to think that the bishops
in this dangerous time take a very evil and unadvised course' in
driving the non-conformist preachers from their cures. He said
that good local schoolmasters and schools were particularly
necessary, because the proper teaching of children could be more
effective than the kind of preaching to adults in reducing the
number of Catholics.

Another feature of his advice was that Catholics should be able
to take a modified oath of loyalty, so that they would not be
driven to acts of desperation.

A reference to Bacon's maiden speech in the Commons reports
two highly characteristic remarks, one in which he confessed the
weakness of his argument with a bluntness claimed as a sign of
candour, and the other an oblique reference to his inheritance,
intended to draw the Queen's attention to its meagre size, and
how much she had done for his father. His very first speech
made a bad impression, by what was taken to be an affectation of

NICHOLAS BACON

BURGHLEY

IV. Bacon's Father and Guardian

ELIZABETH I   ESSEX

V. Bacon's Earlier Masters

BUCKINGHAM

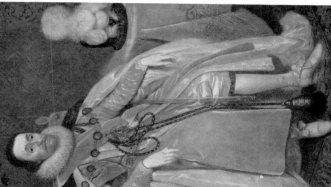

JAMES I

VI. Bacon's Later Masters

EDWARD COKE

ROBERT CECIL

VII. Bacon's Rivals

candour, and a lack of taste in referring to personal money matters.

In the following year, Bacon wrote to Walsingham to inquire whether the Queen had come to any decision on the legal work he had proposed some time before, as if she decided that she did not require it, he would 'take a course of practice', and become an ordinary working lawyer.

When Bacon became convinced that nothing was coming of his proposal, he asked Burghley to use his influence to secure the advancing of the date when he would be qualified to plead in the courts. While Burghley evidently helped in this, he also took the occasion to tell Bacon that people were alleging that he was arrogant. Bacon, in his letter of thanks couched in humble words but expressing noble ideas natural to him, says that he finds 'that such persons as are of nature bashful (as myself is), whereby they want that plausible familiarity which others have, are often mistaken for proud', but he beseeches Burghley to believe 'that arrogancy and overweening is so far from my nature, as if I think well of myself in anything it is in this that I am free from that vice . . .'. The young nephew and M.P. was already a difficult case.

Bacon became qualified to plead in the Westminster courts in 1586. While pursuing his legal career and his private studies, he was also active in the House of Commons, and in the social life of the inns of court. He took part in organizing a masque at Gray's Inn for the entertainment of the Queen. In politics he supported the popular cause leading to the execution of Mary Queen of Scots. In 1587, the year before the Armada, he participated in proposing an additional subsidy to the Queen, to be spent mainly on aiding the Netherlands against Spain.

All Protestants were united in resistance to the Spaniards, and even extreme Puritans were prepared to moderate their agitations lest, as it was said, too eager demands for the protection of civil liberty might have created conditions leading to the loss of national independence.

Though Bacon was still under thirty years of age, he had a voice, both in the management of the country's economic affairs and in dealing with the problems of government raised by the deep differences on civil and intellectual opinions.

The first Parliament after the defeat of the Armada again offered the Queen an additional subsidy. She graciously refused

M

it, forcing a grateful Commons to give her two additional subsidies instead. Bacon was a member of the committee dealing with
the bill, and at its instruction incorporated a note indicating that
this double subsidy was not to be taken as a precedent. His name
appeared as a supporter of the Commons against the Crown, a
courageous act, especially for a young politician looking to the
Crown for preferment.

Bacon's studied attempts at obsequiousness, which were so
striking a feature of his career, did not spring from lack of courage, but in part from reading Machiavelli.

Besides following the dangerous course of supporting the
Commons, Bacon undertook the thankless task of trying to find
a way of handling the controversy in the Church. From his upbringing as a member of the ruling class, and as one acquainted
with the Queen since he was a child, and as a pupil of Whitgift
at Cambridge, he was fully conversant with the authoritarian
point of view. From his mother he had learned of the intensity of
the problems of conscience. He understood from his knowledge
of her personality and beliefs that these could not be solved by
force.

In the year after the defeat of the Armada, the pent-up doc-
trinal conflicts burst out under the release of tension brought
by peace. The problems he discussed affect all post-war periods.
Bacon drafted a paper on the situation. He thought it might help
the government, and incidentally draw attention to his qualifications for high office, or at least for drafting of papers for
ministers of state.

He said that it was strange that after 1588, the country should
be riven by controversies. He would not enter into the controversies themselves, 'as judging that the disease requireth rather
rest than any other cure'. He thought that much of the contention was about ceremonies and 'things indifferent'. He advised
that both sides should try to acquire the habits of silence, and
slowness in engaging in argument. Opinions should not be expressed in imperative form—epithets should be avoided. They
should be tendered by way of advice, so that they could receive
the reverence due to kindly counsel.

Nevertheless, the causes of controversy should be openly
examined. The wisest men did not abstain from plainly recognizing the causes of controversy, and 'bitter and earnest writing
may not hastily be condemned; for men cannot contend coldly

and without affection about things which they hold dear and precious'. So, after all, epithets could not be avoided. He thought that the pamphlets written on behalf of the bishops were in general as worthy of suppression as those by the Puritans, for they hurt the Puritans in their most sincere beliefs, and were perhaps even more damaging to good order than the assaults of the Puritans on authority.

He then made some remarks on qualifications for leadership in the Church, and in general. Men should realize that they cannot speak with authority, 'when they have lost their reputation in the consciences of men' by refusing to conduct themselves in the way they recommend to others. A type which was particularly troublesome was 'a kind of Rabbi, master; not in ceremony or compliment, but in an inward authority which they seek over men's minds in drawing them to depend upon their opinion, and to seek knowledge at their lips. These men are the true successors of Diotrephes, the lover of pre-eminence, and not lords bishops. Such spirits do light upon another sort of natures, which do adhere to them . . . and zeal marvellously for those whom they have chosen as masters. This latter sort, for the most part, are men of young years and superficial understanding, carried away with partial respect of persons, or with the enticing appearances of goodly names and pretences . . . few follow the things themselves, more the names of the things, and most the names of their masters. About these general affections are wreathed accidental and private emulations and discontentments, all which together break forth into contentions; such as violate truth, sobriety or peace. The universities are the seat and continent of this disease, whence it hath been and is derived into the rest of the realm. . . .'

There should not be too much purging of obstreperous persons, for otherwise some good men will be purged with the bad, and a permanent wound created in the bowels of the Church, as indeed had already happened.

It was a mistake to imitate foreign churches too closely. Many men who had gone abroad to escape persecution at home had returned with too foreign ideas. But it was better to agree 'that every church do that which is convenient for the estate itself'. The English Church was to find its own specifically English road to Christianity.

He was against synods in the Church for formulating doctrines, for they introduced a democratic principle in deciding opinions, and 'it is hard in all causes, but specially in matters of religion, when voices shall be numbered and not weighed'.

He preferred dictatorship to anarchism: 'better it is to live where nothing is lawful, than where all things are lawful'. He concluded his paper with the observation that neither side in the controversy was 'like to be grateful' for what he had said. But he trusted that those who were not entirely partial, and 'love the whole better than a part' might find his remarks helpful.

He probably showed it to Burghley and Walsingham. Shortly afterwards, Walsingham was consulted by the French Government on how to deal with religious controversies. It is thought that his reply was drafted by Bacon, who appears to have submitted his draft to Whitgift.

In the reply it is said that the Queen's policy in this matter had been based on two principles. Firstly, that consciences were not to be forced, but won by persuasion and the force of truth, with the aid of time and all good means of instruction. Secondly, that when the causes of conscience exceeded their bounds and became matter of faction, they lose their nature, and become practices which princes should distinctly punish, even 'though coloured with the pretence of conscience and religion'.

Elizabeth had proceeded with tolerance and circumspection towards the Papists for about twenty years, until plots against her life multiplied, and it became evident that the Papists were no longer merely a religious sect, but a faction. Likewise, so long as Puritans merely inveighed against priests who held more than one living, and the like, and even when they proposed to bring democracy into the Church, they were listened to, and treated with consideration.

'Because multitudes of rogues and poverty were an eyesore and dislike to every man,' the Puritans had 'put it into the peoples' head that if discipline were planted, there should be no beggars nor vagabonds; a thing very plausible. And in like manner they promised the people many other impossible wonders of their discipline.' They proposed governing themselves through their own parish meeting, which was 'no less prejudicial to the liberties of private men than to the sovereignty of princes, yet in the first show very popular'.

These extravagances had in general been treated tolerantly because they were advanced merely as theoretical propositions. But latterly, when numbers of persons 'combined themselves by classes', and made others doubtful whether they should take oaths, on which the administration of justice depended; and when they began to boast of the strength of their numbers and that their cause would prevail through uproar and violence, 'it appeared to be no more zeal, no more conscience, but mere faction and division'. The state was then compelled to restrain them with a 'somewhat harder hand', but still only 'with as great moderation as the peace of the church and state could permit'.

This impressive statement of classical British policy was probably written by Bacon. If it did not earn him an immediate state pension, he received about a year later the reversion of the clerkship of the Star Chamber. This carried the large salary of £1,600 a year.

However, the occupant continued to survive for no less than nineteen years. Bacon had to wait all that time, in frustration and with impatiently repeated regrets, before he received this stable foundation to his economic position.

19. *An Unofficial Officer*

THE continuing lack of an adequate income from official sources prompted Bacon to look for help in other directions. He became closely acquainted with the Earl of Essex, who was six years his junior. Essex, then about twenty-four, had already achieved distinction as a soldier. Elizabeth had appointed him General of the Horse at the threat of the Spanish invasion in 1588.

He had been reared under the guardianship of Burghley, and had studied at Trinity College, Cambridge, when he was ten. Besides courage, education and intelligence, he had literary gifts. Bacon subsequently said he 'knew well' Essex's 'gift and style to be far better than mine own'.

It is possible, too, that Essex possessed great physical charm, though his portraits do not offer conclusive evidence of this. He had a spontaneous generosity and sympathetic interest in people which won everyone's heart, from the Queen to the humblest servant. He had the age, the position in the state, and many of the qualities which enable a man to accomplish great achievements. Bacon had failed to secure substantial support from the Queen and Burghley, who were absorbed in the almost superhuman task of preserving the national independence of state and church, against the double world-power of Spain and Catholicism. They were far too preoccupied by pressing affairs, and probably also by temperament, to be interested in Bacon's forward-looking ideas, trying to devise policy for the future, both in politics and knowledge.

After years of abortive waiting, Bacon found Essex's generous sympathy most refreshing. He concluded that he was 'the fittest instrument to do good to the state; and therefore I applied myself to him in a manner which I think happeneth rarely among men; for I did not only labour carefully and industriously, in that he set me about, whether it were matter of advice or otherwise; but neglecting the Queen's service, mine own fortune, and in a sort my vocation, I did nothing but advise and ruminate with myself to the best of my understanding, propositions and memorials of anything that might concern his Lordship's honour, fortune, or service'.

Anthony joined him in service to Essex. After ten years abroad, he had become deeply versed in foreign affairs. Their rooms in Gray's Inn became a private foreign office and secret service on Essex's behalf. In this period of national and ideological danger, the Crown encouraged every kind of informer, and noblemen competed with each other in trying to unveil the enemies' machinations. An effective secret police was not the least of the weapons by which Elizabethan England survived, and laid the foundations of British greatness.

While Bacon was cultivating Essex, he did not cease his applications to Burghley. After his thirty-first birthday he wrote to him once more. 'I wax now somewhat ancient; one and thirty years is a great deal of sand in the hour-glass.' He thanked God that his health was better than it used to be, in spite of leading a life of study which was more strenuous than practical affairs. He did not aspire to serve her Majesty in anything more than a middle place. He did not find in himself such self-love that he did not deserve well of his friends and especially of his Lordship; who 'being the Atlas of this commonwealth', the honour of his house, and the second founder of his own poor estate, he was tied to him by all duties. But the meanness of his estate still troubled him, though he was neither prodigal nor lazy. 'Lastly, I confess that I have as vast contemplative ends, as I have moderate civil ends: for I have taken all knowledge for my province; and if I could purge it of two sorts of rovers, whereof the one with frivolous disputations, confutations, and verbosities, the other with blind experiments and auricular traditions and impostures, has committed so many spoils, I hope I should bring in industrious observations, grounded conclusions, and profitable inventions and discoveries; the best state of that province. This, whether it be curiosity, or vainglory, or nature, or (if one take it favourably) *philanthropia*, is so fixed in my mind as it cannot be removed. And I do easily see, that place of any reasonable countenance doth bring commandments of more wits than of a man's own; which is the thing I greatly affect. . . .' His lordship would find no supporter with more strength and less opposition, and he particularly did not want a position that he thought too close to him (so possibly interfering with any plans he had for his son Robert Cecil). If his lordship was unable to find a place for himself, he would consider selling his inheritance and retiring, and becoming 'some sorry book-maker, or a true pioneer' in the mine of truth.

Bacon's preoccupation with things which must have seemed to Burghley inappropriate in a man of affairs, could not have been regarded as a good qualification. The lack of ideological solidarity with the rulers of the state disqualified him in the eyes of such judges as Burghley and the Queen. He was not 'one of them'. Bacon's protestations of devotion only emphasized his constitutional isolation from all persons and parties. His approaches must often have appeared to them grotesquely inept.

He tried to 'zeal marvellously' for others, but he had not the pliability of mind for the sort of submission which was demanded. His superficial acquiescence did not deceive persons of judgment who had close dealings with him.

Slow progress in the service of the Queen and of Essex caused Bacon to lean heavily on his mother. Lady Bacon feared that Anthony, through his years abroad, was in danger of being seduced by Roman Catholicism. During her lengthening widowhood she was troubled more and more by the exercise of authority as head of the family, and its conflicts with maternal affection for her sons. She was passionately anxious to do her duty by them, but was uncertain how. She alternately berated and besought them, in letters interspersed with proverbs, and Latin and Greek ejaculations.

Bacon's own style is, to some extent, a rationalization of his mother's. The letters of Bacon to his mother show him very respectful, and also very careful, as if he were gravely concerned not to excite her. This suggests that he recognized her mental instability.

Lady Bacon was deeply concerned with the mode of life of her sons at Gray's Inn. Writing to Anthony, she says of Francis: 'I verily think your brother's weak stomach to digest hath been much caused and confirmed by untimely going to bed, and then musing *nescio quid* when he should sleep, and then in consequent by late rising and long lying in bed; whereby his men are made slothful and himself continueth sickly. But my sons haste not to hearken to their mother's good counsel in time to prevent. . . .' She complained that Francis's reply to her strictures was unintelligible. 'I do not understand his enigmatical folded writing.' But if he trusts in God, he may yet be saved, for 'he was his father's first choice', and has 'good gifts of natural wit and understanding'.

Francis and Anthony found the task of conducting Essex's shadow government complicated by this unquiet maternal authority on the flank.

Besides assisting Essex in political affairs, Bacon helped him in the cultural field. The Elizabethans were aware of the possibilities of the arts as a medium of propaganda. Bacon suggested and organized masques on Essex's behalf, which might be calculated to impress the Queen. He wrote discourses for these entertainments, which were supposed to amuse and instruct their accomplished audience.

One in *Praise of Knowledge*, written for a masque in 1592, contains the earliest statement of his philosophical conceptions. The publication of a philosophy through such a medium is an illustration of the unity of culture at the time. It opens with dialectical aphorisms: 'The mind itself is but an accident to knowledge; for knowledge is a double of that which is; the truth of being and the truth of knowing is all one.'

Knowledge excels the pleasure of the affections, as these excel the pleasures of the senses. It is the only pleasure of which there is no satiety. It relieves the mind from perturbation, raising it above the confusion of things, through 'the prospect of the order of nature and the error of men'.

But is truth to be restricted only to the provisions of serenity, and not to discovery of new things? Is it to be for ever barren? So far the disputations of the learned have not brought to light one effect before unknown. Their activities are a web of wit that can work nothing. What is wanted is the power to 'produce worthy effects', and 'endow the life of man with infinite commodities'. All the philosophy now received comes either from the Greeks or the alchemists. The former is founded in words and disputations, the latter in imposture and obscurity, derived respectively from a few vulgar observations, or a few experiments with a furnace.

'But why do I in a conference of pleasure enter into these great matters, in sort that pretending to know much, I should forget what is seasonable?' It is because other things may be adorned with speeches, 'but knowledge itself is more beautiful than any apparel of words that can be put upon it'.

So far, the greatest discoveries, such as printing, artillery and the magnetic compass, had been stumbled on by accident; what might not be discovered if mind and things were combined in a proper marriage?

'No doubt the sovereignty of man lieth hid in knowledge; wherein many things are reserved, which kings with their treasure cannot buy, nor with their force command; their spials and intelligencers can give no news of them' (so much for Essex's secret service). 'Now we govern nature in opinions, but we are thrall unto her in necessity; but if we would be led by her in invention, we should command her in action.'

How these thoughts must have excited the Court, and raised Essex's prestige! A longer discourse in praise of the Queen may have been more acceptable. Besides presenting the national conception of her personality and policy, it contains a direct personal description.

'What life, what edge is there in those words and glances wherewith at pleasure she can give a man long to think, be it that she mean to daunt him, to encourage him, or to amaze him.'

It is true that she has no children, but 'let them leave children that have no other memory in their times'. Her wisdom and policy in government is to be noted in the prudence with which she controls access, on the one side maintaining her majesty, and on the other, 'not prejudicing herself by looking to her estate through too few windows; her exquisite judgment in choosing and finding good servants (a point beyond the former): her profound discretion in assigning and appropriating every of them to their aptest employment; her penetrating sight in discovering every man's ends and drifts; her wonderful art in keeping servants in satisfaction, and yet in appetite, her inventing wit in contriving plots and overturns; her exact caution in censuring the propositions of others for her service; her foreseeing of events; her usage of occasions—he that shall consider of these and other things that may not well be touched, as he shall never cease to wonder at such a queen, so he shall wonder the less, that in so dangerous times, when wits are so cunning, humours so extravagant, passions so violent, the corruptions so great, the dissimulations so deep, factions so many, she has notwithstanding done such great things, and reigned in felicity.'

If Elizabeth did indeed listen to this discourse, it did not persuade her to place her trust in Bacon, and make him one of her officers. He could not but reflect that to the end of her life he remained unable to satisfy 'her exquisite judgment in choosing and finding good servants'.

In a reply to a foreign libel on Burghley, Bacon made an analysis of the psychology of conspirators against the state. A number of these had recently left England. Abroad 'they are nourished rather in listening after news and intelligence', and after a time their necessitous state impels them to 'devising how to do some acceptable service to that side which maintaineth them'. When their credit waxes cold, and their pensions are ill-paid, 'straitways out cometh a libel, pretending thereby to keep in life the party of ill subjects' in England. As those in olden times were wont to help themselves with 'lying miracles', now these are fain to help themselves with 'miraculous lies'.

In his rebuttal of allegations that Protestantism had ruined England, Bacon said that it had brought the country three particular advantages. Firstly, a mighty treasure that formerly went to Rome now stayed within the realm. Secondly, about one-third of the land, including the best, which had belonged to the monasteries, and the produce of which was 'unprofitably spent', had been transferred to the hands of those who were able to give 'service and strength' to the state. Thirdly, the English Crown had been enfranchised from the recognition of a 'foreign superior'.

His review of the condition of other Christian countries showed that England was 'not inferior to any'. As for the Spaniards, we did not much envy their greatness and glory. They had a reputation for ambition rather than justice, for attempting more than achieving, and of rather 'doing things by treasure and expense than by forces and valour'.

As for the church controversies, which are alleged to have caused great confusion in the state, Bacon says that there are two extremes: the permission of the exercise of more religions than one, 'which is a dangerous indulgence and toleration', and the other is 'the entering and sifting into men's consciences when no overt scandal is given'. English policy had been a mean between them.

It must not be supposed that controversy is necessarily bad. Christ had remarked that outward peace may be a bad sign, for 'when a strong man is in possession of the house (meaning the devil) all things are in peace'. Indeed, the absence of controversy is a sign of atheism, because it indicates that men consider that questions of principle are not worth discussing.

Having already dismissed the Pope as 'the chaplain of Spain', he discussed the threat of foreign powers. The Spaniards were great in resources but weak through the burdens of empire. They were not to be feared by a 'nation seated, manned, furnished, and policied as is England'. Recent events had given a conclusive demonstration of this. 'The invincible navy neither took any one bark of ours, neither yet once offered to land; but after they had been well beaten and chased, made a perambulation about the northern seas, ennobling many coasts with wracks of mighty ships; and so returned home with greater derision than they set forth with expectation.'

Bacon concluded his reply with a panegyric of Burghley, citing the length of his service, his courage and restraint in expressing his opinion, and his loyalty in carrying out the Queen's decisions. He was free from suits and covetousness, and did not raise his rents or expel tenants. He was 'no vindicative man'; no 'breaker of necks', no 'brewer of holy water in court, no dallier, no abuser, but ever real and certain . . .'. He was 'never no glorious wilful proud man, but ever civil and familiar and good to deal with'. He was 'never a factitious commender of men to her Majesty . . . but was ever a true reporter unto her Majesty of every man's deserts and abilities . . .'.

Nor was the libeller any nearer the truth with regard to his son Robert, 'one of the rarest and most excellent wits of England; with a singular delivery and application of the same, whether it be to use a continued speech, or to negotiate, or to couch in writing, or to make report, or discreetly to consider of the circumstances, or aptly to draw things to a point; and all this joined with a very good nature and a great respect to all men . . .'.

Twenty years later, with Robert Cecil in mind, he published his essay *Of Deformity*. 'Whosoever hath anything fixed in his person, that doth induce contempt; hath also a perpetual spur in himself, to rescue and deliver himself from scorn. Therefore all deformed persons are extreme bold: first, as in their own defence, as being exposed to scorn, but in process of time, by a general habit. Also, it stirreth in them industry, and specially of this kind, to watch and observe the weakness of others, that they may have somewhat to repay. Again in their superiors, it quenches jealousy towards them, as persons that they think they may at pleasure despise; and it layeth their competitors and emulators asleep, as never believing they should be in possibility of advancement, till they see them in posession. So that upon the whole matter, in a great wit, deformity is an advantage to rising. . . .'

Bacon also had occasion to rebut the assertion that his father Sir Nicholas Bacon 'was a man of exceeding crafty wit'. This showed that the libeller was throwing out his words at random, for 'all the world noted Sir Nicholas Bacon for a man plain, direct, and constant, without all fineness or doubleness', who held that in both private and public life, a man's proceedings 'should rest upon the soundness and strength of their own courses, and not upon practice to circumvent others . . .'.

Even in composing artistic and political propaganda, Bacon could not help contributing to philosophy and history.

20. *Defending Parliamentary Rights*

WHILE Bacon was engaged in writing parts for artistic entertainments at one moment, at the next he was participating in acts of state. The government received intelligence in 1593 that Spain was organizing a simultaneous attack through Scotland, as well as a new naval invasion in the English Channel, to be carried out by improved ships operating from bases in Brittany.

To meet the threat, Parliament was asked to provide not one, but a triple subsidy, to finance the necessary military defence. Elizabeth again tried to take advantage of the situation to limit the gradually extending invasion of the royal prerogative by parliamentary privilege, by ordering her spokesman to instruct the Commons to discuss only the provision of money, and not to propose new laws of which there were already more than enough. Indeed, the existing laws required abridgement rather than addition. The function of the Commons was not to express opinions, but merely to vote.

Bacon, who was then thirty-two and member for Middlesex, seized on the remark on the laws to propose a project on their reform. The laws were 'so many in number that neither common people can half practise them, nor the lawyer sufficiently understand them . . .'. Spedding suggests that he started by talking about the laws as a covert opposition to the Queen's attempt to restrict the Commons' business to a purely financial discussion.

The Commons did not proceed with the granting of the triple subsidy as quickly as desired, so the Queen, through Burghley, made an obscure proposal which seemed to suggest that the Lords, who were impatiently in favour of it, should discuss it jointly with the Commons. Bacon heard of it in committee. Immediately after Sir Robert Cecil raised the proposal in the Commons, Bacon spoke on it. He said he agreed to the subsidy, but that he did not like the proposal that they should join with the Lords in granting it.

The Commons had the privilege of offering subsidies, and 'it is reason that we should stand upon our privilege'. Joining with the Lords would derogate from themselves, and he therefore desired that they should proceed 'apart by ourselves'. As an answer was required quickly, he drew forth from his bosom one framed by himself, making it absolutely clear that the Commons would discuss the subsidy generously, but not jointly, as this would infringe their privileges. The House approved it. But within the next few days, the government spokesmen got the decision reversed in committee.

The size of the subsidy had, however, not yet been decided, so again the question of privilege was fought on this issue. A resolution 'that no such conference should be had' was passed by a large majority.

When it became clear that the Commons would not surrender its privileges on subsidies, the Crown was forced to withdraw. Cecil now announced in the Commons that it was never desired that they should confer with the Lords 'about a subsidy'. After this, Sir Walter Ralegh moved that the Commons should have a 'general conference' with the Lords, which was agreed unanimously. The Crown's face was saved, and the Commons' privileges preserved.

The Commons now resumed its discussions on the triple subsidy. The government proposed not only treble the usual amount, but that it should be collected yearly at double the usual rate. Bacon again agreed to the triple subsidy, but now opposed the steep rate of collection, on the ground that it raised difficulties and dangers, and could be carried out in a better way. For 'the poor men's rent is such as they are not able to yield it, and the general commonalty is not able to pay so much upon the present. The gentlemen must sell their plate and the farmers their brass pots ere this will be paid. And as for us, we are here to search the wounds of the realm and not to skin them over; whereof we are not to persuade ourselves of their wealth more than it is. . . .'

The danger was that the new rate of collection might breed discontent among the people, and 'her Majesty's safety must consist more in the love of her people than in their wealth'. It might constitute 'an ill precedent upon ourselves and our posterity', of which future princes might take advantage.

Bacon's leadership was an important contribution to the increase of the power of the Commons, and a further advance towards the management of the nation's finances by the representatives of the people.

Elizabeth never forgave this challenge. She referred to 'some persons', who exaggerated the necessities of their constituents, 'forgetting the necessity of the time'. For four years she refused to see Bacon. She judged that he was constitutionally incapable of truly being anyone's servant, try as he might. He could follow only his own mind, and there was no security in a servant who chose to be servile as a matter of policy. Elizabeth no doubt instinctively felt the magnitude of Bacon's mind. If she had made him a minister, he would probably have soon become chief minister, and as, unlike James, she had the endowment to appreciate him, she might have found herself coming under his influence. The problem never arose with the Cecils, for they were by nature administrators rather than innovators.

Besides increasing the power of the Commons, Bacon also improved the efficiency of parliamentary debate as a means of propounding policy.

While Bacon had become involved in a deep struggle for the protection of democratic rights, a new figure appeared in the Commons. This was Edward Coke, who was nine years Bacon's senior, and a brilliant lawyer. In those qualities generally regarded as typically lawyer-like, Coke was outstanding. He was prodigiously industrious, learned in the law, tireless, physically strong, handsome, and shrewd. He had the advocate's gift of fighting for the brief of the moment with all his strength. He could apply his abilities with an insensitive adaptability and brutal force. His high qualifications had secured his appointment to the solicitorship.

He was elected to Parliament in 1593, when he was forty-one, and at the height of his powers. On his legal reputation, he was made Speaker of the House. He got up the procedure of the Commons with typical thoroughness, and then used his skill to conduct the proceedings efficiently, and at the same time ensure, as a good government man, that government policy went through.

Bacon had spoken in favour of a bill for 'the better expedition of justice in the Star Chamber'. The government was opposed to this bill, and Coke secured its rejection by a trick he devised in taking the vote. Such a man was a useful servant of the Crown. Coke naturally aspired to the attorneyship, which was about to become vacant.

The demonstration of his usefulness in facilitating government aims, in addition to his legal qualifications, was a strong recommendation. Coke, however, was of middle-class origin. Bacon was nine years his junior, but a son of a former Lord Keeper, a nephew of Burghley, and a member of ruling circles since birth. So, together with his own abilities, he did not hesitate to contend for the attorneyship. He had had little practical experience in the courts. Youth and lack of experience did not deter him, for had not his own father been 'made Solicitor of the Augmentation (a court of much business) when he had never practised, and was but twenty-seven years old?'

Burghley supported Bacon's candidature, though not enthusiastically. Essex passionately desired the important office for his nominee and friend. Burghley explained to Bacon the depth of the Queen's displeasure over his opposition in Parliament, so he wrote a letter to him, for her eye, 'in excuse of his speech against the Triple Subsidy'.

'I was sorry to find by your Lordship's speech yesterday that my last speech in Parliament, delivered in discharge of my conscience and duty to God her Majesty and my country, was offensive. If it were misreported, I would be glad to attend your Lordship to disavow anything I said not. If it were misconstrued, I would be glad to expound my words, to exclude any sense I meant not. If my heart be misjudged by imputation of popularity or opposition by any envious or officious informer, I have great wrong; and the greater, because the manner of my speech did most evidently show that I spake simply and only to satisfy my conscience, and not with any advantage or policy to sway the cause; and my terms carried all signification of duty and zeal towards her Majesty and her service. It is true that from the beginning, whatsoever was above a double subsidy, I did wish might (for precedent's sake) appear to be extraordinary and (for discontent's sake) mought not have been levied upon the poorer sort; though otherwise I wished it as rising as I think this will prove, and more. This was my mind, I confess it. And therefore I most humbly pray your Lordship, first to continue me in your own good opinion: and then to perform the part of an honest friend towards your poor servant and ally, in drawing her Majesty to accept of the sincerity and simplicity of my heart, and to bear with the rest, and restore me to her Majesty's favour.'

Bacon did not surrender an inch of his position; naturally the Queen was not mollified.

In simultaneous pursuit of high office and the conquest of all knowledge, his financial position became worse. Without aptitude or time for the management of his personal finances, he borrowed in many directions, and his brother considered selling some of his own patrimony to help him.

Bacon wrote to Robert Cecil for support in securing the attorneyship. Cecil advised that he should first regain access to the Queen, and then make application for the place, and he said that Essex was the most likely means to obtain it for him.

Essex had already twice spoken to the Queen on the matter very earnestly, but this had served only to reveal still further the depth of her objection. When Bacon was told of this, it still did not occur to him to apologize for his speeches. He wrote in an injured tone to Lord Keeper Puckering that it was 'a great grief . . . joined with marvel', that the Queen 'should retain a hard conceit' of his speeches in Parliament. 'It mought please her sacred Majesty to think what my end should be in those speeches, if it were not duty, and duty alone. I am not so simple but I know the common beaten way to please. And whereas popularity hath been objected, I muse what care I should take to please many, that taketh a course of life to deal with few.'

He wrote to the Queen herself, saying he perceived that she 'had taken some displeasure' towards him. He wished to repair his error. He did not aspire to any important position, but to a post in his profession. 'Your Majesty's favour indeed, and access to your royal person, I did ever, encouraged by your own speeches, seek and desire; and I would be very glad to be reintegrate in that.' He concluded by most humbly craving pardon for his 'boldness and plainness'. Essex thought that the Queen was being appeased, and her only objection now to Bacon's appointment to the attorneyship was his youth.

The delay dragged on. Bacon borrowed more and more to support the kind of position expected of an attorney-general elect, and as such, various persons were prepared to lend him money. The anxiety and the responsibility affected his health. Lady Bacon was persuaded to agree to the sale of family property, though she desired to manage the proceeds on behalf of the aspirant to the attorneyship, 'seeing so manifestly that he is

N

robbed and spoiled wittingly by his base exalted men, which
with Welsh wiles prey upon him . . .'.

The autumn approached, and still the Queen had not made up
her mind. Essex persisted, until she told him bluntly that Bacon
was more at fault than any of the rest in Parliament. 'If it had
been in the King, her father's time, a less offence than that would
have made a man be banished his presence for ever.' A renewal
of access was as much as he could hope for. Essex told her that if
she did not employ him she would 'lose the use of the ablest
gentleman to do her service of any of your quality whatsoever'.
On a later occasion, she bade him go to bed, if he would talk of
nothing else.

Lady Bacon again approached her brother-in-law Burghley,
who replied with good will but said that he was 'of less power
to do my friends good than the world thinketh'. Burghley had
thought that Bacon would have been wiser to seek the solicitorship before the higher post, but he did not obstruct his bolder
application.

More weeks went by, and Essex informed Anthony Bacon that
the Queen was content to hear him plead at large for his brother,
'but condemned my judgment in thinking him fittest to be Attorney whom his own uncle did name to a second place; and said
that the sole exception against Mr. Coke was stronger against
your brother, which was youth'. She told Essex she would be
advised in these matters by those who had more judgment in
them than himself.

To rebut the criticism that he lacked practical experience in
the courts, Bacon pleaded an important case before the law lords,
and made a good impression. A youthful admirer reported that as
a consequence, 'the Bacon may be too hard for the Coke'.

The attorneyship could not be left vacant any longer. Burghley
now pressed the Queen to appoint Coke. Essex continued his
vehement opposition not only to Coke, but to the other appointments which would follow. Cecil 'prayed him to be better advised', and said that if Bacon had asked for the solicitorship,
'that might have been of easier digestion to the Queen'.

'Digest me no digesting (said the Earl); for the Attorneyship
is that I must have for Francis Bacon; and in that I will spend my
uttermost credit, friendship and authority against whomsoever,
and that whatsoever went about to procure it for others, that it
should cost both the mediators and the suitors the setting on

before they came by it.' He told Cecil that he thought it strange that he and his father 'should seek to prefer a stranger before a kinsman, especially if his 'parts and sufficiency in any respect' were compared with his competitor Coke.

However, in the spring of 1594 Coke was finally appointed. It was regarded as a serious blow to Bacon's prestige. Bacon told Essex that 'this very delay hath gone so near me, as it hath almost overthrown my health'. He felt that 'no man ever received a more exquisite disgrace', in being rejected in spite of such supporters and connexions. 'My nature can take no evil ply; but I will by God's assistance, with this disgrace of my fortune, and yet with that comfort of the good opinion of so many honourable and worthy persons, retire myself with a couple of men to Cambridge, and there spend my life in my studies and contemplations, without looking back.'

Bacon did not succumb to this temptation, which with his temperament and interests, was the greatest to which he was exposed. If he had retired to Cambridge he would have become just one more distinguished scholar, instead of the first statesman of science.

Essex now pressed for Bacon to be appointed to the solicitorship. The absence of an established system of appointment, as in modern administrations, made the canvassing for places not only a means of securing jobs for one's friends, but also a part of the necessary machinery by which personnel was recruited.

21. *No Place for the Unsubmissive*

THE canvass for the solicitorship did not start well, for Essex became involved in a personal difference with the Queen. Bacon was reduced to consulting his cousin Cecil for advice, and was told that the Earl was 'being somewhat troubled at this time', and that this circumstance 'cut the throat' of his access to the Queen. He promised all his assistance and suffered with him in mind that he was 'thus yet gravelled'. But 'time will founder all your competitors and set you on your feet, or else I have little understanding'.

Essex fell into one of his mild illnesses, which he was adept in exploiting. The Queen took pity on him and called to see how he was, so he seized the opportunity to press Bacon's claims once more. She at first answered in jest that 'she came not to me for that; I should talk of those things when I came to her'. When he tried to pursue the matter 'she stopped my mouth'.

A little latter he again raised the question, no less than three times in one day. Essex wrote to Bacon that she had said: 'you had a great wit, and an excellent gift of speech, and much other good learning. But in law she rather thought you could make show to the uttermost of your knowledge, than that you were deep.' By this she probably meant that he was not widely experienced in the practice of the law. She said that she had shown as much dislike for the suit as Essex had shown affection for it, and if anyone was to yield it would be fitter that it should come from his side.

Essex had taken the leading part in exposing the affair of Dr. Lopez, the Queen's Portuguese Jewish physician. The King of Spain had exploited the dissatisfaction and poverty of Portuguese anti-Spanish refugees in London, and organized through them a plot in which Lopez was to poison the Queen. Essex's part in exposing the conspiracy brought him into close discussions with the Queen on the subject of security.

Bacon accordingly considered this question, and in characteristic manner began to compose 'a discourse touching intelligence and the safety of the Queen's person'. The two points in the fragment that has survived are that the intelligence service should not only provide good intelligence, but it should publicly have 'the reputation and fame thereof'; and that while the service should be conducted with the utmost efficiency, every effort should be made to put the King of Spain morally in the wrong, by pointing out through negotiations that his actions were contrary to the law of nations and the honour of kings.

The Lopez conspiracy had been discovered through a complete surveillance of all Portuguese letters entering the country, and the interrogation in secret of each suspected person, on the basis of the information gained, unknown to him, from the interrogations of others. Among the conspiracies investigated by Bacon was one voluntarily confessed, in which the Queen was to be killed by a poisoned weapon, and the crown, with the support of the King of Spain, offered to the Earl of Derby. Even contributions like these did not, however, persuade the Queen to appoint Bacon her Solicitor.

Bacon did not have much to do. He retired to his country cottage at Twickenham, where 'one day draweth on another'. He was well-pleased in being there, 'for methinks solitariness collecteth the mind'. But the dreary canvass went on. Christmas approached, and still the solicitorship was vacant. The finances of the Bacon brothers became still more embarrassed. Anthony burdened himself further by raising money on behalf of his brother, but never complained. He apparently considered the loans were justified.

After the end of 1594 the members of Gray's Inn planned an ambitious series of entertainments in the twelve days of festivity customary at Christmas time. At the first of the open performances, the crowd surged over the stage. It became impossible to perform the elaborate diplomatic play which had been prepared. This was cancelled and replaced by dancing, followed by a scratch performance of Shakespeare's *Comedy of Errors*. The chaotic proceedings were not appreciated, and were accounted a disgraceful failure. The occasion became known as the *Night of Errors*.

With Bacon's help a more dignified entertainment was organized. He composed speeches, supposed to be delivered at a prince's privy council, on the comparative merits of war, philosophy, construction, absolute rule, good government, and sport as political aims. He made them the medium for the expression of his own opinions. The task of the statesman was to choose the port to which the ship of state should be bounden. Judgment was superior to technical advice and administrative skill: one must not employ 'the right way to the wrong place'.

War offered the possibility that 'in your later years you shall find a sweet respect into the adventures of your youth . . . and leave deep footsteps of power in the world'.

The philosophic councillor advised that the Prince should pursue 'four principal works and monuments'; a 'most perfect and general library', a 'spacious, wonderful garden', in which all plants, 'divers moulds', rare animals would be collected, so 'you may have in small compass a model of universal nature made private'; a 'goodly huge cabinet', wherein specimens of everything which the hand of man has made by 'exquisite art or engine' shall be kept; and finally a still-house or laboratory furnished with 'mills, instruments, furnaces, and vessels, as may be a palace fit for a philosopher's stone'.

With these, the Prince will discover the natural causes of all miracles and wonders, and thereby become 'the only miracle and wonder of the world'. Bacon's suggestion of a collection of 'moulds' is particularly interesting, in the light of the modern development of antibiotics, which has led to an intense collection and exploration of moulds and fungi.

The constructionist councillor contended that the only durable way to fame was the building of pyramids, temples, colleges and the like.

The absolutist advised consolidation of power at home, no adventures abroad, and the increase of wealth.

The protagonist of good government outlined Bacon's own policy. First of all, peace. Then good administration and intelligence, promotion of virtuous and not mercenary men, repression of faction, and reform of the laws. But 'trust not to your laws for correcting the times, but give all strength to good education'.

The sporting councillor advised that the 'Sweet sovereign' should 'take only counsel of your five senses'.

On this occasion, the arrangements in the hall were carefully organized, and the performance was accounted a great success.

After the Christmas revels, the serious business of canvass for the solicitorship was resumed. Lady Bacon came up specially from the country to see Sir Robert Cecil about it. She said that Francis was 'the very first young gentleman of some account made so long a common speech of'. The world marvelled that it should happen to one with such friends and abilities. Some thought that if Lord Burghley had been in earnest, the appointment would already have been made. Sir Robert then told her that only on the last Tuesday his father had asked the Queen to fill the place, saying that the judges regarded Bacon as suitable, and his appointment was generally expected. The Queen had replied that she dare not name any for fear of the opposition of himself and Essex. Cecil added that he himself was Secretary in fact, though he had not been nominated for the position, and he felt himself as hardly used as his cousin.

Bacon let it be known that he contemplated retiring from public life and going abroad. This disturbed both Essex and the Queen. Bacon was sent for by the Court, but was seen by Cecil, not the Queen. He told him she had said that Bacon was demanding that the solicitorship should be given to him 'in his own time', or else she would be made to appear as if she were casting him away. The Queen had sworn that if Bacon continued in this manner, she would seek all England for a Solicitor rather than take him.

Bacon gained the impression that she was more angry with Essex than with himself, and indeed that he was the victim of conflicting forces, and was 'the least part of mine own matter'. The Bacon family's suspicions of Cecil grew deeper. They believed that he was deceiving them by pretending to support Bacon's candidature, while indirectly creating obstacles. Bacon presently drafted a letter to him, saying he had heard that he had been 'bought by Mr. Coventry for two thousand angels', and that he had used his influence with his father against him. Further, he had put 'in the Queen's mouth' a word pretending to be a commendation when it was intended to discredit him.

Perhaps Cecil had praised his speculative mind, as an indirect way of discrediting him for business. Bacon said that he did not believe these assertions, but though this was 'much to write', he thought his fortune set him at liberty to do so, and he was 'weary of asserviling myself to every man's charity'.

In another letter or draft to Cecil he remarked that 'it is my luck still to be akin to such things as I neither like in nature nor would willingly meet with in my course, but yet cannot avoid without show of base timorousness or else of unkind and suspicious strangeness . . .'. He would neither 'fawn nor retire'.

'To speak plainly, though perhaps vainly,' he wrote to Burghley, 'I do not think that the ordinary practice of the law, not serving the Queen in place, will be admitted for a good account of the poor talent which God hath given me. . . .'

In the summer of 1595, when Burghley was ill, the Queen called on him. He took the opportunity of again recommending Bacon for the solicitorship. The Queen apparently still resented Bacon's parliamentary speeches of 1593, and queried the practical ability of the philosopher. In reply to Burghley's account of this interview, Bacon still did not offer to apologize abjectly for his speeches, but suggested that they should be regarded 'as a discord in music', to make the harmony 'more perfect'. As to his lack of practical experience, he mentioned the case of his father which has already been quoted.

Bacon seems to have heard of a comment by the Queen about this time on the clerkship to the Star Chamber, of which he had the reversion. The occupant had committed some irregularity, and might be expelled from his post if proceedings were taken against him. Bacon interpreted this as a hint that he could secure the post if he started proceedings against the occupant. But he wrote to the Lord Keeper that he did not like 'coming in upon a lease by way of forfeiture', and he never in his life had proposed any such action, though he had 'been incited thereto'. The world would naturally believe that it had been 'underhand quickened and nourished' by him, and he 'would not be thought to supplant any man for great gain'.

He now suspected that the Lord Keeper was failing him. Puckering was a Yorkshireman of humble origin, a son of a curate of Bempton, the village near the high cliffs north of Flamborough Head. His dialect was so broad that Elizabeth had difficulty in understanding him. His rise had been due to his ability and Nicholas Bacon's patronage. Bacon asked Puckering 'to call to mind from whom I am descended, and by whom, next to God, her Majesty, and your own virtue, your Lordship is ascended; I know you will have a compunction of mind to do me any wrong'.

Essex went to Twickenham to confer with Bacon on this difference. He wrote to Puckering, entreating him to suspend his judgment on Bacon's attitude towards him. 'This manner of his was only a natural freedom and plainness, which he had used with me, and in my knowledge with some other of his best friends. . . .'

Lady Bacon reported that she had heard that Francis 'looked very ill'; he suffered from 'inward grief', and he was 'thin and pale'. Though the Earl 'showed great affection, he marred all with violent courses'.

Finally, in November 1595, after keeping Bacon waiting for more than two-and-a-half years, Elizabeth passed him over once more, by appointing Fleming to the solicitorship.

Bacon conceived that the event might be for himself 'a beginning of good fortune, or at least of content'. Whether the Queen 'look towards me or no, I remain the same, not altered in my intention. If I had been an ambitious man, it would have overthrown me'.

After Elizabeth had finally decided not to give Bacon office, though continuing to make use of his services, she withdrew her ban on his presence.

Essex was mortified, for he had failed to gain a point on which he had staked his credit. Bacon wrote to him that he trusted the Queen would alter her opinion of himself 'when she knoweth me better'. He had 'lost some opinion, some time, and some means . . . but then for opinion, it is a blast that goeth and cometh; for time, it is true it goeth and cometh not; but yet I have learned that it may be redeemed. . . . For means, I value that most. . . .' For he had decided not to practise the law, though if her Majesty commanded him to undertake any particular case he would of course do so. 'For your Lordship, I do think myself more beholding to you than to any man. And I say, I reckon myself as a *common* (not popular, but *common*); and as much as is lawful to be enclosed of a Common, so much your Lordship shall be sure to have.' Bacon evidently felt it necessary to indicate to Essex that he was fundamentally independent of him.

As he was unable to surrender himself entirely to the Queen, so he was unable to surrender to Essex.

Nine years later Bacon gave a celebrated account of what passed during the conference with Essex at Twickenham. 'Master Bacon,' said Essex, 'the Queen hath denied me yon place for you, and hath placed another; I know you are the least part of your own matter, but you fare ill because you have chosen me for your mean and dependence; you have spent your time and thoughts in my matters. I die (these were his very words) if I do not somewhat towards your fortune: you shall not deny to accept a piece of land which I will bestow on you.'

He pressed the offer, and finally Bacon said: 'My Lord, I see I must be your homager and hold land of your gift: but do you know the manner of doing homage in law? Always it is with a saving of his faith to the king and his other lords: and therefore, my Lord: (said I) "I can be no more yours than I was, and it must be with the ancient savings: and if I grow to be a rich man, you will give me leave to give it back to some of your followers".'

Bacon afterwards sold the piece of land for £1,800, which he used for meeting his creditors' demands.

His next task was to compose more discourses for a masque organized by Essex for the Queen's entertainment. They were to be introduced and reviewed by a Squire, as 'the master of the best behaviour or compliment'. The part was played by Toby Matthew, who became Bacon's great friend.

A Hermit advises that the Muses should be followed, because

their gardens 'keep the privilege of the golden age; they ever flourished and are in league with time. The monuments of wit survive the monuments of power: the verses of a poet endure without a syllable lost, while states and empires pass many periods. . .'

Let not a man 'borrow other men's opinions to direct himself', for they 'set him the way to their own journey's end'. He should make 'the time to come the disciple of the time past and not the servant'.

A 'tedious Secretary' advises that a statesman should 'not trouble himself too laboriously to sound into any matter deeply, or to execute anything exactly; but let him make himself cunning rather in the humours and drifts of persons than in the nature of business and affairs. Of that it sufficeth to know only so much as may make him able to make use of other men's wits, and to make a smooth and pleasing report. . . . Let him entertain the propositions of others . . . and ever rather let him take the side which is likeliest to be followed . . . that everything may seem to be carried by his direction. . .'

The Squire did not like these views. 'Corrupt Statesman', he said, 'you think by your engines and motions to govern the wheel of fortune; do you not mark that clocks cannot be long in temper, that jugglers are no longer in request when their tricks and sleights are once perceived? Nay do you not see that never any man made his own cunning and practice (without religion, honour, and moral honesty) his foundation, but he overbuilt himself, and in the end made his house a windfall?'

No doubt Sir Robert Cecil was with the Queen in the audience. As for her, 'the Muses, they are tributary to her Majesty for the great liberties they have enjoyed in her kingdom during her most flourishing reign; in thankfulness whereof they have adorned and accomplished her Majesty with the gifts of all the sisters . . .'.

A contemporary report said that the world identified two of the characters as eminent lords, 'but the Queen said that if she had thought there had been so much said of her, she would not have been there that night, and so went to bed'.

22. *Private Interests and Public Affairs*

THE failure of Bacon's canvass for the attorney- and solicitor-ships released more of his energy for legal and other work, 'though in practicing the law I play not all my best game'. He gave lectures on law at Gray's Inn, and composed a memoir on *Maxims of the Law*, which he dedicated to the Queen. He opened his preface with the famous phrase: 'I hold every man a debtor to his profession; from the which as men of course do seek to receive countenance and profit, so ought they of duty to endeavour themselves, by way of amends, to be a help and ornament thereunto.' One should especially 'strengthen the roots and foundation of the science itself . . .'. He expressed his views in the form of aphorisms 'because this delivering of knowledge in distinct and disjoined aphorisms doth leave the wit of man more free to turn and toss, and to make use of that which is so delivered to more purposes and applications . . .'. All the ancient wisdom and science had been expressed in that form, and especially the civil law.

In the same period, about 1596, he composed a work called the *Colours of Good and Evil*, on the art of persuasion and dissuasion. It dealt with an aspect of the technique of advocacy, and in it Bacon discussed some of the principles of propaganda and advertisement.

At this time, too, he prepared the first edition of his *Essays* for the press. This was published in 1597, though the contents had 'passed long ago from my pen'. The little volume contained only ten essays, compared with fifty-eight in the third edition, published twenty-eight years later. The selection of subjects shows that they were primarily the expression of a man's private interests. They were affectionately dedicated to his brother Anthony, and showed a preoccupation with the considerations by which a man might personally become cultivated. He said he had wished that his brother's infirmities might have been transferred to himself, so that his 'active and able mind' would have been available to serve the Queen, while he might 'be with excuse confined to these contemplations and studies for which I am fittest . . .'. The statesman's interest in public life had not yet taken precedence, as in the third edition dedicated to the Duke of Buckingham.

Though Bacon's *Essays* have become the best-known and most widely-read of his works, he did not consider them of primary importance. In his later years, he wrote to a correspondent 'As for my *Essays*, I count them but as the recreations of my other studies, and in that sort purpose to continue them; though I am not ignorant that those kinds of writings would, with less pains and embracement perhaps yield more lustre and reputation to my name than those other which I have in hand.'

In the spring of 1596, Puckering died suddenly. Sir Thomas Egerton, the Master of the Rolls, was immediately appointed his successor. Bacon wrote to Essex to ask that he should recommend him as successor to Egerton, remarking incidentally that 'it hath pleased God to establish mightily one of the chief pillars of this estate, that is, the justice of this land, which began to shake and sink; and for that purpose no doubt gave her Majesty strength of heart of herself to do that in six days which the deepest judgments thought would be the work of many months'.

The speed of Egerton's appointment showed how fast the Queen could act when her judgment was satisfied. It was in remarkable contrast to her indecision over Bacon, and made this all the more significant. Egerton was an upright, able, courageous and handsome man who believed wholeheartedly in the principle of the royal prerogative. He was a paternalist. He spoke scornfully of More's *Utopia*, dismissing it as a 'pamphlet', and was completely opposed to political democracy. He appreciated Bacon's ability. Bacon deeply admired him and indeed became devoted to him almost as a son.

Essex wrote to Egerton that he approached him because his own intercession with the Queen had hitherto rather hurt Bacon than done him good. He earnestly commended Bacon to him. He had great care of his advancement, 'for his parts were never destined for a private and (if I may so speak) an idle life. That life I call idle, which is not spent in public business: for otherwise he will ever give himself worthy tasks.'

Bacon did not canvass for the mastership of the Rolls with the persistence he had shown over the attorney-and solicitorships.

He sought the position more as a matter of form than with hopes. Having no serious expectations of office, his relations with the Queen improved. He remarked to a friend in the late spring of 1596, that 'the Queen saluted me today as she went to chapel'.

At this time, Essex was in the midst of preparations for the famous attack on Cadiz, a spoiling operation aimed at hindering further Spanish plans for the invasion of England. The English ships sailed into the harbour of the Spanish fleet, and destroyed the fleet in less than one day. Bacon subsequently described the impression of this victory as 'like lightning. For in the space of fourteen hours the King of Spain's navy was destroyed and the town of Cales taken. The navy was no less than fifty tall ships, besides twenty galleys to attend them. The ships were straight-ways beaten, and put to flight with such terror as the Spaniards in the end were their own executioners, and fired them all with their own hands. The galleys, by the benefit of the shores and shallows, got away. The town was a fair, strong, well-built, and rich city; famous in antiquity, and now most spoken of for this disaster. It was manned with four thousand soldiers on foot and some four hundred horse. It was sacked and burned, though great clemency was used towards the inhabitants. But that which is no less strange than the sudden victory, is the great patience of the Spaniards; who though we stayed upon the place divers days, yet never offered us any play then, nor never put us in suit by any action of revenge or reparation at any times after.'

Essex was mainly responsible for the assault on the town, and for the clemency with which the population was treated. He wished to follow up the action by sailing out to capture the home-coming Spanish treasure fleet from America. He was over-ruled by the council of senior commanders in charge of the expedition, so the English fleet sailed home with its glory and its spoil, while the Spanish treasure fleet sailed into the Tagus one or two days later, intact.

The brilliant success of the action in Cadiz raised Essex's prestige to its zenith. To the public he was a martial hero of the first order. But the older commanders of the expedition, which included several of the heroes of the defeat of the Armada in 1588, were aware in their skill and experience that Essex, while showing great dash, had had a good deal of luck as well. They were not disposed to grant him all the credit, nor an excessive share of the spoils. The Queen naturally gave weight to their views, and Essex took umbrage at her not unmeasured approval.

But when the public heard of the escape of the Spanish treasure fleet, apparently as a consequence of rejecting Essex's advice, Essex's popularity became greater than ever, and the professional criticisms of the more experienced naval tacticians could not be pressed home. The Queen resumed her good relations with him.

Essex was still only twenty-eight, with one of the most spectacular, and most popular, military actions in British history to his credit.

In October, after the return and the national celebrations, Bacon chose to send Essex a long letter of advice on how he should conduct himself and his policy in his present situation.

He reminded him that he had formerly counselled him to behave to the Queen with 'obsequious kindness', and that Essex had said that experience had subsequently shown that she had taken advantage of it. Though he gave place to none in congratulations on his recent achievement, he continued to advise him not to estrange himself from the Queen. He did not repent himself of 'safe counsel, neither do I judge of the whole play by the first act'. Essex must 'win the Queen . . . of any other course I see no end'. What could her attitude to him be at this time? The Queen must regard him as 'a man of a nature not to be ruled; that hath the advantage of my affection and knoweth it; of an estate not grounded to his greatness; of a popular reputation; of a military dependence . . .'. Bacon demands 'Whether there can be a more dangerous image than this represented to any monarch living, much more to a lady, and of her Majesty's apprehension?'

Was it not obvious that so long as she had this conception of him, he would find his way full of difficulties and 'inventions to keep your estate bare and low'. He would find his actions crossed, his merit alternately praised and blamed, his enemies supported, his friends won from him, suggestions that he should undertake dangerous offices that might lower his reputation, 'dalliances and demonstrations' that might abuse him, and divert him from a serious consideration of his own case, 'yea and percase' provoking him into 'perilous and desperate enterprises'. He desired his Lordship to understand him fully, for 'I mean nothing less than that these things should be plotted and intended as in her

Majesty's royal mind towards you: I know the excellency of her nature too well.'

Whenever 'the formerly-described impression is taken in any King's breast towards a subject these other recited inconveniences must, of necessity of politic consequence, follow; in respect of such instruments as are never failing about princes: which spy into their humours and conceits, and second them; yea and many times, without their knowledge, pursue them further than they themselves would . . .'.

Bacon was warning Essex in the plainest terms against political provocation and provocative agents. He wrote with great boldness, for if his letter had fallen into the Queen's hands, he might well have been imprisoned, and even executed.

Though Essex might find better ways to deal with this situation he would like to draw his attention to five lines of action. In order to remove the impression that he is opinionated, he should make it plain that past disagreements had arisen entirely from lack of satisfaction and not from his nature or disposition. He would find it helpful to avoid emphasizing the differences between his stepfather, the Earl of Leicester (the Queen's earlier favourite) and himself, and to allege that in various matters he was taking him as a pattern.

He should be careful, when he praises the Queen, to avoid formality in his expression. Then he should stimulate a flow of minor matters, any of which, if the Queen disapproves, can be instantly dropped as if in deference to her opinion, without embarrassment to himself. Not even the smallest things are to be neglected, such as 'habits, apparel, wearings, gestures, and the like'.

He particularly advised him not to emphasize his military interests. 'I cannot sufficiently wonder at your Lordship's course; that you say, the wars are your occupation, . . . you should have left that person at Plymouth. . . . And here (my Lord) I pray mistake me not . . . I am infinitely glad of this last journey, now it is past. . . .'

Bacon had doubted the success and wisdom of Essex's part in the project, and was greatly relieved by its outcome. He now most earnestly advised him to be satisfied with this military achievement, at least for a time. No one, for many years, could approach him in military prestige, and if he added greatness in other directions, the control over appointments and affairs would naturally flow to him. He should keep the substance of military authority, but not make a show of it to the Queen. He should seek not the highest military offices, but high civil office, such as the Lord Privy Seal, which would give him 'a kind of superintendance' over the Secretary, that is, his opponent Sir Robert Cecil. He advised him to 'pretend to be as bookish and contemplative as ever you were', and to recommend the Queen to appoint some military man of his own choice to be a member of the Privy Council. This would increase his influence without arousing a corresponding amount of opposition. He thought Lord Mountjoy would be the most suitable person.

Finally, he should accept such increase in popular esteem as comes to him honourably, but he should 'speak against popularity and popular courses vehemently' to the Queen. He should be careful with his estate, to show he would not depend on the Queen, and was free from 'higher imaginations'.

The relations between Essex and the Queen again became cordial. But news arrived of Spanish preparations for avenging the Cadiz disgrace. Plans were immediately started for a new expedition to destroy the enemy's forces. In flat contradiction to the advice Bacon had given, Essex immediately desired to dominate all of the military affairs. He was angered when the Queen did not at first make him sole commander, but only joint commander with Howard and Ralegh. He threatened to retire to Wales, and presently the sole command was granted to him.

Then the Queen refused to accept his nominee for the wardenship of the Cinque Ports, commanding the English Channel, so he insisted on standing for the place himself. He gained yet another point, for though she would not make him Warden, she gave him the higher post of Master of the Ordnance.

The new expedition, unlike the former, did not enjoy good luck. After leaving Plymouth it ran into a gale, and had to return for a refit. After this, it was no longer strong enough for an attack on the new armada in harbour at Ferrol. Essex was convinced that the Spanish fleet would 'not leave Ferrol this year'. According to his habit, he had surrounded himself with young military men burning for action, so he decided to try to carry out the operation he had proposed after the sack of Cadiz, but in which he had been overruled: the interception of the Spanish treasure fleet returning from America. He sailed to the Azores, but missed the main treasure fleet, though it arrived at the expected time and place. He tried to save face by making the most of the accidental capture of a few stragglers. Since he had been made admiral of the expedition and Ralegh rear-admiral, his relationship with Ralegh had been better. Ralegh performed the only exploit of military distinction carried out during the expedition, the capture of the fortified island of Fayol. Essex was so angry that he attempted to try Ralegh for his life on a charge of insubordination.

The expedition returned home with its captains in conflict, and without having achieved its primary aim.

While the British fleet was away in the Azores, the south-west coast was left virtually unprotected. The Spanish admiral who would 'not leave Ferrol this year', sailed with the plan of capturing Falmouth and converting it into a Spanish base. Unopposed, the fleet arrived off the Scillies, and the Spanish admiral summoned all his captains to his flagship to receive their final instructions. While they were away from their ships, a tremendous storm suddenly blew up. The fleet was shattered. Eighteen ships of war were sunk, including two of the biggest. Monson, who had been one of Essex's captains, said that the Spanish plans had not been foreseen, and that the English had to 'ascribe this success to God only: for certainly the enemy's designs were dangerous, and not to be diverted by our force'.

The experienced Queen was not pleased with the results of Essex's second expedition. Essex soon showed signs of being hurt by what he considered her lack of appreciation. But for the nation, the main fact was that the Spanish fleet was crippled, and in these circumstances, Essex, as admiral, naturally retained his great popular prestige.

The Queen summoned a Parliament for the autumn of that year. The absence of Essex had made his calls on Bacon's time less than usual, and Bacon was very active in the Commons. Owing to the frustration of the Spaniards, the political atmosphere was happy, and Elizabeth was careful not to precipitate any conflict of her authority with the Commons of the kind that had already so significantly affected Bacon's career. Her subsidy, as large as the last, was voted without opposition.

Bacon was a member of all the committees. He introduced bills against enclosures and for the maintenance of tillage. He said that the enclosures had brought 'depopulation, which brings forth first idleness, secondly decay of tillage, thirdly subversion

o

of houses, and decrease of charity and charge to the poor's maintenance, fourthly the impoverishing the state of the realm'.

As the remnants of the frustrated Spanish fleet were still hovering near the English coasts, and defence was very much in the national mind, Bacon linked the ill-effect of enclosures with the shortage of good soldiers, and used military necessity as an argument for a rational control of agriculture.

Just before Essex had returned to England, the Queen raised the Lord High Admiral, Howard of Effingham, the hero of 1588, to the rank of earl. Essex felt injured, for the Lord High Admiral as an earl took precedence over himself. After his return, he withdrew from Court, Council and Parliament.

About this time Bacon became aware that Essex was no longer confiding in him as formerly.

Essex demanded that Howard should be persuaded to surrender his new rank. However, this did not become necessary, for the Queen appointed Essex Earl Marshal, the post which Bacon had particularly warned him not to accept. It was therefore not surprising that he had detached himself from Bacon, for, as Bacon subsequently wrote, 'it is the manner of men seldom to communicate when they think their courses are not approved'.

Among earls, the Earl Marshal took precedence over the Lord High Admiral. Essex now resumed public life with his customary charm.

A few months later a new crisis arose. The condition of affairs in Ireland was causing alarm. Apart from other considerations, this was serious from the military point of view, for the Spanish had ever in mind the establishment of bases there as a preliminary to the invasion of England. The Irish had produced a talented leader, the Earl of Tyrone, who had been educated in England, and had the personal gifts and technical skill for organizing a national movement of Irish resistance. The English government had sent several limited expeditions against him, all of which had failed. It became essential for English interests to take effective action.

Cecil was absent in France, on an important mission to Henry IV, and Essex, in his happy mood, was in charge of affairs at Court. This was the civil position which Bacon had counselled him to acquire, and Bacon now wrote a letter advising him to give special attention to the Irish problem, as 'one of the aptest particulars for your Lordship to purchase honour upon'. It was the most pressing matter of state at the moment, and in the popular opinion, Irish affairs had been neglected, so an improvement of them would raise his prestige both in government circles and with the public.

Bacon remarked that the problem was a particularly suitable one for him because it was 'mixt with matter of war', thus implying that he assumed that Essex was concerning himself primarily with its civil aspects, and would take a hint not to involve himself primarily in the military aspects. Bacon concluded his letter by describing himself as playing 'the ignorant statesman; which I do to nobody but your Lordship: except to the Queen sometimes when she trains me on'.

This remark contained an implication that Bacon was no longer in full receipt of information.

Terms of 'pardon', which amounted to a treaty, were presented to Tyrone, who agreed to most, but not all, of the clauses.

Essex asked Bacon for his opinion on the situation. Bacon recommended that Tyrone's terms should be accepted, to give time for further opportunities to develop. Meanwhile, strong military preparations should be made in England, not for use but to impress Tyrone in case he should think of breaking the treaty, and Essex might strengthen the impression by letting it be known that he would, if necessary, lead the forces in person into Ireland. But the objection to this course was that 'your Lordship is too easy to pass in such cases from dissimulation to verity'. If, however, he could 'pretend' that he would do this, it would help to make Tyrone accept the accord, and 'win you a great deal of honour *gratis*'. Meanwhile, the abuses in the government of Ireland should be reformed, to weaken the causes of Tyrone's influence.

The Queen proposed sending Essex's uncle to govern Ireland, but Essex insisted that another man should be sent, apparently because he had quarrelled with him and wanted to get him away from the Court. In the course of a heated argument with the Queen he turned his back on her, which provoked her to slap him. He turned round in a fury, put his hand on his sword, and swore that he would not have borne that, even from Henry VIII. He withdrew himself from the Court, and refused to apologize. As Spedding puts it, Essex was 'now once more on the brink of his favourite precipice'; an eminent performer in a kind of statesmanship familiar in our own day. Nearly six months passed before his relations with the Queen were patched up, but this time his behaviour did not extract any additional place.

The situation in Ireland deteriorated still further. Tyrone ignored the treaty, and won a brilliant victory at Blackwater, killing fifteen hundred English troops. This was followed by further successes, which rendered the English government's problem very grave.

In the midst of these troubles, in 1598, the aged Burghley died. His presence had dominated the Privy Council, and after his departure the struggle for leadership among the younger generation became more uncontrolled. The long collaboration between Elizabeth and Burghley had hindered any younger man from acquiring pre-eminence, for as long as their partnership lasted, no younger man, however gifted, could have the experience of making major decisions.

The Irish situation demanded large operations and major decisions. The Queen, herself ageing, was compelled to depend on her younger statesmen. Essex was a greater man relative to Cecil than to Burghley, so his authority had increased. In spite of her anger, the Queen tried to make a compromise with him.

She needed the support of his influence with the military. She proposed to send Mountjoy to Ireland to recover the situation. He was Essex's friend, and the very man Bacon had suggested that Essex should make his deputy. It would have been a marvellous opportunity for Essex, for it would have enabled him to occupy Burghley's old place as chief minister at home, while one of his friends who, later events proved, had the necessary talent to reconquer Ireland, would have solved for him the major problem of the day.

But Essex would not agree that another man, even Mountjoy, should be in command in Ireland. In order to prevent his appointment, he began to be more submissive, so that he was presently restored to outward favour. He resumed his seat in the Privy Council. He there made it clear that he would not tolerate any man other than himself being appointed the Queen's Lieutenant in Ireland. But he went through the form of asking Bacon's advice, whose 'silence' in respect to his recent affairs he had noted, as to whether he should accept.

During this period, Bacon had been experiencing a little Blackwater setback of his own. In the autumn of 1598, while returning from the Tower where, as one of the Queen's counsel extraordinary, he had been interrogating conspirators against the state, he was arrested in the street for debt, on behalf of a money-lender. He sent urgent messages for succour to the chief minister of state, who secured his release.

In spite of the fact that Bacon had difficulties in coping with such trivialities as these, Essex and the Queen listened to his advice on major matters of state.

Bacon subsequently wrote that he not only tried to dissuade Essex, but protested against his going to Ireland. It would be ill for him, ill for the Queen and ill for the state. He pointed out the danger of a campaign against a people 'which placed their felicity only in liberty and the sharpness of their sword', as illustrated by the failure of the Romans against the Germans. He pressed these and other arguments with extreme earnestness, 'for I did as plainly see his overthrow chained as it were by destiny to that journey, as it is possible for a man to ground a judgment on future contingents. But my Lord, howsoever his ear was open, yet his heart and resolution was shut against that advice'.

Essex had privately determined that he would be commander-in-chief, and he followed this by demanding that he should be provided with a large army and extraordinary powers, including the authority to grant pardons for treason. He was so insistent that even at the time his demands aroused comment. He seemed to be chiefly interested in attaching a large army to himself, and acquiring royal powers. Young military men flocked from all parts of the country to become his officers.

He demanded commands for his friends, and when these were not immediately granted, he told the Queen that he would retire, for 'he must work with his own instruments'. He had his step-father, Sir Christopher Blount, who was a Roman Catholic, made Marshal of the Army. He was granted 16,000 foot and 1,500 horse, and £300,000 in treasure. Before he had left England, he was complaining of the supply system. He behaved as if he expected the expedition to be a failure, and was recording complaints beforehand, so that the responsibility would be on the Queen and the Privy Council.

After landing in Ireland in the spring he spent three months in desultory marches, in which his troops and supplies were dissipated by disease, and skilful guerilla fighting by the Irish. In July, when the main campaign should have started, his 1,500 horse had dwindled to less than 300, and his infantry were 'very weary and unfit for any new journey', but he reported that 'as fast as I can call these troops together I will go back upon yonder proud rebel'. If he found him in hard and open country he would dislodge him, even if outnumbered three to one. Two thousand more troops were sent to him from England, but this was not enough. He was given permission to levy 2,000 Irish besides.

Yet Essex reported shortly afterwards that he had only 4,000 effective troops. In September he marched against Tyrone with but 2,500 of these, and found the 'proud rebel' on the top of a hill, and supported by twice as many troops. The two armies manoeuvred for seven days, after which Tyrone accepted an invitation to parley. This was conducted by Essex and Tyrone by themselves, shouting at each other over a stream: most careful precautions were taken to keep all eavesdroppers at a distance. A verbal truce was concluded, and Essex went to 'take physic' at Drogheda, while 'Tyrone retired with all his forces into the heart of his country'. No signed statement existed of what had been agreed.

By this time, the Queen had become suspicious. She told Bacon that she considered Essex's proceedings 'unfortunate, without judgment, contemptuous and not without some private end of his own'. The Queen had already ordered Essex not to return from Ireland without her permission. She also mobilized troops in England, on the pretext of threats from Spain, and after taking these precautions she intended to demand an explanation from Essex.

23. *Rebellion*

BEFORE the demand could reach him, Essex left his post, against orders, to go to London. He confidently told his friends Blount and Southampton 'that he found it necessary for him to go into England, and thought it fit to carry with him so much of the army as he could conveniently transport, to go on shore with him to Wales, and there to make good his landing till he could send for more: not doubting but his army would so increase in a small time, that he should be able to march to London and make his conditions as he desired'.

He rode to London accompanied by 'a great number of captains', and then to the palace, where he went straight into the Queen's bedroom in his dirty travelling clothes. Her immediate reaction was true to her genius: she greeted him cordially, as a personal friend whom she was glad to see. He was greatly relieved, retired, bathed and dressed, and dined cheerfully with his friends. But in the evening he was commanded not to leave his room, and was placed under house arrest, for leaving Ireland against orders.

Bacon had not known of Essex's return until he heard the news of his arrest. He succeeded in having a quarter of an hour's conversation with him on the following day, and advised him not to appear proud of the truce with Tyrone, nor to try to force the Queen to send him back to Ireland, and to seek access to her on every pretext. Essex made little comment, but shook his head as if he thought his advice was not good.

Essex was interviewed by the Privy Council which, after hearing his account, committed him to the custody of Egerton, their member who was most friendly with him. Under vows of secrecy, he divulged Tyrone's proposals for a treaty. These were found to be much like the terms of modern commonwealth status, or independence under the Crown.

While the Queen and her ministers were trying to understand Essex's account, strange information arrived from Ireland. Tyrone informed an envoy sent to confer with him 'that within two months he should see the greatest alteration and the strangest that he . . . could imagine, or ever saw in his life . . .'. The envoy could not understand what Tyrone meant, nor did Tyrone explain but went on to say, several times, that before long he 'would have a good share in England'.

It was unsafe, without adequate explanation, either to release Essex or to keep him under restraint. The Queen proposed to publish the official criticisms of his conduct of the expedition, but without his answers. Bacon 'told her plainly' that if she did this, 'the people would say that my Lord was wounded in his back'. She did not accept his advice, but ordered the publication of a dispassionate summary of the main facts then known to her.

As Bacon had foreseen, the statement stimulated sympathy for Essex, for popular opinion assumed that Essex could have given crushing replies if he had had the opportunity. It concluded that the Earl had been misrepresented to the Queen and Council, and a suspicion arose that Bacon was responsible.

Bacon had been having much more business with the Queen than formerly, in connexion with legal and financial matters, and it was assumed that one so closely connected with Essex, and now with the Queen, must be the cause of the trouble. His life was threatened, and he wrote to the Queen that such threats came from 'those whose despairs are dangerous, but yet not so dangerous as their hopes'. They were 'the devices of some that would put out all your Majesty's lights, and fall on reckoning how many years you have reigned . . .'. He wrote to Lord Henry Howard that rumour said he had advised the Queen that Essex had committed treason. 'The untruth of this fable God and my sovereign can witness. . . .' He said he was not servile to Essex, and had 'spent more time and more thought about his well doing, than ever I did about mine own'. On the same rumour, he wrote to Sir Robert Cecil, saying that he intended 'to avoid a suspicious silence, but not to make any base apology . . .'

Essex had hoped to return to Ireland, where he would have had an army at his back, but he had not succeeded. His friend Mountjoy was sent to replace him. He welcomed this, because Mountjoy was in his confidence. Mountjoy had informed the King of Scots, at Essex's request, that Essex would support his claim to the succession to the English Crown. Essex's aim was to secure the King's backing, so that he would then be able to count on an army in Scotland as well as in Ireland. Elizabeth had years ago given the strictest orders that there were to be no negotiations on the succession to her crown. Anyone engaging in them was committing treason. It was therefore essential not to be caught in them red-handed.

When Mountjoy became involved in the responsibilities of his new command, and saw that Essex was being treated with consideration in London, he withdrew from the intrigue, for he was not prepared to enter into any enterprises 'to satisfy my Lord of Essex's private ambition'. The secret of the negotiations with the King of Scots was not revealed until Essex himself confessed it. He used to keep papers bearing on it in a 'little black bag' hidden under his clothes, on a string round his neck.

Essex was presently allowed to return to his own house, where he lived in retirement under surveillance.

To satisfy public feeling, the Queen appointed a commission of eminent persons to inquire into the affairs of the Irish expedition. It was conducted in a judicial manner but not under ordinary law, so that Essex would not be subject to the usual penalties. The Crown's criticisms were to be presented by Coke, who was instructed not to suggest that Essex had been disloyal. It was arranged that Essex should appear before the commission with a prepared speech, which he would deliver with passionate accents of repentance. The commission would give him an admonishment, which he would modestly and dutifully accept. After this he would be reconciled with the Queen.

The arrangement was almost upset by Coke, who prosecuted in his customary lawyer's manner. Essex was not used to such treatment and was provoked to answer back. The Commission anxiously smoothed the disturbance, and sentenced Essex to be suspended from the execution of his offices and confined to his house during her Majesty's pleasure.

Bacon reported the proceedings to the Queen, telling her that now all was well, and Essex could again be received into favour. She requested him to write an account of what had happened. Bacon spent two afternoons reading it to her. She did not immediately act as Bacon advised, for six weeks passed before she restored Essex's liberty, and she did not restore access to herself.

Bacon laboured to improve the relations between the Queen and Essex. He offered his services once more to Essex, saying that, after the Queen, he loved few persons better than him. Essex sent a most becoming but conspicuously cautious reply, and asked Bacon (no doubt at Bacon's suggestion) to draft letters meant to be indirectly read by the Queen. Essex would say that he was out of touch with her present interests and ideas, as he had not met her for so long. Among these drafts was one purporting to be from Anthony Bacon to the Earl, and another was the Earl's purported reply.

How a reader could imagine that these letters had been drafted by any person other than Bacon is hard to understand. In the first of these, Anthony is supposed to say that Essex's friends at Court 'do not only toll the bell, but even ring out peals, as if your fortune were dead and buried', and he feared that this untimely despair would cause his Lordship 'to slack and break off your wise, loyal, and seasonable endeavours and industries for reintegration to her Majesty's favour; in comparison whereof all other circumstances are but as *atomi*, or rather as *vacuum* without any substance at all . . .'. Anthony was supposed to mention in his reply 'my brother Francis Bacon . . . is too wise (I think) to be abused, and too honest to abuse, though he be more reserved in all particulars than is needful . . .'.

Essex's supposed reply was drafted in a quiet demure tone of sad nostalgia. In it Bacon writes (again referring to himself) 'For your brother, I hold him an honest gentleman, and wish him all good, much the rather for your sake. . . .' This Machiavellian naivety was too clever by half.

Bacon said that he was never more welcome to the Queen than when he spoke 'fullest and boldest' in Essex's favour.

While Bacon was regarding Essex as a penitent, and Elizabeth was trying to do so, Essex presented a very different aspect to a few of his closest friends. He lived in seclusion, seeing scarcely anybody. Besides writing incessantly to the Queen for the restoration of her favour, he sued also for the continuation of his monopoly of sweet wines, which was running out, and had not been renewed. It provided a large part of his income.

While he appeared to be living quietly, his private activities were very different. He continued secret negotiations with the King of Scots, and suggested to Mountjoy that if the monopoly of sweet wines were not renewed he should send a protest to the Queen, which would provide Essex with the opportunity 'by means of his friends' to 'present myself to the Queen'. He implied that he would then secure his requests by force.

Sir John Harrington (a god-child of Elizabeth) saw him at about this time and made a note on his impression. 'It resteth with me in opinion that ambition thwarted in his career doth speedily lead on to madness: and herein I am confirmed by what I learn of my Lord Essex; who shifteth from sorrow and repentance to rage and rebellion so suddenly as well proveth him devoid of good reason or of right mind. In my last discourse he uttered strange words bordering on such strange designs, that made me hasten forth and leave his presence. Thank heaven I am safe at home, and if I go in such troubles again, I deserve the gallows for a meddling fool. His speeches of the Queen become no man who hath *mens sana in corpore sano*. He hath ill advisers, and much evil hath sprung from this source. The Queen well knoweth how to humble the haughty spirit, the haughty spirit knoweth not how to yield, and the man's soul seemeth tossed to and fro like the waves of a troubled sea.'

Bacon no doubt perceived that rebellious notions were passing through Essex's mind, but he did not know they were uppermost, and Essex concealed this decisive fact from him. Characteristically, Bacon did not guess the truth. His strength was in expressing subtle ideas, but he was deficient in ordinary perceptions.

The Queen had deeper perceptions, and also probably better information. In spite of Bacon's almost officious attempts to reconcile her with Essex, she would not forgive him. She became suspicious of Bacon's persistence, and for three months refused to see him. As he wrote later, 'she had me in jealousy, that I was not hers entirely, but still had inward and deep respects towards my Lord, more than stood at that time with her will and pleasure'.

He had lost the confidence of both, and did not know the most important things that were happening.

This was not a complete disaster for him, because public affairs were only a part of his life. He could turn with zest, in every moment free from public and professional work, to his intellectual projects.

Essex and his inner circle of friends decided that the refusal of the renewal of the sweet-wines monopoly should be the occasion for seizing control of the Court. They sounded personalities in various directions to secure support. Mountjoy had come to disapprove the project and refused his support, which meant the withdrawal of the backing of the army in Ireland. Essex informed the King of Scots that the present English governing circles were in favour of a Spanish claim to the crown. He promised Roman Catholics toleration, and he informed Puritans that he would oppose a Spanish succession.

Plans to seize the Queen and dismiss Cecil, Ralegh and others were worked out. Early in 1601, Essex's house became a centre of so much activity that the authorities felt it necessary to inquire what was going on. Essex was requested to attend the Council and explain. He said he was too ill to go, and called his inner circle together to decide what to do. As the government was evidently on the alert, it was not possible to surprise the Court and seize the Queen, so Essex decided to appeal to the people in the City of London, where he was personally popular. Rumours were started that the Crown had been promised to the Spaniards, that Ralegh the atheist was attempting to waylay and murder

Essex, that Roman Catholics and Jesuits were also trying to murder Essex. A message of unknown origin came from the City, pledging its support for Essex.

Some three hundred armed gentlemen assembled at Essex House, courageous and capable fighting men who had been carefully selected from the various counties of England, so that they might subsequently return to their homes to lead Essex's cause in their own regions, providing a framework of control for the whole country.

The Queen now sent Egerton and three other dignitaries to inquire whether Essex had any complaint; that if he had, it would be heard; and that the assembly at his house should be dispersed.

Essex decided that action was now essential. He locked the four emissaries in his library, and went into the City to rally the people to his side. His military organization was so bad that the horses were not ready, and he and two hundred of his armed gentlemen had to proceed on foot. The party, shouting that the Earl was in danger of being murdered, walked to the house of the Sheriff, who was in command of armed citizens, and was believed to be one of Essex's supporters. He was indeed one of the many who enthusiastically admired Essex from a distance. But the presence of the Earl on his doorstep, surrounded by two hundred armed men and calling for protection against being murdered, perplexed and embarrassed him. He did not know what to do, so he went to consult the Lord Mayor.

As Essex was associated in the public mind with military glory and not with any political programme and organization, there was no machine by which the people could be set in motion. They stood amazed, and in effect motionless.

During this chaotic inaction, heralds from the Court arrived in the City, and denounced Essex as a traitor. Individuals who had thought of following Essex, out of good-will and curiosity, reconsidered their decision. Very few joined him, and he was reduced to returning to his house in the Strand, apparently with the main aim of destroying papers which should 'tell no tales'. A few hours later, the house was surrounded by the Queen's forces, and Essex and those with him were arrested.

Bacon, not in the inner confidence of either Essex or the Queen, was outside these developments. He sought an audience with the Queen as soon as possible, and most earnestly assured her of his loyalty. He decided to have nothing more to do with Essex.

24. *Prosecution*

AFTER the arrest, the government started an investigation. This was conducted by Coke under the supervision of the Council. So many persons had to be interrogated and documents examined that as many legal personnel as possible were brought in to assist. Bacon came in with the rest.

At the beginning of the process against Essex, Bacon had not a very prominent part. The Council reserved to itself the examination of principal prisoners, and succeeded in learning from one of them that there was an inner circle of about half-a-dozen conspirators. Essex and Southampton, the chief leaders, were not informed of this discovery, but the others were confronted with the facts revealed in the confession, and all, seeing that the primary truth was known, confessed with very little qualification.

Coke, Bacon and the other lawyers were then told not to pursue further details, but to prepare an immediate prosecution of Essex and Southampton. Essex contended at the prosecution that he had, rightly or wrongly, been acting only to protect his life, and that morally his actions were not treasonable. But Coke revealed details of the plan for the seizure of the Queen, and gave the names of those who were to lead the various actions in the occupation of the palace.

This made Essex anxious. He requested that he be allowed to comment on the assertions forthwith. This was granted, with the effect that the normal legal process was broken by continual interruptions from Essex. Sir Walter Ralegh was called to deny that he had been trying to murder Essex, and Sir Robert Cecil suddenly appeared from behind a curtain to deny that he had sold the crown to Spain. In the midst of the irregular procedure and excitements, Coke lost control of his case. He did not focus the evidence into a clear proof of treason, moral as well as legal. Presently he paused in his floundering, as if wondering what to say next.

At this point Bacon rose, and pulled the proceedings together.

He said that all history had shown that traitors never attacked the throne directly, but under a pretence, such as the reformation of corruptions in the state and religion; the restoration of ancient liberties, or the removal of evil ministers. Essex had said that he was only trying to protect the Queen against some of the great men around her, and that he had fled into the City for protection against those trying to murder him. His behaviour was not unlike that of the Greek tyrant Pisistratus, who wounded himself and then ran bleeding through Athens, to secure the sympathy of citizens and then rally them to gain control of the city.

'You, my Lord,' he said to Essex, 'should know that though princes give their subjects cause of discontent, though they take away the honours they have heaped upon them, though they bring them to a lower estate than they raised them from, yet ought they not to be so forgetful of their allegiance that they should enter into any undutiful act; much less rebellion, as you, my Lord, have done. . . .'

'To answer Mr. Bacon's speech at once,' Essex broke in, 'I say thus much; and call forth Mr. Bacon against Mr. Bacon.' He referred to the two letters Bacon had drafted, purporting to come from Anthony Bacon and the Earl. He said that in one of these, Bacon had given the grounds and reasons of his discontent as well as he could do himself. 'If those reasons were then just and true, not counterfeit, how can it be that now my pretences are false and injurious? For then Mr. Bacon joined with me in mine opinion, and pointed out those to be mine enemies and to hold me in disgrace with her Majesty, whom he seems now to clear of such mind towards me; and therefore I leave the truth of what I say and he opposeth unto your Lordship's indifferent considerations.'

Bacon was not put out. He said that 'those letters, if they were there, would not blush to be seen for anything contained in them', and that he had 'spent more time on trying to make the Earl a good servant to the Queen and state, than on anything else'.

Coke tried to attack Essex on religious grounds, but Essex answered him with a consistency which was in marked contrast to his replies to the charges of political treason.

The prosecution again floundered by trying to trip Essex over minor legalities, and Essex said to Coke, 'Well, plead your law and we will plead conscience.'

Again the case was knitted together by Bacon. He said that he had 'never yet seen in any case such favour shown to any prisoner; so many digressions, such delivering of evidence by fractions, and so silly a defence of such great and notorious treasons . . .' he therefore held it necessary briefly to recite the judges' opinions.

Was Essex's intent 'to go only as a suppliant to her Majesty. Shall their petitions be presented by armed petitioners? This must needs bring loss of liberty to the prince . . . to take secret counsel, to execute it, to run together in numbers armed with weapons,—what can be the excuse? Warned by the Lord Keeper, by a herald, and yet persist! Will any simple man take this to be less than treason?'

'To this,' it is reported, 'the Earl answered little.'

The prisoners were found guilty, and condemned to death.

During the trial Essex behaved with extraordinary 'boldness, and show of resolution and contempt of death'. But after the condemnation, he had a revulsion of feeling, and began to reveal not only his own part, but that of others. In particular, he accused his secretary Henry Cuffe, described by Bacon as 'A base fellow by birth, but a great scholar.' He asked for Cuffe to be brought to him, and then, before Egerton, Cecil and two other councillors, denounced him, saying: 'You have been one of the chiefest instigators of me to all these my disloyal courses into which I have fallen.'

Cuffe acted as organizing secretary to the conspiracy. After Essex's denunciation he made a confession, writing as one 'whom public justice hath pronounced the child of death', in which he gave the best-expressed account of the details of the conspiracy.

Shortly before his execution Essex confessed to three divines, who recorded that he had acquired 'a deeper insight into his offence, being sorry he had so stood upon his justification at his arraignment, for he was since that become another man . . . if his project had taken effect, God knows . . . what harm it had wrought in the realm . . .'.

He humbly thanked her Majesty that his execution should be in private, 'lest the acclamation of the people might have been a temptation unto him . . . all popularity and trust in man was vain', and he thanked God that he was 'justly spewed out of the realm'.

The three divines wrote that at his execution he desired 'God to forgive him his *great*, his *bloody*, his *crying*, and his *infectious sin'*, explaining to his confessors that 'it was a leprosy that had infected far and near'. He was in such a state of obsession that 'he never mentioned nor remembered there wife, children, or friend, nor took particular leave of any that were present, but wholly abstracted and sequestered himself to the state of his conscience and prayer'.

Bacon was ordered by the Queen to draft an account of the affair. It was 'perused, weighed, censured, altered, and made almost into a new writing' by certain of the principal councillors, and then 'exactly perused by the Queen herself, and some alterations made again by her appointment'. This *'Declaration* of the Practices and Treasons attempted and committed by Robert late Earl of Essex and his Complices', is substantially accurate and keeps closely to the original statements and confessions.

Bacon's part in the Essex affair drew on him unpopularity and contempt. To those who had an emotional conception of politics he had betrayed a friend, and should, if he had come to the conclusion that Essex was mistaken, at least have withdrawn and not participated in his prosecution. In their view, he was faithless and ungenerous.

These sentiments were held against him in his own lifetime, and still more strongly in the liberal period of the nineteenth century, when England was the leading imperial power, and seizure of the Queen and government was a notion which belonged to romantic fiction rather than reality.

In the twentieth century, Bacon's behaviour is more easily understood. Essex was a young man of great gifts and personal attraction. He found it easy to acquire a large following of admirers. His sensitive and emotional nature enabled him to sympathize with other people and see things from their point of view. He 'could vary himself into all shapes for a time', and men of many conditions liked him and attached themselves to him. But though he could understand many men and many ideas, he was lacking in administrative gifts. He was unable to organize a party and a programme. Consequently, he tended to depend on the direct support of the multitude. 'His own courses inclined ever to rest upon the main strength of the multitude, and not upon surprises, or the combinations of a few.'

Bacon in his youth had been excluded from political power by the early death of his father, and his own lack of means. The

Cecils, who occupied the central posts, naturally did not wish to surrender them. He was personally dissatisfied by this exclusion but, like many others, he was not happy about the conditions of the state, with an ageing Queen, a tired old Burghley, and the chief working position in the state held by Robert Cecil, with his devious methods.

Bacon saw no way of guiding the state directly, so he sought for the best means of influencing it indirectly. The most promising seemed to be through the attractive, impressionable and admired young Essex, a potential leader, who might bring a fresh energy and ability to deal with the country's many difficulties of defence, religion, and social and agricultural reform.

Bacon had hoped in the earlier years to strengthen the rational side of Essex's nature, and bring it into balance with his emotional gifts. But this hope was not realized. As Essex grew older, he grew more emotional, and depended more and more on his personality. He did not develop his powers of political thought and organization. Bacon had soon perceived this tendency and had warned him against it.

The most significant sentence in all Bacon's speeches and writing on Essex was his comment that he had never yet seen in any case 'so silly a defence of such great and notorious treasons'. Essex's stupidity was unpardonable, and left no alternative to the performance of conventional duty. Other intelligent and able men, such as Mountjoy, naturally took the same line.

In the world of the twentieth century, Essex would have tended to be a fascist. Bacon's attitude towards him, trying to cure him of his faults and help him while there was hope, and when all hope had gone, firmly detaching himself and following a rational policy however unpleasant, has been justified by subsequent history.

The affair of Essex was of supreme personal importance to Elizabeth and to Bacon. In both cases it provided the ultimate test of their characters, of their final choice of the interests of the state before their personal affections.

Elizabeth's mastery of herself in the necessity of signing Essex's death warrant gave her greatness a tragic quality.

Bacon lost his brother Anthony, with whom he had such a sympathetic understanding, early in 1601. Anthony had long been a bed-ridden invalid. His very close association with Essex, living for a long time in his house, no doubt heightened the

P

shock he received from the affair and execution, and precipitated his early death.

Bacon's profound and undisturbed affection for his brother is one of the most signficant features of his character. They were one in mind as well as heart. The steadfastness of his affection for his brother shows that he was capable of the deepest emotional attachments, and heightens the contrast of his attitude to Essex.

Francis inherited from Anthony the estate at Gorhambury, which meant so much to him thereafter as a place of residence, meditation and filial piety. Though Anthony's possessions were heavily encumbered by debt, and Gorhambury was in disrepair, the country house was a delicious place of retirement and an exquisite spur to Bacon's imagination. His mind dwelt on its improvement, and he subsequently built a beautiful summer house nearby, which became an object of wonder and admiration.

But the inheritance gave him little immediate relief from financial embarrassment. Later in 1601 he had to mortgage his country house at Twickenham, and secure the intervention of the Lord Treasurer to obtain for him an agreed settlement with his creditors.

After the suppression of the rebellion, Parliament was called. Subsidies were voted virtually without opposition, and it was announced that various monopolies would be suppressed. The Commons received this with great joy. All the members waited on the Queen, by her leave, to deliver their thanks. She received them with an affectionate grandeur, perfectly though unconsciously fitted to the occasion, for it proved to be the last at which she met the representatives of the people.

Bacon was very active in Elizabeth's last Parliament. He introduced a bill on Weights and Measures, remarking that the use of false weights had grown 'intolerable and common'. Their suppression was necessary for 'true and just dealing', and 'things necessary in use are better than those things which are glorious in estimation'.

He proposed, once more, the repeal of superfluous laws. On such matters, which might be unpopular, it is better 'to venture a man's credit by speaking than to stretch a man's conscience by silence'. He opposed a bill which would have declared monopolies to be in contradiction to the common law. He contended that the grant of monopolies was a royal prerogative, and the Commons 'ought not to deal or judge or meddle with her Majesty's prerogative'. The suppression of monopolies should be sought not through a bill, but by a petition to the Queen.

Incidentally, in his discussion of various kinds of monopoly, he defined his conception of the aim and principles of the patenting of inventions. 'If any man out of his own wit, industry or endeavour, find out anything beneficial to the Commonwealth, or bring any new invention which every subject of this kingdom may use; yet in regard of his pains and travel therein, her Majesty perhaps is pleased to grant him a privilege to use the same only by himself or his deputies for a certain time.'

His interest in economic and technical measures was shown by speeches on a bill on assurance for merchants with cargoes abroad. 'A certainty of gain is that which this law provides for,' he said. 'By Policy of Assurance the safety of goods is assured unto the merchant. This is the lodestone that draws him out to adventure, and to stretch even the very punctilio of his credit.'

A very interesting incident occurred in connection with charitable trusts. The bishops had been granted special powers in an act to prevent the misapplication of funds for colleges, hospitals and other charitable institutions. It was felt that these powers were excessive, and it was proposed to repeal the act, and replace it by a new one. For some reason which has not been recorded, Bacon was passionately opposed to the repeal. He said that 'It would be a most uncharitable action to repeal and subvert such a mount of charity.' He became so excited that he was unable to express himself coherently. 'I speak (quoth he) out of the very strings of my heart; for I speak not now out of the fervency of my brain. . . .'

It seems that Bacon's concern about endowments for learning was so passionate that it was capable of upsetting his usual composure. His ordinary mode of expression both in speech and writing was a conscious intellectual construction. It had superlative merits for putting ideas into words, but it had drawbacks in dealing with emotional subtleties and semi-conscious ideas and intuitions. For dealing with these, his intellectual machinery was sometimes clumsy, and not always appropriate.

The last months of Elizabeth's reign saw Mountjoy's great victory in Ireland, in which he defeated a strong Irish army, led by Tyrone and assisted by four thousand Spanish troops.

According to his manner of offering unsolicited advice, Bacon
sent a letter to Cecil on the policy to be pursued in pacifying
Ireland after the victory. It consisted of four points: the repair
of war-damage; the recovery of the hearts of the people; the
removing of the root and occasions of new troubles, and the construction of plantations and buildings.

'A toleration of religion' seemed to him to be 'in policy of
absolute necessity'. Besides this, good Protestant preachers,
'especially of the sort which are vehement and zealous persua-
ders', should be established there, at her Majesty's expense, and
'the college begun at Dublin' (Trinity College) should be
developed. The Bible and other works should be published in
the Irish language. Justice was to be made quick and inexpensive
by local judges. The English and the Irish should be treated
equally, whether in competition or controversy, 'as if they were
one nation'.

Among the steps to be taken to remove the seeds of the troubles
are the suppression of barbarous customs among the native
inhabitants, including their 'habits of apparel', and 'their poets
or heralds that enchant them in savage manner'.

With regard to Plantations and Buildings, they were to be
carried out by men who were 'gracious and well beloved and are
like to be well followed'. And it was not to be 'left (as heretofore) to the pleasure of the undertakers and adventurers, where
and how to build and plant; but that they do it according to a
prescript or formulary'. They were to have a plan.

Such were the kind of activities in which Bacon was engaged,
when Elizabeth died in 1603. For many years he had been employed as a Queen's Counsel, though without a written appointment. He was a leading Parliamentarian, much esteemed and
used in committees, and often spokesman for the government in
the Commons. In addition to this, he sent on his own initiative
weighty suggestions on policy to chief ministers.

He was now forty-two years old, and still without any official
position or salary. To the end, Elizabeth would not give him
office. With his small inheritances he had little means to support
so much unpaid public service.

25. *Statesman or Scientist?*

ELIZABETH'S blocking of Bacon's attempts to become a statesman brought him nearly to abandon them. For many years he had sought office, until it had become almost an unconscious habit. He continued with the same series of activities, his legal work, his work in Parliament and his giving of advice solicited and unsolicited. At the same time, his taking of all knowledge to be his province never ceased, nor did his financial embarrassment.

He returned in every moment of leisure to the pursuit of the notions he had formed in his youth. He formulated his ideas and results over and over again, and planned a work on the *Interpretation of Nature*, in which his project was to be carried out. In the years about the end of Elizabeth's reign, or the beginning of James's, he drafted a preface for the work, in which he discussed his aims and his personal qualifications for undertaking the project. It is one of the few, and the most substantial, of his autobiographical notes.

'Believing that I was born for the service of mankind, and regarding the care of the commonwealth as a kind of common property which like the air and the water belongs to everybody, I set myself to consider in what way mankind might be best served, and what service I was myself best fitted by nature to perform. . .'

Among all the benefits that could be conferred upon mankind, he found none so great as the discovery of new arts, endowments, and commodities for the bettering of man's life. For he saw that the work of inventors lasted forever, whereas that of the fathers of the people and other heroes of that sort lasted but for a short time.

'If a man could succeed not in striking out some particular invention, however useful, but in kindling a light in nature . . . and bring into sight all that is most hidden and secret in the world,—that man (I thought) would be the benefactor indeed of the human race,—the propagator of man's empire over the universe, the champion of liberty, the conqueror and subduer of necessities.'

He had found that his qualities of mind had fitted him 'for nothing so well as for the study of Truth', and he thought that his 'nature had a kind of familiarity and relationship with Truth'.

But because his birth and education had seasoned him in business of state, and 'because opinions (so young as I was) would sometimes stagger me; and because I thought that a man's own country has some special claims on him more than the rest of the world; and because I hoped that, if I rose to any place of honour in the state, I should have a larger command of industry and ability to help me in my work;—for these reasons I both applied myself to acquire the arts of civil life, and commended my service, so far as in modesty and honesty I might, to the favour of such friends as had any influence . . .'.

But when he found that his 'zeal was mistaken for ambition', and his 'life had already reached the turning point', and his weak health reminded him how ill he 'could afford to be so slow', he reflected that he should not leave undone that which he could do by himself, through devoting the whole of his efforts to that which could be done only with 'the help and consent of others', so he decided to betake himself entirely to his personal contribution.

He was not discouraged by 'signs in the times of the decline and overthrow of that knowledge and erudition which is now in use'. He did not expect any more barbarian invasions, though perhaps the Spanish empire might crush other nations and then sink under its own weight, but he foresaw danger from 'the civil wars which may be expected . . . (judging from certain fashions which have come in of late) to spread through many countries . . .'. These, 'together with the malignity of sects, and those compendious artifices and devices' which have replaced solid erudition, portend a danger to literature and the sciences which may be fatal, and against which printing will not be an effectual security for the survival of knowledge. Fair-weather learning, nursed by leisure and blossoming under reward and praise, would not be able to withstand such dangers.

But 'far otherwise is it with that knowledge, whose dignity is maintained by works of utility and power'. He was not afraid of the injuries which the times could do to these, and he was not concerned with the injuries done to them by men. If anyone charged him with 'seeking to be wise overmuch', he answered simply that 'modesty and civil respect are fit for civil matters; in contemplation nothing is to be respected but Truth'. If anyone called on him for *works*, he would tell him frankly that for a man not old, of weak health, with his hands full of civil business, entering without guide or light upon an argument of all others the most obscure, he held 'it enough to have constructed the machine' though he 'may not succeed in setting it to work'. He believed that the most serious error of previous investigators of nature had been eagerness to proceed to practical works before fundamental principles had been elucidated. Existing knowledge was so limited that it does not 'teach a man even what to *wish*'.

He warned politicians, who 'make their calculations and conjectures according to persons and precedents', not to interpose their judgment in the project, for in it no thought is 'to be taken about precedents, for the thing is without precedent.'

He proposed to publish the more general parts of the work, in order to bring the project to the notice of men and interest them in it. The more special parts he would pass from 'hand to hand, with selection and judgment'. He believed that 'the formula itself of interpretation, and the discoveries made by the same, will thrive better if committed to the charge of some fit and selected minds, and kept private'.

At this time, Bacon believed that secrecy might be of assistance to the progress of research. 'This however,' he says, 'is other people's concern. For myself, my heart is not set upon any of those things which depend upon external accidents. I am not hunting for fame: I have no desire to found a sect, after the fashion of heresiarchs; and to look for any private gain from such an undertaking as this, I count both ridiculous and base. Enough for me the consciousness of well-deserving, and those real and effectual results with which Fortune itself cannot interfere . . .'.

With these long-cherished and developing ideas in his mind, he found that in the latter years of Elizabeth's reign, he had lost the full control of his activities and had begun to drift. Her death, and the accession of the new king provided a sharp break in the tenor of his life. The change aroused great hopes. Britain had never before been under one king, and this immediately brought two major benefits, the unity of the whole British island, and the increase in military security arising from it. These fundamental advantages, together with the rule of a Scottish Protestant king, greatly reduced the danger of Spanish invasion in the interest of Roman Catholicism. This was an ideological advantage of the first order.

Security in Elizabeth's time had depended more on heroic endeavour in a dangerous situation. Now the conditions of security were more concrete. Assured by their improved situation, the people heaved a sigh of relief. The future, looking more secure, appeared to be full of opportunity. There was no longer the same need to be so much concerned with the fight for survival on the stage of the world, and men became more interested in systematic pursuit of personal interests at home. Gifted men changed from adventurers into business men. In the new atmosphere of social values, men like Sir Walter Ralegh, who had formerly appeared a hero, now looked like pirates and bandits.

Bacon shared in the initial general exhilaration. In a letter to his friend Toby Matthew, he referred to the effect of the coming of James on himself: 'In my particular I have many comforts and assurances; but in mine own opinion the chief is, that the canvassing world is gone, and the deserving world is come. And withal I find myself as one awaked out of sleep; which I have not been this long time, nor could, I think, have been now, without such a great noise as this. . . .'

In spite of the departure of 'the canvassing world', Bacon had written to all of the most important persons whom he knew, who had access to James, offering his services. One of the most interesting of his letters was to the poet John Davies, in which Bacon desired him 'to be good to concealed poets', one of Bacon's remarks which has stimulated speculation on whether he had written poetry under another name.

He sent an offer to the King to write his proclamation, 'it being a thing familiar in my Mistress's times to have my pen used in public writings of satisfaction'. No use seems to have been made of this offer, but his draft contained notable ideas. One of these was that the union of England and Scotland had made a balance, which 'will be a foundation of the universal peace of all Christian princes, and that now the strife that shall remain between them shall be but an emulation who shall govern best and most to the weal and good of his people'. This is a prevision of the modern notion of an era of social and cultural emulation between the nations, after a universal ideology and peace have been established.

When James took over the government, he announced that for the present all officials were to remain in their posts. He believed in looking around, and told the French Ambassador that he considered that a new king should reign for a year and a day before making important changes. As Bacon had no official position under Elizabeth, he was not covered by the order. But as soon as his position was explained to James, it was confirmed.

Bacon continued to offer information to Cecil, in his attempts to remain on good terms with him. 'Your Lordship shall find a prince the farthest from the appearance of vain-glory that may be, and rather like a prince of the ancient form than the latter time. His speech is swift and cursory, and in the full dialect of his country; and in point of business, short; in point of discourse large. He affecteth popularity by gracing such as he hath heard to be popular, and not by any fashions of his own. He is thought somewhat general in his favours, and his virtue of access is rather because he is much abroad and in press, than that he giveth easy audience about serious things. He hasteneth to a mixture of both kingdoms and nations, faster perhaps than policy will conveniently bear. I told your Lordship once before, that (methought) his Majesty rather asked Counsel of the time past than of the time to come. But it is early yet to ground any settled opinion. . . .'

His description of James may be compared with that given by a French agent about nineteen years earlier: 'He is wonderfully clever . . . and has an excellent opinion of himself. Owing to the terrorism under which he has been brought up, he is timid with the great lords . . . yet his especial anxiety is to be thought hardy and a man of courage. . . . He dislikes dances and music and amorous talk, and curiosity of dress and courtly trivialities. He speaks, eats, dresses, and plays like a boor, and he is no better in the company of women. He is never still for a moment, but walks perpetually up and down the room, and his gait is sprawling and awkward; his voice is loud and his words sententious. He prefers hunting to all other amusements, and will be six hours together on horseback. . . . His body is feeble, yet he is not delicate; in a word, he is an old young man. . . . He is prodigiously conceited. . . . He irritates his subjects by indiscreet and violent attachments. He is idle and careless, too easy, . . . leaving his affairs to be managed. . . . He told me that, whatever he seemed, he was aware of everything of consequence that was going on. He could afford to spend time in hunting, for that when he attended to business he could do more in an hour than others could do in a day. . . . '

Such was the man whom Bacon was trying to take the best possible view of. Cecil was more powerful under James than under Elizabeth, because he had had the leading part in secret negotiations with James before Elizabeth had died, to smooth his way to the English crown. James was dependent on him for knowledge of English affairs, and through his laziness in leaving disagreeable administrative work to his subordinates.

During this early period when James's dependence on Cecil was very great, Bacon's numerous efforts to secure attention failed almost completely. Cecil was superficially friendly to Bacon at this time, and gave him substantial help over his debts, and minor help in getting professional work, but appears to have distinctly avoided putting him in the way of any important official work. He helped him to secure one of the knighthoods which James was making extremely cheap, as a means of creating followers and funds. He made about six hundred in six months, and ordered all who had an income of not less than £40 a year in land to be knighted or pay a fine. Bacon's first hopes of promotion were dashed.

In a letter to Cecil, describing his efforts to extricate himself from his debts, he said that his aim was to live in a small country house on £300 a year. 'I desire to meddle as little as I can in the King's causes, his Majesty now abounding in Counsel; and to follow my private thrift and practice, and to marry with some convenient advancement. For as for any ambition, I do assure your Honour mine is quenched. In the Queen's, my excellent Mistress's, time the quorum was small: her service was a kind of freehold, and it was a more solemn time. All those points agreed with my nature and judgment. My ambition now I shall only put upon my pen, whereby I shall be able to maintain memory and merit of the times succeeding.

'Lastly, for this divulged and almost prostituted title of knighthood, I could without change, by your Honour's mean, be content to have it . . . because I have three new knights in my mess at Gray's Inn commons; and because I have found out an alderman's daughter, an handsome maiden, to my liking. . . .'

Bacon said that he was grieved not a little that Cecil made no use of him. 'For my knighthood, I wish the manner might be such as might grace me, since the matter will not; I mean, that I might not be merely gregarious in a troop. The coronation is at hand. . . .' However, Bacon received his knighthood as one of a batch of three hundred.

He found himself with less legal work than at any time for many years. He very seriously considered retiring from public business, and devoting himself entirely to his philosophical and scientific studies. Believing that his prospects as a statesman might have come to an end, he began to organize a purely intellectual life.

He decided to write a general review of learning which might widely prepare men's minds for the acceptance of his project for the interpretation and mastering of nature. He entitled it *The Advancement of Learning*, and put together the first half of it from the notes he had accumulated during the previous twenty years.

Probably after he had written this first half, as the first fruits of his intended private life of study and research, he conceived the idea that the work might be used as a new way of gaining James's attention. As James was a learned man, one of the most learned who ever occupied a throne, Bacon decided to dedicate the work to him, in the hope that it might secure his sympathy and support for carrying out its main object. The idea may have been conceived when, after the absence of demand for his services, some use began to be made of them again, especially in connexion with Parliament.

James's first Parliament was extremely important for the consolidation of his rule. Among the numerous major matters to be dealt with was the uniting of England and Scotland. It was essential that this should be handled capably. The Commons elected Bacon the first member of its commission on this primary question. His abilities as a reporter of committees were outstanding and in frequent demand, and he had an inherent taste for drafting documents. The Commons acquired the habit of entrusting him with the exposition of their views. It is a mark of his disinterestedness. They liked to make use of his technical ability, whatever they thought of his political line. Bacon's clarity of style and processes of mind were unsuited to intrigue. When he tried by an effort of his intellect to be Machiavellian, it was against his nature. It created distrust and was unsuccessful. His extraordinary originality and boldness of thought puzzled people and made them uncomfortable. He tried to adjust himself to their understandings by an exaggerated deference, which was often taken for impertinent conceit.

At the end of the heavy work on the legal aspects of the union, Bacon 'in conclusion prayed the House that at other times they would use some other, and not oppress him with their favours'. On a later occasion, he was expected to make a report on a conference with the House of Lords on a petition of merchants concerning grievances against the Spaniards. 'And it please you (Mr. Speaker),' he said, 'I do not find myself any ways bound to report that which passed at the last conference touching the Spanish grievances: having been neither employed to speak nor appointed to report in that cause. But because it is put upon me by a silent expectation, grounded upon nothing (that I know) more than that I was observed diligently to take notes; I am content (if that provision that I made for mine own remembrance may serve this house for a report) not to deny you that sheaf that I have in haste bound up. . . .'

Bacon had a disinterested enjoyment in the exercise of his natural capacities, which was quite distinct from his ambition.

In his Parliamentary speeches he frequently expressed original thoughts on the subject under discussion. He could hardly help doing so, owing to the cast of his mind. In his speech on the problems of naturalization of Englishmen and Scotsmen as one people, he incidentally gave his views on the population problem. He earnestly argued that the country was under-populated, and that the means of production could be increased to support a much larger population. 'Our industry', he said, 'is not awaked to seek maintenance of any over-great press or charge of people.' He inclined to the modern view that the application of science will enable the production of food and goods to expand faster than the increase of population.

He addressed to the King a paper on the problem of the unity of the Church. It contains parallels in the government of religious and political institutions. He expressed his dislike of 'all immodest bitterness, peremptory presumption, popular handling and other courses', which tended to impress the vulgar rather than produce effects and the observation of duty. Solitary and unpopular policies could not always be avoided, for 'if man shall not by his industry, virtue, and policy, as it were with the oar row against the stream and inclination of time, all institutions

and ordinances, be they never so pure, will corrupt and degenerate . . .'.

He thought that in important matters of policy 'he that is not
with us, is against us;—' but that in unimportant ones, 'he that
is not against us, is with us . . .'. He noted that the periods of
persecution 'were excellent times for doctrine and manners, so
they be unproper and unlike examples of outward government
and policy'.

He believed that religious peace depended especially on good
teaching. 'I am partly persuaded that the Papists themselves
should not need so much the severity of penal laws if the sword
of the spirit were better edged. . . .' If the ideological instruction
were improved, they would more easily accept the line without
being forced.

Bacon's outstanding services in the Parliamentary political
union of England and Scotland obtained James's direct appreciation and approval. Bacon was no longer entirely dependent on
Cecil for political advancement.

He began to write, think and aspire with a new confidence,
which was reflected in his style. He made notes on the problem
of the union for James's personal assistance. He provided a
concise analysis of the various aspects of the problem; 'for length
and ornament of speech are to be used for persuasion of multitudes,
and not for information of kings'. He had noticed 'his Majesty's
rare and indeed singular gift and faculty of swift apprehension',
even in matters quite outside the path of his 'education, reading,
and conference'. In view of the King's natural talents, it was
not necessary to provide more than 'a brief and naked memorial
of the articles and points of this great cause'.

In 1604, at the age of forty-three, he received for the first time
an official appointment. His position as a King's Counsel, previously unofficial, was made official, and he was given a pension
of £60 a year. Hitherto, his services had been taken virtually for
nothing.

After his strenuous parliamentary work on the union, Bacon
was free from public work for nearly a year. He devoted it to the
completion of the *Advancement of Learning*, which was published
in 1605. He addressed the work to the King, with the hope that it
would secure his sympathy. He merely added two opening paragraphs to the first chapter, which he concluded by explaining
that as James stood invested with 'the power and fortune of a

King, the knowledge and illumination of a Priest, and the learning and universality of a Philosopher', he thought it proper that
his fame should be celebrated by a 'solid work, fixed memorial,
and immortal monument', and that no better oblation could
be made to him than a treatise contributing to that end, on 'the
excellency of learning and knowledge, and the excellency of the
merit and true glory in the augmentation and propagation
thereof'. Though he could not positively advise the King how
these ends could best be achieved, yet, he said, 'I may excite
your princely cogitations to visit the excellent treasure of your
own mind, and thence to extract particulars for this purpose
agreeable to your magnanimity and wisdom.'

Shortly after the publication of the *Advancement*, the nation
was convulsed by the discovery of the Gunpowder Plot, in which
Roman Catholic conspirators aimed to exterminate King and
government. This no doubt deflected some attention which
might otherwise have been given to Bacon's book. But the affair
scarcely involved Bacon. He still was not much engaged in public
work. He remained undecided whether he should retire and become a private student, or continue to aspire to become a
statesman.

He sent a presentation copy of the *Advancement of Learning*
to Sir Thomas Bodley, who also, like Bacon, had been hindered
by Cecil from advancing in public service. As a consequence,
Bodley had withdrawn from public life and founded the Bodleian Library at Oxford. Bacon was tempted to follow his example.
In his letter accompanying the book, he described the conflict
in the mind, which Bodley had also felt. 'I do confess, since I was
of any understanding, my mind hath in effect been absent from
that I have done; and in absence are many errors which I do
willingly acknowledge; and amongst the rest this great one that
led the rest; that knowing myself by inward calling to be fitter to
hold a book than to play a part, I have led my life in civil causes;
for which I was not very fit by nature, and more unfit by the
preoccupation of my mind. Therefore calling myself home, I
have now for a time enjoyed myself; whereof likewise I desire
to make the world partaker. My labours (If I may so term that
which was the comfort of my other labours) I have dedicated
to the King; desirous, if there be any good in them, it may be as
the fat of a sacrifice, incensed to his honour: and the second copy
I have sent unto you, not only in good affection, but in a kind of

congruity, in regard to your great and rare desert of learning. For books are the shrines where the Saint is, or is believed to be: and you having built an Ark to save learning from deluge, deserve propriety in any new instrument or engine, whereby learning should be improved or advanced.' Bacon's love of the intellectual life shines through this letter.

The copy of the *Advancement* which he sent to Cecil, now Earl of Salisbury, was accompanied by a perfunctory letter. 'I present your Lordship with a work of my vacant time, which if it had been more, the work had been better. . .'

While half of Bacon's mind was still on retiring to private life, promotion among the leading lawyers created the prospect that the solicitorship might again be vacant. Bacon thereupon wrote to Salisbury a rather cool letter, asking for his support for the place, because, he says, 'I would be glad now at last to be Solicitor, chiefly because I think it will increase my practice, wherein God blessing me a few years, I may amend my state, and so after fall to my studies and ease, whereof one is requisite for my body, and the other sorteth with my mind.'

While he was canvassing once more, he married Alice Barnham, the alderman's daughter. He was then forty-five, and she was under twenty. Such differences in age were not then uncommon, for the mortality of wives in childbirth was very severe, and many middle-aged men became widowers seeking a second wife.

The event was described by the letter-writer Carleton:

'Sir Francis Bacon was married yesterday to his young wench in Maribone Chapel. He was clad from top to toe in purple, and hath made himself and his wife such store of fine raiments of cloth of silver and gold that it draws deep into her portion. The dinner was kept at his father-in-law Sir John Packington's lodging over against the Savoy, where his chief guests were the three knights, Cope, Hicks, and Beeston; and upon this conceit (as he said himself) that since he could not have my L. Salisbury in person, which he wished, he would have him at least in his representative body.'

Few details of Bacon's married life are known. His wife seems to have had an upsetting tongue. When Bacon subsequently became Lord Chancellor it was said that his wife made much less good use of her time than Lady Ellesmere, the wife of his predecessor, and that this was because Lady Ellesmere was discreet in her remarks, whereas Lady St. Alban was 'forward'. The comparison of the two ladies was the more piquant because Lady Ellesmere had helped Bacon to get married.

In the letter in which he reveals this, Bacon incidentally remarked that the status of the legal profession had declined.

When receiving congratulations on his marriage from his cousin Sir Thomas Hobby, he replied that 'no man may better conceive the joys of a good wife than yourself, with whom I dare not compare. But I thank God I have not taken a thorn out of my foot to put it into my side. For as my state is somewhat amended, so I have no other circumstances of complaint. . . .'

The views he expressed in his essay *Of Marriage and Single Life*, are unpromising in a husband: 'He that hath wife and children hath given hostages to fortune; for they are impediments to great enterprises, either of virtue or mischief. Certainly the best works, and of greatest merit for the public, have proceeded from the unmarried or childless men; which both in affection and means have married and endowed the public. . . . Wives are young men's mistresses; companions for middle age; and old men's nurses. . . .'

After his marriage Bacon pressed harder than ever for the solicitorship. He wrote to the King, reminding him of his Parliamentary work on the Union 'the labour whereof, for men of my profession, rested most upon my hand'; on Subsidies, Ecclesiastical Petitions, Grievances, etc., and that the King had told him that such services were to be esteemed no less than those of commanders in the wars. The King had then promised him the solicitorship, but still he had heard no more of his preferment, to his 'great disgrace and discouragement'.

In 1607, at last, he was appointed to the office. It was worth about £1,000 a year. The anxieties of his financial situation were for the first time substantially relieved. But the appointment still did not raise his position in political affairs. Salisbury did not make use of him on any matters except the routine legal duties of his office.

At this time, Salisbury was already among the score of prominent Englishmen who were receiving large secret pensions from Spain. This was originally £1,000 a year, and was raised to £1,500. If this had happened in Elizabeth's reign, it would probably have been found out, and Salisbury would have been executed for treason. But under James the situation was different.

It may be that Salisbury took the pension with the connivance of James, in order to learn enemy secrets by counter-espionage. But there seems to be no evidence that it was other than what it appears to be.

It is a striking fact that the Spaniards did not bribe Bacon. Like Elizabeth, Essex and Salisbury, the Spaniards no doubt judged that he could never be theirs; that he was incapable of putting himself entirely in any other person's power; and was fundamentally incorruptible.

As he was drawn into high politics as little as possible, he had leisure for his studies. Arrangements were discussed for a translation of the *Advancement of Learning*. He wrote a letter to the proposed translator, Dr. Playfer, in which he explained what his purpose had been in writing the work, in order to persuade him to undertake the translation. 'Since I have only taken upon me to ring a bell to call other wits together, (which is the meanest office) it cannot but be consonant to my desire, to have that bell heard as far as can be. . . .'

This particular project fell through, for when Bacon saw a specimen of Playfer's translating, he found the Latin over-fine. He let it be known that he desired, so Tenison says, 'not so much neat and polite, as clear, masculine, and apt expression'. Indeed, he wanted a style like his own.

Bacon worked on the plan of his *Great Instauration*. But whether he would be the statesman of the project on behalf of mankind, or a specialist within the ranks of science, was still not decided.

26. *The Planned Life*

Bacon's appointment as Solicitor-General was followed by the reversion of the clerkship of the Star-Chamber, which came to him in 1608, nineteen years after it had been promised to him by Elizabeth. The Star-Chamber was the meeting room of the court appointed by the Privy Council, and dealt especially with legal cases involving affairs of state. The salary for the clerkship had risen to £2,000 a year, so within a period of twelve

Q

months Bacon's financial position had been transformed. But his living from hand-to-mouth, which had persisted for about a quarter-of-a-century, had established bad habits of financial management. The sudden improvement in his fortune caused him to review his situation, aims and prospects.

He spent six days on this task in the summer of 1608, and entered the results in his own writing in an intimate notebook. This survived, and was discovered by Spedding in 1848, after having been unpublished for 240 years. Bacon headed it *Commentarius Solutus*, or a book of loose notes, which he described as being 'like a merchant's waste-book; where to enter all manner of remembrance of matter, form, business, study, touching myself, service, others; either sparsim or in schedules, without any manner of restraint . . .'.

Spedding decided against the suppression or restricted publication of the notebook. Bacon's passion for frankness, which is an essential feature of his style, is one of his greatest qualities, for it underlies the possibility of giving an objective account of any phenomenon, whether of nature or himself. It is basic to a scientific view of existence.

Bacon went to immense pains in making records of his writings, letters, speeches and memoranda. One of his last acts was to make arrangements for the presentation of his papers, including those of a confidential character, which he specifically desired should not be lost, even if not published. The organization and cost of all this recording has been insufficiently appreciated. In his day there were no typewriters or tape-recorders. Everything had to be taken down by clerks, and copies made by hand. In spite of his lack of means, Bacon insisted on having everything of importance written down. He must have spent far more on secretarial assistance than he could conveniently afford. But he put mankind in his debt by doing so. If he had been punctilious over his debts, a large part of his works would almost certainly have been lost. The nineteenth century might well have preferred Bacon to have balanced his accounts, rather than have benefited the human race, but the twentieth century is tending to take the other view.

Bacon devoted about one-quarter of the book to memoranda on personal behaviour and professional advancement, another quarter to his books and scientific work, a further quarter to his fortune and finances, and one-eighth to politics and affairs. The remainder was about equally divided between two subjects in which he was particularly interested: his health and his house and garden.

He made the notes by abstracting items from earlier notebooks which were still of current interest to him. He preserved the book, in spite of its very intimate character, probably because of the notes on his plans for his scientific work, which contain a skeleton of his *Great Instauration*.

He started his first day's work with a good resolution to keep 'a stock of £2,000 always in readiness for bargains and occasions', and to make arrangements so that he could at any time easily borrow a considerable sum.

Then he proposed to 'set on foot and maintain access with his Majesty' in various ways. This was to be done through particular persons, and by presenting the King with suggestions at the beginning of active terms, when projects were to be carried out; and of vacations, when they could be food for thought. He proposed to attend some of the King's repasts, and 'fall into a course of familiar discourse'.

He would find means of privately, but not openly, winning the affections and confidence of the Scots, and try to take over the cultivation of relations with the Scots which Salisbury had formerly carried on, but no longer had time for. He made a list of Scotsmen who might be useful in this connexion.

He proposed 'to have ever in readieness matter to minister talk with every of the great counsellors respective, both to induce familiarity and for countenance in public place'. He made many notes on points by which he might improve his relations with Salisbury.

He proposed to insinuate himself 'to become privy to my Lord of Salisbury's estate', and to speak to his secretary Hicks about it. To impress Hicks he would cause the walks about the wall of his garden 'to be sanded and made handsome' against his coming. He would correspond with Salisbury 'in a habit of natural but noways perilous boldness, and in vivacity, invention, care to cost and enterprize (but with due caution . . .)' for he judged that this manner was most likely to help him to converse without inhibitions, and enable him to obtain his ends most easily. Bacon was lacking in natural cunning, so he tried to substitute artificial cunning.

He was to think of policies which he could propose in Parliament and raise his prestige by giving satisfaction to both King and people. He was to remember to renew the lease of his chambers in Gray's Inn, and this led him on to note the possibility of letting various houses.

When an elegant phrasing occurred to him, he at once jotted it down. Thus 'Death comes to young men and old men go to death.' This suggests to him that he should 'send message of compliment to my Lady Dorset the widow'.

After notes of legal work to be remembered, which would increase his reputation for efficiency, and might augment his income, he made a list of twenty-eight of his manuscript books, concerning learning, the law, and his personal affairs.

This concluded his first day's review.

He started the second day by considering how he could make the best use of this collection of papers, and what further abstractions should be made, so that related subjects could be assembled together. Then he made notes on persons who might collaborate in his plans of research, or might subscribe funds for paying for the work to be done by others.

He should cultivate the acquaintance of his nephew Edmund Bacon, who was interested in medicine and natural history. He would 'make much' of Russell, who was engaged in experiments for the government on separating silver from lead. He would collect technical information from him, and through him interest Sir Thomas Chaloner, a chemist and author of a treatise on nitre, who was governor of Prince Henry's household.

Bacon thought that he might thus in time draw the Prince into his project. He thought of 'the setting-on work my Lord of Northumberland and Ralegh, and therefore Harriot, themselves being already inclined to experiments'. Northumberland and Ralegh were prisoners in the Tower, the former having been implicated in the Gunpowder Plot. They spent some of their time in scientific pursuits.

Harriot, the eminent mathematician and astronomer, who had forestalled Galileo in some of his discoveries, besides making several other first-class discoveries, had taught Ralegh mathematics. Ralegh sent him on the expedition to Virginia, of which country he wrote a notable scientific account.

Bacon proposed to acquaint himself with Poe, one of Salisbury's doctors, 'as for my health', and thereby learn from him about his experiments in medicine, and gain 'entrance into the inner of some great persons'.

He would see and try whether he could interest the Archbishop of Canterbury in his project, 'being single and glorious, and believing the sense'. He would try to draw in another bishop, probably his old friend Lancelot Andrewes, with whom he used to discuss his ideas and work. Andrewes was James's favourite preacher. Bacon notes that he was 'single, rich, sickly, a professor to some experiments'. He thought he might be set to work on his plan for research on motion.

There was the question of which medical men might be brought into the scheme. The likeliest among the King's doctors were Paddy and Hammond.

An inquiry should be made of 'learned men beyond the seas', and 'harkening who they be that may be so inclined'.

After these notes about persons who might be drawn in, he considered pieces of research which required finishing. There were plans for research on motion, heat and sound. The aphorisms which subsequently formed the first book of *Novum Organum*, were to be finished. He was to consider publishing them in France, and to whom a dedication would be most helpful.

Bacon's shifts to secure appreciation and help for his scientific work show, as Spedding has remarked, how little authority he possessed at this period. It is said that when an early draft of his *Great Instauration* was shown to Henry Cuffe, the noted Oxford scholar executed after the Essex rebellion, Cuffe said that 'a fool could not have written it, and a wise man would not'. Subsequently, when Coke received a presentation copy of *Novum Organum* from Bacon, he wrote on the title page in Latin, 'gift from the author', and the lines:

> *It deserveth not to be read in Schooles*
> *But to be freighted in the ship of Fooles*

Then, beneath this, 'You propose to reconstruct the teaching of wise men of old. Reconstruct first our laws and justice.'

Bacon was trying to cope with these attitudes by systematic searching for interest and support. Conventional scholars thought he was a little crazy, and consequently feared becoming entangled with him. It seems probable that most men must have perceived that he was engaged in some kind of scheming, and have been exceptionally reserved with him; and the more they were reserved, the more Bacon schemed to try to get round them.

He made various notes for points which he subsequently elaborated in *Novum Organum*. Among these was his intention of 'discoursing scornfully of the philosophy of the Grecians, with some better respect to the Egyptians, Persians, Chaldees, and the utmost antiquity and the mysteries of the poets'. He was to recommend his notions by a composition 'delightful, sublime, and mixed with elegancy, affection, *novelty of conceit* and yet sensible . . .'. He would consider how 'to grift the new upon the old', that is, to express new ideas through the medium of ancient stories; a project he carried out in his *Wisdom of the Ancients*. This was one of Bacon's favourite ways of making novelty palatable.

He would secure the adoption of his method by pointing out the 'ordinary course of incompetency of reason for natural philosophy and invention of works'.

A history was to be compiled of 'the experiments and observations of all mechanical arts'. It should consist of the quantities and proportions of the materials needed, the places where they are to be found, the instruments and engines required, the use of instruments, the processes in which they are applied, and the errors to be avoided. To this should be added all observations, axioms, and directions, containing the general principles of the subject.

Bacon then noted the suggestion of 'laying for a place to command wits and pens. Westminster, Eton, Winchester, specially Trinity College in Cambridge, St. Johns in Cambridge, Maudlin College in Oxford . . .'. Presumably he considered securing the headship of one of these institutions. He made a note of 'bespeaking this betimes' with the Archbishop of Canterbury who was the Chancellor of the University of Oxford, and with Salisbury who occupied the corresponding position at Cambridge.

He had already made a note on the possibility of directing how the great fortune of the philanthropist Thomas Sutton, the founder of Charterhouse School, should be used. Bacon subsequently made strenuous efforts, which have been particularly obnoxious to Old Carthusians, to prevent the money being spent on a grammar school. Of these, he said, there were already more than enough, breeding an excess of idle clerks for whom there were an insufficient number of jobs. These unemployed men became rebellious persons, instead of industrious servants. Houses of correction for giving vocational training to apprentices, and

where 'sturdy beggars' could be 'buckled to work', were much
more necessary. But there was nothing more wanting towards
the flourishing state of learning than 'the honourable and plentiful salaries' for readers in the applied sciences and professions.
He wanted the reward to be so great that it would 'whistle for
the ablest men out of all foreign parts' to fill the chairs of English
universities.

Bacon's ·demand for a better balance between grammar and
technical education, his call for something like labour camps,
and adequate remuneration for scientists have a modern ring.
His attempts tò secure the ultilization of great fortunes for science
resemble those of the advisers who persuaded Rockefeller and
other magnates to endow foundations for research.

The diffidence that Bacon felt about his success in getting
his ideas and suggestions accepted is reflected in a note that he
should take 'a greater confidence and Authority in discourses of
this nature'.

He was not yet very much regarded, had little of the reputation of his later years, and nothing of his great posthumous fame.
He was still very far from being able to leave his notions and
works merely to speak for themselves.

Further ideas occurred to him for the achievement of the work.
There was the question of the 'young schollars in the Universities'. But, he noted in italics, these must be future scholars:
little could be expected of the present, who were quite inade-
quately taught, as he had found in his youth. This caused him to
consider how the situation could be improved. Research fellow-
ships should be instituted. Pensions should be given to four research workers, to enable them to compile the history of mechanical arts, etc. He desired the 'Foundation of a college for
Inventors. Two Galleries with statues for Inventors past and
spaces or Bases for Inventors to come. And a Library and an
Inginary.'

There was the question of 'the Order and Discipline, to be
mixed with some points popular to invite many to contribute
and join'. The 'rules and prescripts of their studies and inquiries'
were to be considered; 'allowance for travelling; allowance for
experiments. Intelligence and correspondence with the universities abroad'. The 'manner and prescripts touching Secrecy,
tradition, and publication' were to be considered.

The question of 'removes and expulsions' if, 'within a time

some Invention be not produced', was to be thought out. Research workers without talent were to be got rid of with the least inconvenience to all concerned. Suitable honours and rewards for inventions should be established.

Equipment and laboratories should be provided: 'vaults, furnaces, terraces for insolation; work houses of all sorts . . .'.

Finally, he should 'endeavour to abase the price of professory sciences and to bring in estimation philosophy or universality, —name and thing'.

He concluded his second day's review with the enumeration of fifteen heads of 'legitimate enquiries', or main divisions of research.

He spent the whole of the third day in outlining a comprehensive plan of research on motion; in astronomy, physics, chemistry and biology.

The extent of this technical section, in comparison with the amount of space devoted to his other interests, is striking. He was evidently more interested in science than in personal ambition, politics or property, and this was the centre around which the rest of his life revolved.

On the fourth day Bacon started with a series of notes on policy. The King was in danger of being brought low by poverty and empty coffers. If revolt or war came, it was more likely to start in Scotland than in England.

Bacon never published this opinion. In reference to it Spedding quotes the remarks of David Hume concerning the discontent in 1637. 'It seemed probable, therefore, that affairs might long have continued on the same footing in England, had it not been for the neighbourhood of Scotland, a country more turbulent, and less disposed to submission and obedience. It was thence the commotion first arose. . . .'

Attention should be paid to the greatness of particular subjects; for example, Salisbury was acceptable to the House of Commons. The Privy Council might become the dominant power. Bacon considered 'the order of sitting and manage of things in Council as a state'. Then there was 'the greatness of the Lower House in Parliament'.

The jurisdictions of the various courts of law should be brought into a more regular system.

Consideration should be given to 'books in commendation of monarchy mixed, or aristocracy'. He might aim to 'succeed

Salisbury, and amuse the King and Prince with pastime and glory'.

He noted members of the House of Commons worth conciliating.

The fairest policy, 'without disorder or peril, is the general persuading to King and people, and course of infusing everywhere the foundation in this isle of a monarchy in the west, as an apt seat, state, people for it; so civilizing Ireland, further colonizing the wild of Scotland. Annexing the Low Countries. . .'.

He thought of writing legal works on the authority of the Privy Council, which would impress Ellesmere and Salisbury, and other works which would be 'specially fitting for an Attorney, and make them think they shall find an alteration to their contentment over that which now is'.

Then he made detailed notes of his plans for a 'place of pleasure', a country house for summer residence. This was to be on an island in an artificial lake. The island was to be square, with 100-foot sides, and 'in the Middle thereof . . . a house for freshness with an upper gallery open upon the water, a terrace above that, and a supping room open under that a dining room, a bed chamber, a cabinet, and a room for music, a garden; in this ground to make one walk between trees; the galleries to cost northwards; nothing to be planted here but choice . . .'. He proposed to discuss all the details casually with 'my Lord of Salisbury', in order to impress him.

He subsequently carried out his plan in the construction of Verulam House in the grounds of his Gorhambury estate. The house was long an object of wonder and comment.

Then he thought of applying himself 'to be inward with my Lady Dorset', the rich widow of the former Lord Treasurer, whom he had already noted for suitable condolences. No doubt he hoped to influence the disposal of her wealth towards suitable ends.

The hunting for legacies from rich bishops, widows and merchants was one of the available methods of the period for endowing new institutions. Many of the colleges at Oxford and Cambridge had been founded in that way. There was little hope of securing funds from the King or government, as long as they were in a condition of virtually continuous insolvency, and no adequate financial system had been introduced.

After this note on Lady Dorset, he made a long entry on his

health and regimen. It seems that, like many sedentary workers, he suffered much from constipation and indigestion. 'I have found a diet to feed of boiled meat, cool salads, abstinence of wine, to do me much good, but it may not be continued for palling and weakening my stomach.' Then he 'ever had opinion that some comforting drink at four o'clock hour which is the hour of my languishing were proper for me'.

Finally, 'I have found now twice upon amendment of my fortune disposition to melancholy and distaste, specially the same happening against the long vacation when company failed and business both, for upon my Solicitor's place I grew indisposed and inclined to superstition. Now upon Mill's place I find a relapse into my old symptom as I was wont to have it many years ago, as after sleeps; strife at meats, strangeness, clouds, etc.' Bacon's uneasiness at good fortune is yet another symptom of a slightly abnormal psychology.

He concluded his fourth day's review with a detailed examination of his finances. The total income, including £220 of his wife's was £4,975; of which the biggest items were £2,000 from the Star-Chamber clerkship, £1,000 as Solicitor, and £1,200 from his legal practice. He estimated that his property and offices could be sold for £24,155, and that his debts at this time totalled £4,481. He gave a list of twenty-one considerable debts which he had 'absolutely cleared'.

On the fifth day, Bacon made notes on important current legal matters, including the limits of jurisdiction of the various courts of law. This question subsequently led to the conflict between the King and Coke, on the relations between the rights of the Royal Prerogative and the Common Law. As this struggle developed, Coke changed from his earlier attitude when, as Attorney-General, he was the watchdog of the Prerogative, into the defender of the Common Law.

Bacon made notes, too, of views recently expressed by the King on the legal treatment of Papists. He was in favour of moderation, and said that there must be 'no torrent of blood'. It seems that 'My Lord of Salisbury at that time opined that this violent proceeding of the Pope in condemning the Oath of Allegiance was to draw the King to blood, and so the people to greater despair and alienation, and foreigners to malice and quarrell, the better to expose this realm to a prey.'

Then Bacon made a list of the deficiencies of the Attorney-

General Hubbard, to whose place he aspired. Among other things he was a 'solemn goose. Stately least wise nodd crafty.' Spedding presumed this to mean that he wagged his head in a wise manner when he was most at sea. Then 'they have made him believe he is wondrous wy' (wise). Hubbard was not a very talented lawyer, and handled various official matters rather indifferently. Bacon got him 'kicked upstairs' into a place of more honour but less power, six years later, and succeeded him as Attorney-General.

After this, Bacon made notes of services that he might render to prominent persons, in order to increase their dependence on him, and his own prestige and influence.

He might 'furnish my Lord of Suffolk with ornaments for public speeches'. Suffolk, as Lord Thomas Howard, had been one of Elizabeth's admirals, and was now James's Lord Chamberlain. Bacon no doubt thought that the old salt might find a few ideas and striking phrases useful for his public speeches. He might try 'to make him think how he should be reverenced by a Lord Chancellor if I were; Princelike.' He would 'prepare him for matters to be handled in Council or before the King aforehand and to shew him and yield him the fruits of my care'.

He proposed to find out before every term what the King desired to be done, and take notes during Council sittings, with a view to providing suggestions and draft documents. He proposed on every appropriate occasion, 'fit and grateful and continual, to maintain private speech with every the great persons and sometimes drawing more than one of them together . . . specially in public places and without care or affectation'.

At the Council table, he would chiefly attempt 'to make good my Lord of Salisbury's motions and speeches, and for the rest some times one sometimes another . . .'.

He will attend to his elocution: 'to suppress at once my speaking with panting and labour of breath and voice'. He was 'not to fall upon the main too sudden but to induce and intermingle speech of good fashion'. He was to free himself 'at once from payment of formality and compliment though with some show of carelessness pride and rudeness'.

So great a speaker, at the age of forty-seven, still felt it necessary to keep these points in mind, and even write them down. The effects of Bacon's care were recorded by Ben Jonson:

'There happened in my time one noble speaker, who was full of gravity in his speaking. His language (where he could spare or pass by a jest) was nobly censorious. No man ever spake more neatly, more weightily, or suffered less emptiness, less idleness, in what he uttered. No member of his speech, but consisted of his own graces. His hearers could not cough, or look aside from him, without loss. He commanded where he spake; and had his judges angry and pleased at his devotion. No man had their affections more in his power. The fear of every man that heard him was, lest he should make an end. . . .'

The internal and the external view of the same process are here seen in their most illuminating contrast.

Bacon's uncompromising objectivity in his notes provides facts of a most valuable character, rarely obtainable without using the techniques of modern psychology. But their effect in the nineteenth century was to depress his reputation, as Anthony Trollope's was depressed by his exceptionally objective *Autobiography*.

Bacon finished the sixth day of his review with a list of his outstanding creditors, of which there were thirty-seven. Thus he ended, as he had begun, the review of the state and aims of his life with a note on money. It was the weakest point in the management of his affairs, and the review, both in its origin and contents, exhibits an awareness of his duty to put his finances in proper order, especially after becoming a rich man, with an income of about £5,000 a year. Henceforth he could not be excused for being in financial difficulties.

This six days' work is reminiscent of *Genesis*. It shows a man in the making, and preparations for the creation of the future. It ranges from dust to destiny, by the earthiest means to the noblest ends.

27. *Becoming a Statesman*

THE death of Salisbury in 1612 greatly improved the possibilities of Bacon's advancement. Bacon was not liked or trusted by James's entourage, but among its pleasure-loving and lazy members there were few to do the work of government after Salisbury's death. In two months and twenty days in 1610 Salisbury had 'directed and signed 2884 letters', besides performing his 'other continual employments'. The King tried for two years to be his own prime minister, but was gradually forced to depend more and more on Bacon's industry and competence.

Bacon never became a member of James's inner circle of intimate friends, and was treated by him as a civil servant, whose peculiar ideas did not matter so long as they did not interfere with the King's will. Bacon tried to meet this situation by providing a stream of suggestions and drafts of documents to anticipate every requirement. Often he provided more than enough, and in spite of the most determined efforts to please, many of them were not to the King's liking. Bacon accepted the rejection of proposals without resentment, and immediately replaced them with new ones which he thought might be more acceptable. He reserved emotional attachment for his intellectual interests, which he pursued in parallel with his public activities. He bore snubbing in public life because his hopes were centred in his ideas, about which he was incapable of being discouraged.

He had made a private note in 1608 that he was 'out and not favoured' by Northampton, who, with Cecil and Northumberland, had conducted the secret negotiations with James for the succession, in Elizabeth's last years. After the death of Cecil, Northampton became one of the small group which virtually governed the country. Though he did not like Bacon, he ultimately found his assistance indispensable.

The pressing need for improving the King's finances required an investigation of the administration of the customs and the sweet wines monopoly. This was carried out by Bacon, and Northampton reported that it was 'pursued extremely well by the Solicitor'. He asked that the King should show gracious approval of Bacon's 'diligence and industry' in the matter. Bacon could look after the King's finances, but not his own.

Northampton also drew the King's attention to Bacon's good work on collecting the dowry for the marriage of the Princess Elizabeth. In Salisbury's time the task would have been given to the Attorney-General, but now the Council preferred his subordinate, who was more efficient. Northampton described Bacon as 'a person very apt . . . both to apprehend and add' in the legal work involved.

Bacon described himself as having been 'as a hawk tied to another's fist' during Salisbury's time. He was treated as a state

lawyer, or a government spokesman provided with a brief, and
not as a constructive politician. He consequently acted with the
civil servant's diffidence in initiative, aiming mainly at making
the official policy work.

But this was not his natural tendency. When he had to choose
between the legalistic and the statesman-like view of a situation,
he chose the latter. The Commons had received a message purporting to be from the King, which in fact had been composed
by the Privy Council during the King's absence in the country.
The Commons refused to receive the message. Afterwards the
King asked whether they would receive a message either from
him or the Privy Council, when warranted as such by the
Speaker.

In the ensuing debate, Bacon argued that kings may be subject
to illness, or absence and other disabilities. 'In these cases, if
their council may not supply their person, to what infinite accidents do you expose them?' As for the dignity of Parliament, may
it not receive messages from the Privy Council, as the greatest
kings consent to receive them from ambassadors? In other words,
when in a crisis the chief authority is not available, the next in
authority must act without a mandate.

The most pressing political problem of the period was the
relation between Crown and Parliament. It arose most acutely
in the economic field. A tax for a subsidy to the Crown, which had
yielded £194,326 in 1558 at the beginning of Elizabeth's reign,
yielded only £124,000 at the same rate in 1606; yet the country
was much richer.

The subsidies came largely from taxes on land. The new
wealth, which had been created by the development of trade
and industry, was relatively less taxed. The government found
that its income for administering an increasing population and a
more complex social organization was becoming less and less.

The King desired to be relieved by two means; more subsidies,
and fresh taxes on the new commercial wealth. He contended that
he had the right, through the Prerogative, to impose these new
taxes on commerce without necessarily securing the prior agreement of Parliament. Salisbury tried to negotiate a bargain between the King and Parliament, by which the King's income
would increase. His proposal implied that Parliament was an
independent power, and that relations between the King and it
should be conducted more on business lines. The Commons post-

poned its decision on the proposal. Bacon could find so little to say for it that when he spoke he said at once: 'I will not blast the affections of this House with elaborate speech,' and sat down after making some perfunctory remarks about viewing the proposal with 'a great hope in the heart'.

Then came the question of the King's right to impose taxes on commerce. The Commons contained many merchants, and lawyers associated with town interests. They were vehemently opposed to the conception, because it would have allowed the King to tax commerce at will, and make himself economically independent of Parliament. In that situation he could have governed as he chose.

Bacon made the chief speeches on behalf of the Crown in the Commons. He said that the right to impose taxes was of very great importance, touching the King's prerogative on one side, and the liberty of the subject on the other. He argued that there were no legal decisions against impositions. Merchants already made payments without consent of Parliament, and the customs existed. Hitherto, impositions had been abolished only through petitions to the King. The fact that in the past impositions may have been made with the consent of Parliament did not necessarily mean that such consent was essential. It might be true that no impositions had been made for two centuries, but this did not make them illegal. The ancient records were 'reverent things, but like scarecrows'. Impositions 'reposed a special confidence in the King'. Such confidence was necessary because 'the law cannot provide for all occasions'. The King was already entrusted with the pardoning of offenders, dispensing laws, making the coinage, conducting war and making peace. Though in his opinion members had no remedy in law, they could complain through Parliament, as their ancestors had done, by petition. The King has the right to impose the tax, but the judges have the right to moderate it.

After strenuous debate, the Commons decided to condemn the imposition on imported currants, but not to raise the question of the King's right to make impositions. They made a petition for the removal of the imposition. They chose Bacon to present it to the King. Thereupon, the King abolished several unpopular impositions out of his 'mere grace', and said that he would be willing to assent to an act by which his power of making any more impositions on merchandise should be suspended. He still did

not give way on the main point of his right to make impositions.
The Commons was deeply dissatisfied. It would not vote sufficient supplies to meet his debts and expenditure, so James dissolved the Parliament.

This left Bacon with more free time for the projects outlined
in his diaries. News of Galileo's revolutionary discoveries with
improved telescopes reached him. He was stimulated to write a
description of the astronomical universe for his *Great Instauration*, and papers on the tides, and on the principles of natural
philosophy. He also prepared a second edition of his *Essays*,
which was published in 1612. It was to have been dedicated to
Prince Henry, but Henry had in the meantime died prematurely,
probably by catching typhoid fever through swimming in the
Thames. In the unused draft Bacon defined his conception of
the essay. It consists of 'certain brief notes'. The word 'essay' is
'late, but the thing is ancient'. Something of the kind is to be
found in Seneca. Bacon 'endeavoured to make them not vulgar,
but of a nature whereof a man shall find much in experience, and
little in books; so as they are neither repetitions nor fancies'.

Bacon's *Essays* are, like his science, part of his philosophy of
experience; they spring from the same root. He expanded the
number of his essays from ten in the first edition to forty in the
second, with a corresponding variety of matter. The manner
was, of course the same, and the new edition had all the more
riches for reading, but it necessarily could not have the same
impact of originality as the first edition, which appeared against
the romantic background of the literature of Marlowe and Shakespeare. The third edition of 1625 was substantially similar to
the second, but with eighteen more essays, bringing the total to
fifty-eight.

At this time, when the conflict between Crown and Commons
had become more clearly defined and absolute, and the King
more isolated than ever before, the danger to the state was patent.
Bacon chose this moment to ask the King for the reversion of the
attorneyship. He wrote that he did not wish to spend his wits
and time in the laborious place in which he served, if it did not
lead to 'those outward ornaments and inward comforts which it
was wont to have', in the shape of succession to a place of 'more
dignity and rest'.

He would rather retire from the course which he was in, and
do the King honour by writing a history of his times, or recom-

piling his laws, or some other like work. 'Perceiving how at this time preferments of the law fly about mine ears, to some above me and to some below,' he felt it would be a sign of dullness not to propound to his Majesty that which would not so much raise his fortune as settle his mind; that is, the assurance that he would receive the attorney's place. By reason of his 'slowness to sue and apprehend occasions upon the sudden', he might be in danger of being forgotten.

Bacon was told that he might expect to receive the attorney-ship in due course. In thanking the King he remarked that he had known an Attorney Coke, and an Attorney Hubbard, both worthy men and far above himself, but if he did not find a middle way between their two dispositions and carriage, he would not be satisfied with himself. With regard to the succession, he wished no man's death, nor very much his own life, except to do the King's service. 'I account my life the accident, and my duty the substance.'

After the death of Salisbury Bacon drafted several letters of offers and suggestions to the King, which may or may not have been sent, but reveal his thoughts. He said that the King had in Salisbury lost a great subject and a great servant. But if he should praise him in propriety, he should say 'that he was a fit man to keep things from growing worse but no very fit man to reduce things to be much better. For he loved to have the eyes of all Israel a little too much upon himself, and to have all business still under the hammer and like clay in the hands of the potter, to mould it as he thought good. . . .' He was greater in the processes of business than in the achievement of works. Bacon now advised the King that the most important business of the moment was the calling of a new Parliament, 'for two effects: the one for the supply of your estate; the other for the better knitting of the hearts of your subjects unto your Majesty, according to your infinite merit; for both which, Parliaments have been and are the ancient and honourable remedy'.

As one with a little Parliamentary skill who was a 'perfect and peremptory royalist' and yet 'never one hour out of credit with the lower house', and has always wished that the King's causes should not only prevail, but 'prevail with satisfaction of the inner man', he asked whether the King would give him leave to propound unto him 'some preparative remembrances touching the future Parliament'.

R

If his Majesty found any aptness in him, he might think it
fit to remove him to 'business of state'. He made a 'most humble
oblation' of himself; his heart had not been in his profession:
'for my life hath been conversant in things wherein I take little
pleasure . . .'.

The King and the small group of ruling ministers began to
make use of Bacon in executing the Privy Council's business. He
immediately introduced improvements in administration. He
arranged that the King should sign a few major documents only,
and all subsidiary documents should be signed by the Council.
He was always in favour of taking the utmost pains to make
administrative machinery work. In politics Bacon was primarily
an adviser and administrator. In science he was a leader, and
brought to it the understanding of administration that he had
learned in politics.

The King requested Bacon to consider how the revenue from
his lands could be increased. He replied that it required a great
deal of consideration and judgment. Bacon worked very hard
on the attempt to make the management of the King's lands more
businesslike. Among the many details considered, he recommended that control over the King's wastes and commons should
be retained, as they were a potential source of much wealth
through enclosure and agricultural improvement.

Bacon also considered the desirability of establishing a bank
for financing trade, but reported against it on the ground that
trade was carried out mainly by the 'younger sort of merchants'
on the basis of credit, who could get better terms for private
loans from friends, than from a bank to which their financial
situation and business affairs would have to be revealed.

Generally, the King was advised to refrain from touching
trade and industry, and to lease various activities to private
interests, as 'profit is like to be improved by private industry'.
The King should not descend to any means which were not
consonant with his majesty and greatness. 'He is gone from whom
those courses did wholly flow.' Salisbury had published details
of the King's financial affairs which should have remained private,
and had enabled 'worms of aldermen to lend for ten in the hundred upon good assurance'.

After reviewing the management of the King's estates, Bacon
investigated the administration of the customs, and the tax on
wines. He reported that 'The deceits of eight years' were

examined 'in the like or less number of days', and revealed such frauds as could not be looked back upon without 'a great deal of grief'.

The King was informed of the 'diligence and industry' of his 'two faithful and painful servants', the Solicitor and Serjeant, 'whereby the great mass is now digested into that order that may seem best' to the King's service.

Debates on reform in the navy provided Bacon with occasion to discuss the limits within which a lawyer may give advice to a client. He contended that a lawyer who advised a 'jesuitical papist' that the acts of Parliament during the reigns of Elizabeth and James were void because there were no lawful bishops sitting in the Lords, was guilty of high treason. So also a lawyer who advises 'a tribunitious popular spirit' that the oath of allegiance is to the kingdom and crown only, and not to the king, he too will be in danger of treason.

'The privilege of giving counsel protects not all opinion.' It is necessary for the lawyer not to be blind, for 'counsel is the blind man's guide', and it is unfortunate when the blind lead the blind.

Bacon regarded attacks on the prerogative as attacks on the supreme authority in the state, and hence subversive. Lawyers giving advice based on a subversive ideology could not, in his opinion, be protected by the principle that a lawyer's advice to his client is confidential and secret.

Bacon drew up a list of his arguments for persuading the King to call a Parliament. It was the ordinary remedy to supply the King's needs. It made no great difference to the King's reputation abroad whether they saw that he was in need, and Parliament refused to help him, or that they saw he dare not call a Parliament. The King was on better terms with his people than formerly, because 'Salisbury and Dunbar have drawn much envy in a chariot into the other world.' The government had not acted harshly, and the King had shown himself a champion of justice in insisting that a nobleman should not escape the consequences of having committed a premeditated murder. The opposition party had been disorganized by death, the prospects of ministerial appointments, and the King's princely temper in not persecuting or disgracing them, and at the same time not advancing them. The refractoriness of the last Parliament was due mainly to a bad presentation of the King's needs, and to influence from outside.

Any man who opposes the calling of Parliament is 'exposed to the imputation that he is creating or nourishing diffidence between the King and his people'. Finally, he supposed that good or evil would not follow so much from the calling or not calling of a Parliament, as from the policy the King pursued in relation to Parliament.

Bacon then noted twenty points for consideration in drafting such a policy. These should include the questions of measures in hand for improving the King's estate which do not draw upon taxation; the conduct of preliminary propaganda, so that members may attend in an interested and hopeful frame of mind; gracious and plausible laws 'for the comfort and contentment of the people'; the bridling, or winning, of lawyers to the King's causes; the rally of members for the town, and the prevention of splits among the courtiers, some of whom in the last Parliament were against the King. Consideration should be given to what policy should be pursued in order to disintegrate the popular party, by causing divisions, intimidating them, or by holding out hopes, so that they may be 'dissolved, weakened or won'. The judges should be put on the alert with regard to legal questions that might be raised in Parliament. Persons of 'gravity, discretion, temper, and ability to persuade' should be sought as prospective members, who could be brought into the House 'without labouring or packing'. Conversely, steps should be taken to keep back from the House, similarly without 'labouring and packing', persons who were 'violent and turbulent'. Nevertheless, the best use should be made of boroughs for placing 'well affected and discreet persons' in the Commons. This, apparently, was not 'packing'!

Methods of suppressing abuses in elections should be considered. These might be used to keep out some 'that think themselves assured of places'. All of these manoeuvres were to be managed so that they caused no scandal, but produced a Parliament 'truly free and not packed against the King'. It was necessary to consider how to 'make men perceive that it is not safe to combine and make parties in Parliament, but that men be left to their consciences and free votes'. Care should be taken to prevent magnates outside Parliament from influencing its proceedings. Consideration should be given to the stiffening of the Commons with privy councillors. It would be hard to steer its business through conferences with the House of Lords, as in

Salisbury's time, for he 'had a kind of party in both houses'. The King should indicate that the Parliament would not last for too long a time, so that members would be impelled to get on with business; and finally, a suitable candidate for Speaker should be held in mind.

On the basis of these notes Bacon wrote a letter of advice to the King, emphasizing the importance of the way in which he handled Parliament, and that 'a Parliament simply in itself is not to be doubted'. His Majesty should 'put off the person of a merchant and contractor and rest upon the person of a King'. He should approach the new Parliament in an experimental spirit, being prepared to try various things. 'Until your Majesty have tuned your instrument you will have no harmony. I, for my part, think it a thing inestimable to your Majesty's safety and service, that you once part with your Parliament with love and reverence.' He should indicate that it would be held to deal with not merely money but other important matters, such as the increase of trade, the rationalization of the laws, and the colonization of Ireland, on which Bacon had already supplied suggestions which led to the development of Ulster.

In the summer of 1613, the Lord Chief Justice died. Bacon wrote yet again to the King, mentioning that he was already fifty-two and had laboured for seven years as Solicitor-General, 'one of the painfullest places' in the kingdom. He hoped for a step forwards to 'a place either of more comfort or more ease'. He followed this with a scheme for removing Coke from his place as Chief Justice of the Common Pleas to be Lord Chief Justice, the Attorney-General Hubbard to succeed Coke, and himself to succeed Hubbard.

As Chief Justice of the Common Pleas Coke dealt with cases of conflict between the subject and the King. He had become an ardent supporter of the common law against the prerogative, and consequently his judgments were often opposed to the desires of the King and government. Bacon suggested that his promotion to be Lord Chief Justice, where he would be dealing with criminal rather than civil cases, might be seen as 'a kind of discipline to him for opposing himself in the King's causes, the example whereof will contain others in awe'. If Coke's hope of becoming a member of the Privy Council, which was then the aim of every man in public life, was raised but not satisfied, he could be made to 'turn obsequious'.

James accepted Bacon's plan. However, he went beyond Bacon's advice in appointing Coke a member of the Privy Council immediately, instead of keeping him in suspense.

Bacon became Attorney-General in the autumn of 1613. He had at last achieved a position of some influence. But his promotion was not popular. Chamberlain reported that 'there is a strong apprehension that little good is to be expected of this change, and that Bacon may prove a dangerous instrument'.

Coke was extremely reluctant to leave his favourite place, where he had done so much to oppose the King through his interpretation of the common law. When he met Bacon afterwards, he railed at him, saying, 'Mr. Attorney, all this is your doing.' He wept when he took leave of his fellow judges of the common pleas.

But Coke's appointment to the Privy Council had the effect of giving the leading spokesman of the common law a platform within the chief council of the state. Coke interpreted the common law in favour of the new men of property, the improving landlords, the merchants and capitalists who were the core of the opposition to James and his principle of royal authority. Thus James placed this formidable opponent within his own executive committee. But the immediate effect was to discomfit Coke.

Bacon now raised his sights still higher. The King's favourite, Rochester, married Lady Frances Howard, who had been divorced by her husband, the Earl of Essex. Bacon organized a masque at Gray's Inn in honour of the marriage, which cost him more than £2,000. Subsequently, he found himself as Attorney-General having to prosecute the Rochesters as murderers.

His first work as Attorney-General was in the suppression of duelling, which had become a fashionable vice. He had a passionate hatred of romantic stupidity, naturally considering that the intellect as a weapon was incomparably superior to the sword. When he spoke on this subject, his style became unselfconscious, and showed his deep feeling about it. He personally conducted the prosecution of two duellers, and arranged that his presentation of the case should be published, to explain the illegality of duelling, and to act as a warning against it.

28. *Friendship*

WHILE Bacon was struggling to secure political place and influence, he allowed nothing to interfere with his friendships, which were few but deep. He described himself as 'a most unfortunate man' when two friends with whom he could 'freely and safely communicate', and who were no 'stage friends', died within a brief interval.

Intellectual discussion was at the heart of his happiness. He found this among the lawyers and scholars who lived about the inns of court. One of his intimate friends was the lawyer Jeremiah Bettenham of Gray's Inn, who died in 1609. Bacon's relations with him happen to be known because he was one of his executors. In a letter dealing with his estate, Bacon writes of the grief he felt at his departure. 'For in good faith I never thought myself at better liberty than when he and I were by ourselves together.' He erected in his memory an octagonal seat covered with a roof, among the elm trees in the gardens of Gray's Inn, under which they had so often strolled and discussed, in understanding and affection. Bacon placed on the memorial an inscription recording his friend's virtues.

His chief friend seems to have been Toby Matthew, the son of an archbishop of York. Toby was born in 1577, and was sixteen years Bacon's junior. He was educated at Oxford, where he made an impression as an orator and disputant. He was eighteen when he played in the *Device* at Gray's Inn. He came in conflict with his father, who was severe, and was out of sympathy with his mother, who inclined to Puritanism. He was elected M.P. for Cornwall in 1601, and at about this time Bacon became intimate with him. When Bacon was returned for three constituencies in the Parliament of 1604, he arranged for Matthew to sit as his substitute for St. Albans, as he preferred to sit for Ipswich himself.

Matthew received permission in 1604 to go abroad for three years. He promised his parents that he would not go beyond

France, but he went to Florence, where he met English Catholics. They acquainted him with a Protestant's account of having witnessed the liquefaction of the blood of St. Januarius. This shook Toby's religious beliefs. He went on to Rome and met the famous Jesuit, Robert Parsons, and was received by a cardinal. After this, he returned to Florence, where he cut himself off from English people, and lived 'freely and dissolutely' in a small house.

He was converted to Roman Catholicism, and returned to England in 1607. He first went to see Bacon, to seek his advice on what he should do with regard to his change of faith. Bacon appears to have advised him to lay his case before the Archbishop of Canterbury, as the highest authority on questions of doctrine. Archbishop Bancroft listened to him, and then committed him to prison; probably in the form of detention in Lambeth Palace. He was permitted to visit Bacon at will, accompanied by a warder, while his case was under consideration. He was given hope that he would soon be set at liberty.

During these visits, Bacon discussed some of the scientific and historical works that he had recently composed. He lent Matthew manuscripts, which he asked him not to leave with others because they were to be first censured by him, and then considered again by himself. 'The thing which I expect most from you is, that you read it carefully over by yourself; and make some little note in writing, where you think (to speak like a critic) . . .' that the author had nodded and overlooked himself, or had indulged his favourite themes, 'or where, in fine, I give any manner of disadvantage to myself'. He was asked to note 'all such words and phrases' as he could not like, for he knew: 'In how high account I have your judgment.'

Matthew's case was referred to the King, who decided that it would be sufficient for him to take the oath of allegiance. Matthew felt unable to do this, and was consequently committed to the Fleet prison. Bishop Lancelot Andrewes, Sir Edwin Sandys, Dr. John Donne, the poet, and others visited him there, attempting to reconvert him, but without success.

Bacon wrote to him in prison: 'Do not think me forgetful or altered towards you. But if I should say I could do you any good, I should make my power more than it is. . .' He had no doubt that he had been 'miserably abused' when he was 'first seduced', but what he took in compassion, others might take in severity. 'I pray God, that understandeth us all better than we understand one another, contain you (even as I hope he will) at the least within the bounds of loyalty to his Majesty, and natural piety towards your country.' He asked him to meditate on the 'extreme effects of superstition' exhibited in the Gunpowder Plot. 'Good Mr. Matthews, receive yourself back from these courses of perdition.'

Bacon in fact interceded for him, and secured his release. Matthew was called before the Privy Council, admonished, and ordered to leave the country within six weeks.

Matthew's exile caused the two friends to correspond, and thus write down their opinions on topics which they would otherwise have generally discussed in conversation. Bacon wrote that he was glad to receive from him 'matter both of encouragement and advertisement' on his writings. He did not aim at making them appeal to the present times, as they would thereby be 'the less like to last'.

He described two letters of his as 'already walking towards' him. If only they could meet, it would not matter whether their letters went astray. He was glad of his approaches, and would be even more glad to be 'an agent' for his presence, for he had himself been a 'patient' through his absence. 'As my trust with the state is above suspicion, so my knowledge both of your loyalty and honest nature will ever make me show myself your faithful friend without scruple. . . .' He sent him copies of his *Advancement*, for which Matthew had asked, but added: 'My *Instauration* I reserve for our conference; it sleeps not.' He valued Matthew's 'own reading' of his writings, rather than his 'publishing them to others'.

He had scribbled to him in extreme haste he knew not what, which therefore would be the less affected, and for that very reason will not be esteemed the less. He had sent him copies of his memorials of *Julius Caesar* and of *Elizabeth*. It seems that Matthew preferred the *Caesar*. Bacon replied by quoting the opinions of friends in the English Embassy in Paris in favour of the *Elizabeth*. He did not do this for his 'own glory, but to show what variety of opinion rises from the disposition of several readers. And I must confess my desire to be, that my writings should not court the present time, or some few places, in such sort as might make them either less general to persons, or less permanent in future ages. As for the *Instauration*, your so full approbation thereof I read with much comfort, by how much more my heart is upon it, and by how much less I expected consent in a matter so obscure. Of this I can assure you, that though many things of great hope decay with youth (and multitude of civil businesses is wont to diminish the price, though not the delight, of contemplations), yet the proceeding in that work doth gain with me upon my affection and desire, both by years and businesses. . . .'

In the matter of *Elizabeth*, 'I will not question whether you be to pass for a disinteressed man or no; I freely confess myself am not. . . .' He was very glad of Matthew's approbation of his other writings, especially because it concurred with the opinion of others, else he might have conceived that affection had increased it above his neat and free judgment.

Bacon told Matthew that he would not be moved by the opposition of churchmen to his work, though he was prepared to give it a just respect, so long as he had not to go too far about to 'fetch a fair wind'. He thought the opposition would not arise from theological grounds, but through the excessive involvement of theologians in Aristotelianism. He saw 'that controversies of religion must hinder the advancement of sciences'.

Bacon described himself as like the miller of Huntingdon, who, grinding by the aid of a water wheel, 'was wont to pray for peace amongst the willows; for while the winds blew, the windmills wrought, and the water-mill was less customed'.

He prayed Matthew 'to believe that your liberty in giving opinion of those writings which I sent you, is that which I sought, which I expected, and which I take in exceeding good part; so good as that it makes me recontinue, or rather continue, my hearty wishes of your company here, that so you might use the same liberty concerning my actions which you now exercise concerning my writings . . .'.

Bacon's desire for an understanding critic of his actions is very significant, and all the more remarkable for being addressed to an exiled Catholic, that is, a follower of an opposing ideology. Bacon was aware that he did not understand his own behaviour as fully as he should. He knew that his actions were influenced by motives which he could not fully identify. In his youth he probably received a great deal of help in this way from Anthony. After his brother's death, he must have missed his understanding criticism and companionship greatly, and this may have made him turn to Toby Matthew. His willingness to listen to the criticisms of a convert to the opposition is a sign of his courage, breadth of mind and fundamental honesty.

Fourteen years later, in the agony of his fall, Bacon spoke again of the value of a candid friend for criticizing his actions, and in fact explaining himself to himself. In that testing time, Matthew tranquilly stood by him as he had stood by Matthew during his spiritual crisis. After this experience, and at Matthew's request, he extended his essay on *Friendship*, for the final edition of the *Essays*.

While Matthew was in exile he happened to meet in France a poor young gentleman named George Villiers, who was then quite obscure and had not come to the King's notice. After Villiers had become the King's favourite, he was persuaded to add his support to requests that Matthew should be allowed to return. This was permitted in the autumn of 1617, after Matthew had been abroad nearly ten years, and Bacon had become Lord Keeper. Matthew regarded his return as due primarily to Bacon's intercession, and was his guest while he remained in England.

Matthew's father had in the meantime assisted Bacon to achieve one of his dearest desires by leasing to him the house where he was born, York House in the Strand. Matthew stayed with him at York House and at Gorhambury. The consideration with which Bacon treated him was so great that it became a subject of gossip. Chamberlain reported that one in Bacon's office should not behave so to a man of such opinions, and that 'former private familiarity should give place to public respects'. Bacon could be inflexible on matters of principle.

In 1618 Matthew wrote a dedication of the Italian translation of the *Essays* and the *Wisdom of the Ancients* to the Grand Duke of Tuscany, in which he said of Bacon that 'having had the honour to know him for many years as well when he was in his lesser fortunes as now that he stands at the top and in the full flower of his greatness, that I never yet saw any trace in him of a vindictive mind, whatever injury were done him, nor ever heard him utter a word to any man's disadvantage which seemed to proceed from personal feelings against the man, but only (and that too very seldom) from judgment made of him in cold blood. It is not his greatness that I admire, but his virtue: it is not the favours I have received from him (infinite though they be) that have thus enthralled and enchained my heart, but his whole life and character. . . .'

Matthew described him as a man sweet in conversation, grave in judgments, unchanging in fortunes, and splendid in expenses.

At about this time, Matthew was the intermediary through whom two of the gifts of money to Bacon, which were subsequently condemned as bribes, was made.

After Bacon's fall and sentence, Matthew sent him a very sympathetic letter, to which Bacon replied that it had the quality of 'old gold' and said that 'Your company was ever of contentment to me, and your absence of grief: but now it is of grief upon grief.'

Matthew had been ordained a priest by Cardinal Bellarmine in Rome in 1617. After he returned to England, it was reported that he visited Gondomar nightly. He continued to refuse to take the oath of allegiance, and the King banished him again in 1619. He was allowed to return once more in 1621, and was in touch with Buckingham's mother, who became a Catholic. In 1623 he gave James secret information of a scheme for creating titular Roman Catholic archbishoprics in England. Through this, he gained James's confidence, and was sent to Madrid to advise Charles in his *incognito* visit with Buckingham, to secure the Infanta's hand in marriage.

Charles wrote to his father that 'littel prittie Tobie Matthew' had made 'a pictur of the Infanta's drawen in black and white'. He prayed him to 'let none lafe at it but yourself and honnest Kate' (the Duchess of Buckingham). 'Honnest Kate' subsequently wrote that while she had not seen it, 'I do immagen what a rare pesce it is being of his doing.'

Matthew was knighted in 1623 at Royston. His father then softened towards him and invited him to York. Toby went, and tried to convert the Archbishop to Roman Catholicism.

In 1633 the French Ambassador in London reported to Paris that Toby Matthew was the cleverest of the Catholic seminarists. He was 'a man of parts, active, influential, an excellent linguist'. He penetrated cabinets and insinuated himself into all affairs, knew the temper and purpose of those who governed the kingdom, and had the Lord Treasurer in the hollow of his hand, accomplishing through him his schemes for Spain.

Matthew was banished yet again in 1640, and died at Ghent in 1655. During his sojourns abroad he received in allowances from his parents altogether £14,000. He was described as the most 'Italianate' Englishman of his time. Harrington said he was 'likely for learning, memory, sharpness of wit, and sweetness of behaviour'. Sir John Suckling described him as 'whispering nothing into somebody's ear', and Horace Walpole as 'one of those heteroclite animals who finds his place anywhere'.

Such was Bacon's closest friend. Toby Matthew helped him, but had not the qualities which were necessary to save him from his particular kind of personal disaster.

29. *The Ladder of State*

As Attorney-General, Bacon ascended the ladder of state with increased confidence, proposing policies, drafting documents, flattering the King and his favourites, soliciting the highest ministerial office, like an agile, strong and indefatigable climber.

The chief political problem continued to be the provision of finance for the government of the country. Economic power was passing to the House of Commons, which contained the spokesmen of the new commerce. The current monarchical framework and theory of government became less and less fitted to the economic situation. James tried to resolve the contradiction by an extension of the ancient principle of royal authority. According to his view, kings were God's deputies. They were qualitatively different from other men, such as members of the Commons. When this had been clearly explained and understood, difficulties would disappear. Relations between king and parliament would be reduced to discussions on quantities, such as amounts of money, and would not be concerned with questions of principle.

James attempted to justify his theory of kingship by researches in history and theology. Like Coke, he sought the justification of his point of view by an appeal to the past; James and Coke were in effect apologists for two different social groups. The King's group was the nobility, a considerable part of which was related to him by descent. Coke became the spokesman of the new acquisitive men of business, of whom he was himself one of the wealthiest.

Bacon did not belong to either group. He never gained the confidence of the nobility and blood-relations around the King. His only means of confidential access was through John Murray, a gentleman of the bedchamber.

His differences with Coke were fundamental, both ideologically and temperamentally. Coke had a talent for rationalizing his interests. His remarkable power of finding excuses, good, bad and indifferent for justifying the causes in which he was personally interested, and his great natural aptitude for the conduct of business hampered and angered Bacon who followed an isolated and individual policy in which he was not emotionally identified with either group. Bacon gave James full support in his struggle for the prerogative because he identified it with the principle of social authority: 'The lawful authority of sovereign kings, which is God's ordinance for the comfort of human society.' He was opposed to Coke's attempt to transfer social authority from the head of the state to business men, through tendentious interpretations of the accumulated common law of the last thousand years.

Bacon's reasons for supporting the prerogative were not the same as James's. He did not share his ideas or tastes. While he excused the King's addiction to field sports, and denounced poaching, in order to indulge the royal tastes, he recommended a policy of agricultural development which would automatically have circumscribed the scope for hunting.

And yet, while James never gave him full confidence, Bacon did not identify himself with the other side. He placed his abilities at the service of the King's favourites, first Somerset and then Buckingham, as the most practicable means of carrying out the King's affairs, but he was always ready to detach himself from them, as from Essex, when they were no longer of political use. No doubt none of these men fully confided in Bacon because they were aware that he was not theirs. The only important personage to whom he seems to have been emotionally attached was Lord Chancellor Ellesmere, the former Sir Thomas Egerton, an eminent lawyer of exemplary character and a passionate royalist, without much taste for politics. Bacon's dearest wish was to succeed Ellesmere; nevertheless, after visiting Ellesmere when he was dangerously ill, he wrote: 'I was with him yesterday almost half an hour. He used me with wonderful tokens of kindness. We both wept, which I do not often.'

Bacon's affections could triumph over his deepest personal ambition, but they were 'not often' involved. The pattern of his relations with nearly all persons was dictated by policy. After securing the attorneyship he worked for the highest attainable position in the state with unfaltering consistency.

By the beginning of 1614, James became convinced that he could no longer avoid calling another Parliament. A group of politicians who regarded themselves as royalists but also sympathized with the opponents of government policy undertook to manage the House of Commons, so that the King should receive his necessary revenue, and the Commons at the same time be satisfied. Their only condition was that they should be given a free hand.

Bacon recommended that discussions with the 'Undertakers' should be pursued, in order to compile a suitable legislative programme. Nearly fifty subjects for bills were drawn up, covering the removal of feudal anomalies, the suppression of piracy, the encouragement of trade and commerce, the better administration of justice, the extension of colonization, etc.

In the ensuing general election, three out of every five members elected had not sat in Parliament before; they were exceptionally young and inexperienced. James could no longer avoid appointing a chief minister to lead the House. He chose Sir Ralph Winwood, a diplomat who had lived abroad, and had had no previous Parliamentary experience. A more complete demonstration of the contrast between James's conception of politics as the personal action of the head of the state, and Bacon's as the management of interests, could scarcely be imagined.

The appointment of Winwood increased James's dependence on Bacon for expert advice, especially on the management of Parliament. Bacon provided him with elaborate notes for his speech from the throne. The essence of them was that members were called upon 'not to bargain, nor to declaim, or to make long and eloquent orations, but to give counsel and consent in the hard and important causes of the Kingdom'.

In particular, provision should be made for the King's recently-born grandchild, which strengthened the future descent of the Crown. Next, provision should be made for the Crown, and for the people. While the need for money was very pressing in war, it could also be very pressing in peace, as at present. It was needed for negotiations with foreign powers, and the conduct of home affairs. Lack of it upset 'the very *economic*' by preventing the Crown from conducting business affairs under the most advantageous circumstances.

But the King would not speak to his Parliament in 'the language of an Accountant', or of a Merchant 'crying his royalties for sale', or of a tyrant in case they would not supply him. He preferred to rest upon their affections, rather than give them orders. While he wished it to be understood that he would not quit 'any point of his just power', he wanted to make it clear, contrary to rumour, that he was in favour of holding parliaments. He would be in favour of yearly parliaments, except for the danger that they might be regarded as a device for securing more money.

When James came to make his speech he followed Bacon's points, but expressed them in his own style, so that they became personal, and in some degree ridiculous. He said it was to be 'the Parliament of Love'. In his delivery, the politic content of Bacon's advice, with its due consideration of the needs of the business classes, had evaporated. James was of Scottish feudal origin, and had no grasp of the rôle of the productive forces in the state.

Bacon was returned for three separate constituencies, including the University of Cambridge, but when he sought to take a seat in the House, opposition was raised on the ground that it was not customary for the Attorney-General to be a member. After discussion, it was agreed that he should be allowed to sit, but that this decision should not be regarded as a precedent. The opposition feared his influence in the Commons on behalf of the Crown, and acquiesced in his membership only because they believed that the conduct of the forthcoming bills granting concessions to them would be in his hands.

The delay in taking his seat prevented him from facilitating the reception of the King's proposals, which did not start well. An opposition speaker was quick to point out that they tended to the advantage of 'the gentility, not to cities, boroughs, burgesses or merchants'.

Winwood, new to the House, started by asking for money, not knowing that this was without precedent in time of peace. Bacon tried to retrieve the situation as soon as he was able to sit. He asked members 'to consider what hangeth over us, viz. danger; what upon us, Want . . . a state environed by envious foreigners on the one part, and encroachments on matter of trade on the other side, and religion so much questioned, our peace may flatter us, not secure us.—The state of Europe never so dark.— To look a year before him, trouble the best watchman in Europe. —Provision of arms for travelling in the night, as well as going to war.—What treaty with strangers for wrongs, but basely on our part, and gloriously of their part, while we in wants?'

The House still would not proceed to discuss the question of finance. They were extremely concerned about the 'Undertakers', and appointed a committee to draft a protestation against them, for what shall be done for the King 'shall be merely out of the love of the whole House to him'. The 'Undertakers' were denounced as more dangerous than the 'powder-traitors who would have blown us up by force', for they were destroying the House in a more subtle way, by perverting its machinery. If they succeeded, a group of self-appointed men would have secured control of the government and superseded Parliament.

Bacon presently joined in the debate with a major speech. He said he had not spoken earlier because he had not fully grasped what all the commotion was about. 'I do not love to offer at that that I do not thoroughly conceive. That private men should undertake for the Commons of England! why, a man mought as well undertake for the four elements. It is a thing so giddy, and so vast, as cannot enter into the brain of a sober man. And specially in a new Parliament; when it was impossible to know who should be of the Parliament: and when all men, that know never so little the constitutions of this House, do know it to be so open to reason, as men do not know when they enter into these doors what mind themselves will be of, until they hear things argued and debated. . . .'

The accents are the same as in his early speeches, which brought him into collision with Elizabeth: the conception of the House of Commons as a creative social institution, capable of arriving by debate at conclusions of a new character, which could not have been foreseen.

He said he had heard of 'undertakings' of various kinds. For instance, some Undertakers had engaged to discover the North West passage. 'Must there be a new passage found for the King's business by a point of the compass that was never sailed by before?' Or must some forts be built in the House, by which it may be commanded and contained? For his part, he knew but of

S

the forts of affection and of reason, by which this might properly be done.

He agreed with the opinion of those who held 'that it is not a particular party that can bind the House'. Any man who raised rumours that it was 'a packed Parliament; to the end nothing may be done . . .', had been engaged in 'engines and devices nought, malign, and seditious'.

He thought an investigation into alleged 'undertaking' would be a useless work. As for 'protestations, and professions, and apologies, I never found them very fortunate; but they rather increase suspicion than clear it'.

Presently the House considered the still more vexed question of the impositions by the Crown of taxes on merchandise. The House was almost unanimously of the opinion that the Crown had no legal right to levy these taxes without the consent of Parliament. Notwithstanding Bacon's position as the King's Attorney, he was nominated as one of those to present their case against the impositions. As this would involve him in arguments against some of the King's strongest prejudices, it is an example of the Commons' confidence in Bacon, though some no doubt voted for him on the consideration that in this rôle Bacon could do the minimum harm to the opposition. In accepting the part, Bacon said it was 'an argument of their good opinion'. The 'trust in his person discharged the suspicion of his place'. He probably considered it would be to the King's advantage, if one of his spokesmen took part in presenting the House's case against the impositions when their defence was impracticable.

However, the House of Lords refused to join in a conference on the matter, so Bacon was not called upon to present the case.

A rumour arose that the conference had been prevented by a bishop, who had said that the Commons were meddling in a matter in which they had no right.

This provoked more angry resentment in the Commons, which in turn increased the King's annoyance. He sent a peremptory message that unless they attended to his wants, Parliament would be dissolved. Yet more angry speeches ensued, complaining of Popish plots to wreck Parliament, the undue influence of Scots and other personages about the Court, described as 'spaniels to the King and wolves to the people'. The sittings were 'many times more like a cock-pit than a grave Council, and many sat there that had been more fit to have been among the roaring boys than in that assembly'.

Bacon kept out of all this, and spoke little. Parliament was duly dissolved, possibly through the influence of the Earl of Northampton, and others who wished it to fail, so that the King could be driven into some sort of dictatorship. Bacon was opposed on principle to conflict between Crown and Parliament, and considered the first aim of statesmanship was to propound and execute a policy in which each would have their proper rôle, and act together in harmony.

The attempts of ecclesiastics to interfere with proceedings in Parliament had exacerbated religious conflict. Some unpublished writings of a Puritan preacher called Peacham came to the King's notice. In them were references to situations which might lead to the execution of the King and the rising of the people. James suspected that these were connected with a real plot for his assassination, and ordered Peacham to be interrogated. If he was obstinate, then he was to be put 'to the manacles'. As Attorney-General, it was Bacon's duty to participate in this interrogation. It was carried out by Winwood, the chief minister, and seven other high officers of state of whom Bacon was one. The aim of most of the questions was to discover whether there was a plot, and whether Peacham had accomplices. Winwood wrote in his own hand at the end of the official report of the interrogation, signed by the eight officers, including Bacon, that Peacham had been 'examined before torture, in torture, between tortures, and after torture'. But notwithstanding this, 'nothing could be drawn from him'.

Bacon held that torture 'in the highest cases of treason, for discovery' was legal. He did not consider that confessions extracted by torture were of value as evidence in a court of law, for they could be retracted. But a discovery made through torture might afterwards be confirmed by other evidence arising out of it, which was of a legitimate character. He was fond of the Latin adage that 'the torture of laws is worse than the torture of men'.

The King asked for the judges' opinion whether there was a good case in law against Peacham. As the judges were apt to defer to Coke's superior will and ability when consulted collectively, he apparently conceived the idea of consulting them individually, so that none should be overawed by Coke. Bacon was directed to carry out this plan. He reported to the King that he immediately found 'an encounter in the opinion of my Lord Coke, who seemed to affirm that such particular and (as he called it) *auricular* taking of opinions was not according to the custom of this realm; and seemed to divine that his brethren would never do it'.

Bacon pointed out to the judges that it was their duty to follow the King's direction and that Coke should 'leave his brethren to their own answers'. He arranged that other learned counsel should individually ask the judges whether they were ready to read the papers. He took it for granted that they would agree. After they had each given their opinions, he would himself see Coke.

Under Coke's influence the judges were beginning to show the solidarity of a party in the state. This was contrary to Bacon's conception of the judges' rôle.

Coke now repeated to Bacon his view 'that Judges were not to give opinion by fractions, but entirely according to the vote whereupon they should settle upon conference; and that this auricular taking of opinions, single and apart, was new and dangerous'.

Bacon replied that it was reasonable 'for a king to consult with his judges, either assembled or selected, or one by one'. He compared it to a consultation with the Privy Council when the King might ask any of its members to give his opinion apart and in private. Coke answered that a court of law was not like the Council, because it concerned life. Bacon replied 'that questions of estate might concern thousands of lives, and many things more precious than the life of a particular, as war and peace and the like'.

Coke now asked for time to study the Peacham papers, and 'took a pen and took notes' of Bacon's analysis of the case. When Coke gave his opinion, it 'amounted in effect to this—that no words of scandal or defamation, importing that the King was utterly unworthy to govern, were treason, except they disabled his title'.

Peacham was subsequently prosecuted, and convicted of high treason, but he was not executed, dying in captivity.

Coke's action in the Peacham affair, though not immediately successful, advanced the idea of the separation of the administration of justice from the political administration of the state.

The reduction of contact between the king and the judges sub-sequently enabled the latter to develop a political ideology which was different from that of the head of the state. This was of great help to Parliament in its struggle against the Prerogative.

Later on, however, after Parliament had established its supremacy, the separation of law and politics was no longer in its favour. But instead of again defining their relationship, their separation was continued as a social fiction.

A more subtle control over the law was exerted by giving most careful consideration to a judge's political views before promoting him, while the ostensible separation of law and politics was preserved.

Bacon believed that the supremacy of politics over the law should be overt and clearly stated. It should be expressed by the recognition of the supremacy of the King over the judges. He was not inclined to raise law above politics and government. He was a comprehensive thinker, aware of the interactions of every aspect of life, society and thought. He held that each should have its place in a harmoniously designed and operated system.

After the 1614 Parliament had dissolved without granting the King fresh supplies, the Council attempted to improve the management of his estates. The most business-like suggestions came from Coke.

The friends of the King started a voluntary collection of treasure to relieve him. Its legality was questionable, for Benevolences were forbidden by act of Parliament. Bacon advised the King how the collections could be made without infringing the law. He suggested that they should be called Oblations. As might have been expected, they raised only a trifling total.

Bacon was still very much the King's lawyer. The King looked to him primarily for professional legal advice.

A country gentleman called Oliver St. John made a public statement that the 'Benevolences' were against Magna Carta, and accused the King of violating his Coronation oath. St. John was prosecuted. Bacon reported to the King that Coke 'delivered the law for the benevolence strongly', and added that he wished he had 'done it more timely'. (Coke had at first advised that it was not lawful, either to levy or to move for the 'Oblations'.) Bacon said that he himself had not done so badly, 'having spoken out of a few heads which I had gathered (for I seldom do more)'.

He seized the occasion to praise James. Was he not the 'principal conservator of true religion through the Christian world', who 'had summoned the fraternity of Kings to enfrancise themselves from the usurpation of the See of Rome'? Had he not controverted the 'most pestilent and heathenish heresies' of Vorstius?

Incomparable among Kings in learning he had encouraged the universities, those 'seed-plots' of religion and the Church, which 'were never more in flower nor fruit'. He consulted frequently with his judges, who 'are a kind of council of the King's by oath and ancient constitution . . .' and he commonly relied on their opinions.

As for the use of the Prerogative, 'it runs within the ancient banks'. The King had by his wisdom and care prevented it from overflowing, and had thereby strengthened it. Bacon now stated some of the fundamental reasons why it was possible to serve such a difficult master. 'We see the King now hath reigned twelve years in his white robe, without almost any aspersion of the crimson dye of blood. There sits my Lord Hubbard, that served Attorney seven years. I served with him. We were so happy, as there passed not through our hands any one arraignment for treason; and but one for any capital offence. . . .'

As for peace, 'he hath preserved his subjects during his reign in peace, both within and without . . .'.

St. John was sentenced to a fine of £5,000 and imprisonment during his Majesty's pleasure. Ultimately, the fine was remitted and he was released within about three years. The sentencing was delayed owing to the illness of Ellesmere. Bacon described to James how, on visiting him at his sick bed, 'it pleased him out of his ancient and great love to me, which many times in sickness appeareth most, to admit me to a great deal of speech . . . which during these three days he hath scarcely done to any . . .'. Ellesmere wished that his sentencing of St. John would be his last work, and would conclude his services to the King.

A year later, Ellesmere again fell seriously ill. Bacon reported to the King on the steps he had taken in this situation to deal with Chancery business. In the first draft of his letter, he had concluded with a hint that if Ellesmere died he should be promoted; but he thought better of it, and left it out.

A little later he wrote a longer letter, which was virtually an application for the chancellorship. He feared that Ellesmere was going to 'his last day', but the King's service 'must not be mortal'. He never forgot that his appointment as Attorney was his Majesty's 'sole act'. He remarked that Somerset only 'thrust himself into the business for a fee' when he found that it had been resolved upon. He then offered the King his heart, his service, and his official places which were worth £7,600 a year. (He did not offer James a sum, which would have not been unusual, but his offices, which James could have sold to others if he wished.)

He hoped he might be acquitted of presumption in aspiring to the place, which had been held by his father. If the King appointed 'my Lord Coke, this will follow; first your Majesty shall put an over-ruling nature into an over-ruling place . . . you shall blunt his industries in the matter of your finances . . . and lastly, popular men are no sure mounters for your Majesty's saddle . . .'. If he took Lord Hubbard, he would then have lawyers at both ends of his Council table, and 'they will agree in magnifying that wherein they are best'.

The Archbishop of Canterbury would be unsuitable, because 'the Chancellor's place requires a whole man', and no one except a king is fit to be head of both church and state.

For himself, he could only promise that if he sat in that place the King's business would be 'pursued and performed'. The King would be troubled only with his true care, which was to think of the chief things to be done, and not how they should be carried out.

He presumed that the good will he enjoyed in the Commons would be of advantage in 'rectifying that body of parliament men'. As Lord Chancellor he would see that the law was dispensed so that the King's conscience should be satisfied that justice had been done. But the duties he would perform as a moderator of the Privy Council, an overseer of the judges, and an appointer of suitable persons as justices and governors in the country, would be the most important of all.

He would aim also at strengthening the 'inventive part' of the Council. At present, members of the Council exercised judgments on the proposals from 'projectors and private men, which cannot be so well'. Thus Bacon was in favour of the government taking initiative in trade and industry.

Bacon received a message from the King, through the rising favourite Villiers, that he might indeed with confidence expect the Lord Chancellorship. Bacon, who was then fifty-five years old, replied to the young man, who was twenty-three, 'I am yours surer to you than to my own life.'

James's affections, which had been chiefly satisfied during the last half-dozen years by Robert Carr, Earl of Somerset, had been excited by the beautiful youth, who appeared to Simonds D'Ewes at that time 'full of delicacy and handsome features', and 'especially effeminate and curious'. The King's love for him was encouraged by various English courtiers, as a counter to Carr and the numerous other Scots cronies who were receiving more than a fair share of the King's favours.

Bacon made himself useful to Villiers, as he had to other favourites, such as Essex and Somerset. They were among the chief rungs of the ladder of state.

However, Ellesmere recovered, and the vacancy on the Woolsack did not yet occur. Bacon therefore wrote to Villiers, in view of this 'incertainty', that he would be glad to be made a privy councillor. Bacon referred to his letter to the King on his previous services as 'a little remembrance of some things past', which has a sound like the lines in Shakespeare's sonnet that Proust adopted for the title of his famous novel.

Ellesmere, after his recovery, found that Coke had been trying to establish that the court of Chancery could not modify judgments made in the courts of common law. Bacon pointed out to the King that the court of Chancery was his 'court of absolute power'. He should not allow any innovation in the scope of courts, but 'have every court impaled within their own precedents, and not assume to themselves new powers upon conceits and inventions of law'.

He advised that Coke should not be disgraced for his behaviour, because he was 'so well habituate' in dealing with criminal cases, and also because of that 'which I find is in his breast touching your finances and matters of repair of your estate'.

Bacon presently received a more definite intimation from the King about the chancellorship. He wrote a most humble acknowledgment of this great favour, and said he never had great thoughts for himself. It was far from him 'under base pretences to cover base desires', which he accounted them to be, 'when men refer too much to themselves'.

30. *Earning Promotion*

As Somerset was eclipsed by Villiers in the King's affections, his power declined. Men and women acquired the courage to question his activities. Two years before, his great friend and adviser, Sir Thomas Overbury, had died in the Tower of London. It was rumoured that he had been murdered. If true, it would have been the first murder in the Tower since Richard III had had the young princes suffocated.

The officer who had been Lieutenant of the Tower when Overbury died came forward and said that there had indeed been an attempt by an underkeeper called Weston to poison him, but it had been detected and prevented. The Lieutenant had not revealed the matter because of his fear of 'impeaching or accusing great persons', who were thought to be the Earl and Countess of Somerset. Further inquiry showed that Overbury had been poisoned through the bowels with a clyster applied by an apothecary's boy. A Mrs. Turner was implicated in this matter.

Coke was now requested to make an investigation, which he pursued with his usual energy. He rapidly obtained evidence implicating the Somersets. Feeling the need for his own protection, Coke asked for the appointment of other leading officers of state to be joined with him in a commission of investigation. Somerset tried to persuade the King to suspend it, but was unsuccessful. After this, he sent men to search the house of Weston's son, and seize documents bearing on Mrs. Turner. As Mrs. Turner was in custody, the Commission construed Somerset's action as a contempt of court, and placed him and his wife under house arrest. Somerset then attempted to send messages to Mrs. Turner, so he was placed in close custody.

When Weston was arrested he said that he hoped they were not making a net to catch the little fishes, and allowing the big ones to break through. He was tried, found guilty of having administered the poison, and condemned to be executed.

He was brought to the scaffold at Tyburn, where a concourse of aristocrats, consisting respectively of friends of Overbury and Somerset, had assembled to hear his last words. They hoped to learn who the big fishes might be. He was asked by this pushing crowd of interrogators whether or not he had poisoned Overbury. He replied that he had 'left his mind behind with the Lord Chief Justice'.

This badgering of Weston in his last minutes of life was barbarous behaviour, but it was also a questioning of the King's justice. Several of the principal questioners were arrested.

It was Bacon's duty as Attorney-General to prosecute these offenders. In his speech he said of Overbury: 'I knew the gentleman. It is true, his mind was great, but it moved not in any great good order; yet certainly it did commonly fly at good things. And the greatest fault that ever I heard by him was, that he made his friend his idol. . . .'

He described how Overbury had been 'chased to death' by poison after poison, 'first roseaker, then arsenic, then mercury sublimate, then sublimate again; . . . the poets feign the Furies had whips, and that they were corded with poisonous snakes; and a man would think that this subject were the very case . . .'.

He took care to suggest that the affair did not involve the King: 'if it had concerned the King or Prince, there could not have been better nor greater commissioners'.

He mentioned that the defenders in the present case 'are all my particular friends', and persons whose qualities he respected and loved. But now he could 'only do this duty of a friend to them, to make them know their fault to the full'.

Bacon recounted that when Weston was questioned on the scaffold, he answered 'that they did him wrong; and turning to the sheriff, said, You promised me that I should not be troubled at this time . . .' and yet, it was reported, 'for all this vexing of the spirit of a poor man, now in the gates of death', Weston nevertheless refused to answer.

Some had said they wished him to discharge his conscience, and satisfy the world. 'What world I marvel? it was the world at Tyburn.'

'As we have no Spanish inquisitions, nor justice in a corner, so we have no gagging of men's mouths at their death, but that they may speak freely at their last hour. But then it must come from the free motion of the party, not by temptations of ques-

tions. . . .' A cross examination on the scaffold 'were to erect a
court or commission of review at Tyburn, against the Courts at
Westminster'.

The offences were great and dangerous. 'For if we do not
maintain justice, justice will not maintain us. . . .'

The confessions and convictions of Weston and the humbler
agents made the prosecution of Somerset inevitable. But Coke in
the course of his investigations discovered information even more
startling than the poisoning of Overbury. He found among
Somerset's papers dispatches for the King from Digby, the
English Ambassador in Madrid, which revealed that Spain had
been paying pensions to some of James's principal ministers,
and that negotiations had occurred on the possibility of the
Prince of Wales making a Spanish marriage.

Coke had assumed that Somerset must have concealed these
dispatches from the King, and thereby committed high treason,
in addition to instigating murder. But the King had been kept
informed by Somerset, who had discussed the proposed marriage
with the Spanish Ambassador in London. Digby feared that
Somerset might have revealed very secret negotiations on the
management of the religious side of the ceremony to unauthorized persons.

As Attorney-General, Bacon participated in interrogations
on these Spanish discussions. In his report he was careful to
place the responsibility on the King for the line that he had
followed, and to make it very clear that he had himself no prior
information of the affair.

He said that Digby was 'somewhat reserved' on the matter of
'conveying the Prince into Spain, or the Spanish pensions',
and he did not consider it fit to press him before he received the
King's further instructions. 'I for my part am in no appetite
for secrets; but nevertheless seeing his Majesty's great trust
towards me (wherein I shall never deceive him) and that I find
the Chancellor of the same opinion, I do think it were good my
Lord Chancellor chiefly and myself were made acquainted with
the persons and the particulars.'

Most important matters of policy were being formed and
carried out without the knowledge of Ellesmere and Bacon in
spite of their high offices in the state. They were expected
primarily to operate the machinery of administration, not to
create policy.

When Bacon interrogated Somerset in the Tower he formed the opinion that the Spanish affair had little bearing on the poisoning, and that the polite treatment of Somerset, which was proper in connection with the diplomatic matters, would not make him forthcoming about the poisoning. He therefore considered that the matter of the Spanish dispatches should be dropped. This was calculated to restrict the King's embarrassment to the matter of the poisoning, which was serious enough.

Coke had refused during the first three months of his investigation of the poisoning to reveal to the King the information that he had discovered. He said that if the King insisted on having this information before the prisoner was publicly tried, he would resign, implying that it would have been unconstitutional.

Though the evidence was strongly against Somerset and everybody believed he was guilty, it was not conclusive. But if the trial had been delayed or withdrawn, there might have been a civil revolt. The government, in the shape of the King and his officers, had to conduct the prosecution in such a way that what they conceived to be the public safety was not endangered. Bacon analysed the situation that might arise from various possible outcomes of the trial. 'Things duly foreseen may have their remedies and directions in readiness.' He thought it most probable that the Countess would confess, but that Somerset himself would plead not guilty. 'In this case, first, I suppose your Majesty will not think of any stay of judgment, but that the public process of justice pass on. . . .' It would be in his care 'so to moderate the manner of charging him, as it make him not odious beyond the extent of mercy . . .'.

In this way justice and policy were carefully planned together. 'Well remembering who is the third person, whom your Majesty admitted to this secret,' Bacon, without mentioning his name, sent the analysis unsealed to the new favourite, Villiers, for transmission to the King, who returned it with marginal notes in his own writing.

The King suggested that a hint should be given to Somerset that if he would confess, the royal prerogative of mercy might be exercised in his favour. Bacon thought that this 'little charm which may be secretly infused into Somerset's ear some few hours before his trial' was an excellent idea. He suggested that the hint of mercy might be extended to cover the Countess and child (she was pregnant), and to some extent, his fortune and favour. As for the person who should deliver the hint, Bacon was 'not so well seen in the region of his friends, as to be able to make choice of a particular'. He spent four or five hours with the four judges of the King's bench discussing the evidence against Somerset. They all concurred that the prosecution was most honourable and the evidence fair and good.

Bacon forwarded through Villiers to the King for his comments the synopsis of his speech for the prosecution of Somerset. He proposed to quote from Overbury's letters such passages as 'Is this the fruit of nine years love, common secrets, and common dangers,' and 'do not drive me to extremity to do that which you and I shall be sorry for'.

He proposed to say 'that Overbury was a man of nature fit to be an incendiary of a state, full of bitterness and wildness of speech and project; that he was thought absolutely to govern Somerset . . .'. He intended to put the 'imputations rather upon Overbury than Somerset'.

Bacon gave a list of the extraordinary evidence that he did not propose to use, including items that the Prince had been poisoned by a physician with a red beard, that Mrs. Turner tried to kill the Prince by magic, and that the Countess had attempted to influence the Queen by witchcraft.

After Somerset had been given the hint that he would receive mercy if he confessed, the Commissioners tried to persuade him to confess. He refused in a very sober, modest and mild manner.

When Somerset became convinced that he was to be tried, he threatened to publish secrets affecting the King. Bacon noted for prior discussion with the judges what action they should take if Somerset 'should break forth into any speech of taxing the King'.

The Countess was prosecuted first. She pleaded guilty. Bacon outlined the case, relating the story in a very clear and mild manner. He mentioned that Coke had 'taken at least three hundred examinations' in the affair. The trial had been delayed for two causes. Honour, christianity and charity demanded that it should be postponed 'until this Lady's deliverance was due . . . in respect of her great belly'. There was also a delay caused by another kind of deliverance: 'which was that some causes of estate which were in the womb might likewise be brought forth, not for matter of justice but for reason of state'.

When the Countess was asked what she had to say 'she spoke

humbly, fearfully, and so low' that the presiding judge, Elles-mere, could not hear her. Mr. Attorney recounted her words for her: 'The Lady is so touched with remorse and sense of her fault that grief surprizes her from expressing herself: but that which she hath confusedly said is to this effect, That she cannot excuse herself but desires mercy.'

Chamberlain was of the opinion that her demeanour was 'more curious and confident than was fit for a Lady in such distress'. She was sentenced to be hanged, and commonly pitied.

Bacon handled these state trials, so dangerous to James, with great political skill, and the case against the Countess with ingenious delicacy.

When Somerset was tried, the court was thronged with noble-men, who were intensely curious about the fallen favourite. Government policy was to conduct the proceedings as publicly as possible, to make the utmost impression that justice was being done.

Bacon in his speech for the prosecution described how Over-bury had been 'a kind of oracle of direction' to Somerset, who had been used by the King as a provisional foreign secretary. Somerset in this capacity had sent dispatches to Overbury 'sometimes opened by my Lord, sometimes unbroken' for Over-bury to make such notes as he thought fit. There was a time when Overbury 'knew more of the secrets of state than the Council-table did'.

Nevertheless, he did not charge the Earl with any disloyalty, he wished only to establish that there was a great communication of secrets between him and Overbury.

But this excess of friendship ended on the Earl's part in mortal hatred. He entered into 'an unlawful love towards his unfortunate Lady, then Countess of Essex'. He had her marriage with Essex nullified, and then married her himself. In his capacity as a friend, Overbury violently opposed this marriage, on the ground that the Countess was 'an unworthy woman', but the truth was that he was loth to have any partners in Somerset's favour.

Overbury boasted that he had himself won the love of the lady for Somerset 'by his letters and industry'. When, however, he saw that he was in danger of being displaced from a position in which 'he had promised himself to do wonders', he attempted to deter Somerset from that love and marriage, and threatened him with the revelation of 'secrets of all natures. Hereupon grew two streams of hatred on Overbury; the one from the Lady, in respect that he crossed her love and abused her name, which are furies to women, the other of a deeper and more mineral nature, from my Lord of Somerset himself; who was afraid of Overbury's nature, and that if he did break from him and fly out, he would mine into him and trouble his whole fortunes.'

Bacon then described how Somerset had had Overbury imprisoned in the Tower, how he had had the Lieutenant of the Tower replaced by one under his influence, how Overbury's under-keeper was replaced, how Overbury was prevented from communicating with his friends, how all this and more had been carried out within fifteen days, and poison first administered two days later.

Among the proofs of Somerset's guilt Bacon mentioned his efforts to suppress evidence. 'You did deface, and destroy, and clip and misdate all writings that might give light to the impoison- ment; and that you did fly to the altar of guiltiness, which is a pardon, and a pardon of murder, and a pardon for yourself, and not for your lady.'

Somerset gave a good answer to most of the accusations. He was even able to prove that powders he had himself sent to Overbury were proper medicines.

The most serious evidence against him was the forgery of the dates of documents. He seemed to be surprised by the discovery of the forgery, and could give no plausible explanation of it.

But he could not be moved from his protestations of inno- cence, which he expressed courageously throughout. He made no reflection whatever on the King.

The court unanimously pronounced him guilty.

The Somersets were imprisoned in the Tower, and released after five years.

Five days after the trial of Somerset, Bacon wrote to Villiers, whose path in the King's favour was now cleared, that 'the time is as I should think now or never for his Majesty to finish his good meaning towards me, if it please him to consider what is past and what is to come'. If he cared to oblige men through his place and practice, he could have more profit than he desired. But his heart was not on these things. Nevertheless, he 'would be sorry that worthless persons should make a note that I get nothing but pains, and enemies, and a little popular reputa- tion which followeth me whether I will or no'. He knew that if Villiers put his 'strength to the business', it would be done.

He followed this by another letter, saying that though he was ambitious to be Lord Chancellor, his hearty wishes that Lord Ellesmere should live long caused him to ask rather for a privy councillorship.

His wish was granted, and six days later he was sworn a member of the Privy Council.

31. *Chequered Ascent*

SINCE the conviction of Somerset left the way clear for the emergence of Villiers as the King's uncontested favourite, Bacon had to accommodate himself to this position, or retire from official life. As ascent of the official ladder was part of his life's plan, he made the necessary adjustments.

In the 1612 edition of his essay *Of Counsel* he refers to the danger of being unfaithfully counselled by self-seekers, who are more concerned with advancing their own ends than helping the persons they advise. Attempts to prevent this by forming inner groups of trusted persons can be 'a remedy worse than the disease', as had been shown by French experience. This is followed in Bacon's manuscript by the explanation that 'Councils of State to which Princes are solemnly married' are so converted into 'Councils of gracious persons recommended chiefly by flattery and affection'. In the manuscript Bacon crossed out the word 'solemnly'. He inserted 'flattery and' in his own hand between the lines.

This was precisely James's system of government; Bacon did not jeopardize his political career by publishing the passage. As usual, Bacon's earlier draft was the more pungent. As earlier drafts tended to be more outspoken than later ones, so the printed word tended to be more outspoken than verbal advice. 'Books will speak plain when Councillors blanch.' It was therefore good to be conversant with books, especially those written by 'such as themselves have been actors on the stage'.

It follows that he would naturally consider it necessary to gain experience of high office in the state before feeling adequately qualified to say how science should be used for the benefit of mankind.

When Bacon saw that James had fallen in love with Villiers, he did his best to take a favourable view of the young man. He described him to James as of 'a safe nature, a capable mind, an honest will, generous and noble affections, and a courage well-lodged . . .'. Villiers might, with suitable discipline when he was a young man, have grown into an agreeable country gentleman. But he had not the abilities necessary to be an effective understudy for a head of state, and his situation intoxicated his vanity. He was rapidly corrupted, but Bacon's description was not at first entirely illusory. He set out to give Villiers the best possible advice.

In sending him the papers for the title of viscount, Bacon remarked that now his fortunes were established it was time that he should refer his actions chiefly to the good of his king and country. It was the life of an ox always to eat and never to exercise. Men are born 'not to cram their fortunes but exercise their virtues'. He recommended him to encourage and advance able and virtuous men in the King's service. 'For in the time of the Cecils, the father and the son, able men were by design and of purpose suppressed', and though of late choice had been better, 'yet money, and turn-serving, and cunning canvasses, and importunity prevail too much. . . . As for cunning and corrupt men, you must (I know) sometimes use them; but keep them at a distance; and let it appear that you make use of them, rather than that they lead you.'

Villiers seems to have appreciated these remarks, and to have asked for further advice. Bacon discussed the opportunities and dangers of a favourite, and gave rules for dealing with suits, which would facilitate the business of a minister of state.

He says that most of the business will fall under eight headings: religion, law, matters of state (what is now called Cabinet agenda) foreign affairs, war, colonies, trade, and the Court.

On religious affairs it was necessary to take the advice of divines who are discreet and exemplary in their lives.

With regard to the law, the Common Laws of England were the best, if rightly administered. The judges should be chosen from the most learned 'for an ignorant man cannot be a good Judge'.

T

The members of the Privy Council, who administer the state, should be chosen so as to provide a range of authorities 'versed in all knowledges'.

He recommended Queen Elizabeth's methods of conducting foreign affairs; 'who was very happy, not so much in a numerous as a wise Council to advise her'.

As to War, the King was 'settled in his judgment for peace', but he had to say that the best way to a secure peace is to be prepared for war. In Britain, 'where the Seas are our Walls, and the ships our Bulwarks', safety and plenty (by trade) are concomitant.

The most serious of all wars is civil war, and 'the King by his wisdom, justice and moderation must foresee and stop such a storm . . .'.

He advised that the development of colonies should be entrusted only to free men, and the use of 'schismatics, outlaws, or criminal persons', should be avoided. The natives should not be exploited by a 'few merchants and tradesmen' who kept them always in poverty.

On the question of trade, 'I confess it is out of my profession.' He conjectured that exports should exceed imports, so that the stock of gold at home increased. 'Instead of crying up all things which are either brought beyond sea or wrought up here by the hands of strangers,' let the native commodities of our kingdom be advanced, and 'employ our countrymen before strangers'. If home wool and raw materials were turned into manufactured goods it would set thousands of hands to work. One shilling's worth of material would be converted by industry into products of twenty times the value.

He particularly advised the extension of tillage in agriculture. The area of Britain was fixed, but its agricultural productivity could be multiplied by good husbandry.

Navigable rivers were a great help to trade. Therefore let them be made by art and industry, 'but let them not be turned to private profit'.

Finally, he recommended the development of fishing. Half a day's sail with a good wind would bring the fisherman to the catch, but the English were too lazy to undertake it.

He could not advise him on Court affairs, for he had 'scarce stept within the Court gates but as by chance and at the most as a stranger'.

In his remarks on trade and industry, he comments on the value of lead, copper, iron and tin ores to be found in the country, but does not mention coal. He warned against monopolies, which he described as 'the cankers of all trades'.

While Bacon, in an extreme effort of accommodation, was attempting to steer the young Villiers, he submitted to the King his proposals for the *Compiling and Amendment of the Laws of England*. The notion had been one of his favourite thoughts since he had first studied law. He revolved in his mind for more than twenty years various methods of securing its adoption. But his plan did not have an effective result until two hundred years later, when Sir Robert Peel said in the House of Commons that he could not provide better arguments for his own proposals on the reform of the law of theft than Bacon had advanced for the reform of the law in general, and asked leave to submit Bacon's paper as a preface to his speech.

Bacon spent much diplomatic effort on his unsuccessful attempts to persuade James to reform the laws. He informed the King that he had achieved 'the highest degree of sovereign honour' by uniting England and Scotland. After that, he had founded colonies, which was second in honour. Now he should be a lawgiver, which was third in honour. Here Bacon's plan of using political and diplomatic techniques for securing constructive ends is seen in operation. Always, in his efforts to make use of Essex, Somerset, Villiers, and the King himself, he had in mind the advancement of constructive projects as well as his own career.

In his proposals Bacon paid tribute to Coke's *Reports*, saying that while they contained some errors and dogmatisms yet 'they contain infinite good decisions and rulings over cases'. Bacon proposed a comprehensive work of systematization which would consist of a pruning and grafting of the laws, and not a ploughing up and planting again, which would indeed be 'a perilous innovation'. He said that 'books must follow sciences, and not sciences books'.

Bacon's conception of law was very different from Coke's, which was essentially empirical. Bacon saw that a comparative system, in which general principles were derived from experience, would carry the law to a higher stage than it had as yet reached. He hoped to carry this out himself, and he said that 'I am in good hope, that when Sir Edward Coke's *Reports* and my

Rules and Decisions shall come to posterity, there will be (what-soever is now thought) question who was the greater lawyer?'

But Bacon did not do more than make a beginning of his great comparative work.

Coke naturally conceived the law in the manner best suited to his own gifts of memory and shrewdness. He relied on his vast knowledge of cases to overreach others, and he tended to interpret cases, on which others were generally not so well informed as himself, in favour of his own opinions. He used this method in attempting to limit the scope of the royal prerogative. It greatly irritated James, and Bacon fanned the annoyance that it caused.

The King ordered Bacon and the law officers to make a list of doubtful principles of law propounded by Coke in his *Reports*. It was scarcely possible to order the Lord Chief Justice to alter the contents of his own books of law, so he was given the opportunity of voluntarily making the corrections in the desired direction.

The King temporarily suspended Coke from the public exercise of his office, to give him the opportunity to review and correct the 'many exhorbitant and extravagant opinions set down and published for positive and good law'. He was to make a list of these errors and inform the King of them privately.

Ellesmere and Bacon received the answers on behalf of the King. Coke had diligently re-read his eleven volumes of five hundred cases during three months' study, and said that he had discovered only five examples of error; these were trivial in character. He had failed to detect anything erroneous in his obnoxious opinions concerning the prerogative.

Coke had by far the better of this exchange. Ellesmere and Bacon were very careful to leave the next step to the King, for it was obviously dangerous to dismiss or prosecute the Lord Chief Justice for disseminating bad law. Popular opinion would merely assume that he was being victimized.

Coke was now confronted with five particular examples of alleged errors chosen by Bacon and Yelverton from his *Reports*, which appeared to limit the prerogative. Coke took them away with him, and four days later gave answers claiming to show that they threw no shadow on the prerogative.

It was evident that Coke would not change his attitude, so the King decided to dismiss him. Bacon provided the King with a memorandum of the details of the case against him. Besides the points of law, the King had noted that Coke, as Bacon put it, 'having in his nature not one part of those things which are popular in men, being neither liberal, nor affable, nor magnificent, he hath made himself popular by design only, in pulling down government'.

For the moment, Coke was out of the way.

Bacon was standing counsel to the University of Cambridge. The university feared that when he was appointed a member of the Privy Council he might no longer have time to attend to their affairs. But through all his absorbing struggles Bacon never weakened his ties with learning. When the university sent its congratulations and inquired about his situation, he replied that while he proposed to continue to apply himself with unwearied zeal, care and affection to public interests, he regarded colleges and letters as among the parts of the commonwealth that were dearest to his mind. They could regard any addition to his position as an addition to themselves. He hoped, as he had been translated from private to public affairs, so in his later life he might be 'withdrawn again from public cares and fall to leisure and letters'.

While he retained this thought, events advanced his political career. Ellesmere at last succeeded in retiring from his place as Lord Keeper. Early in 1617, Bacon succeeded him as Lord Keeper, the place that his father had held. Memories of filial affection inspired his profound joy on receiving this appointment. He believed he owed the promotion to Villiers, now Viscount Buckingham. He was so overwhelmed with feelings of gratitude that he had difficulty in finding words to express himself. In sending his thanks, he explained that for this reason he had spoken little to him earlier in the day. 'It is both in cares and kindness, that small ones float up to the tongue, and great ones sink down into the heart with silence.' Buckingham was 'the truest and perfectest mirror and example of firm and generous friendship that ever was in court'.

Bacon made the taking of his seat in the court of Chancery a great occasion. The newswriter Garrard reported that 'Our Lord Keeper exceeds all his predecessors in the bravery and multitude of his servants. It amazes those that look on his beginnings, besides never so indulgent a master. On the first day of term he appeared in his greatest glory; for to the Hall, besides his own retinue, did accompany him all the Lords of his Majesty's Council and others, with all knights and gentlemen that could get horses and footcloths.' Chamberlain wrote that 'he was accompanied by most of the nobility, with other gallants, to the number of more than 200 horses, besides the Judges and the Inns of Court. There was a great deal more bravery and better show of horse than was expected in the King's absence; but both Queen and Prince sent all their followers and his other friends did their best to honour him.'

He made an impressive speech on the rules he would observe in conducting the affairs of the Seal and Chancery, so that men who had to do with them should know what to expect. He would expound these in 'no flourishing or painted words, but such words as are fit to go before deeds'. In his plans for the improvement of Chancery procedure, he made special provision for accelerating the administration of justice, which he regarded as particularly important, by increasing the length of the working day, adding 'the afternoon to the forenoon', and reducing the length of the vacation by a fortnight. But 'the depth of the three long vacations I would reserve in some measure free for business of estate, and for studies, arts and sciences, to which in my nature I am most inclined'.

He sent a report of his speech and activities to Buckingham for the King, saying how 'this matter of pomp, which is heaven to some men, is hell to me, or purgatory at least'. He hinted that various proposals in his speech had been regarded as a good preparation for holding a Parliament. Bacon held that good and efficient relations between the King and Parliament were the first principle in policy. But he had no sympathy for popular democracy, or any form of syndicalism in which the working people form their own instruments of government. He took elaborate precautions to control May-day demonstrations, 'at which time there was great apprehension of tumult by prentices and loose people . . .'. He mustered the militia in 'brave fashion', and ordered the mayor and aldermen, and justices of the peace to see that while the apprentices might go abroad 'with their flags and other gauderies', they were not to be allowed to carry pikes and weapons, as formerly. He appointed extra lieutenants of police, with the result that 'there never was such a still' due to the 'terror' produced by his measures.

Buckingham informed him that the King was exceedingly well-satisfied with his speech and activities, and commented on 'the sufficiency and worthiness of his Majesty's choice in preferring a man of such abilities to that place, which besides cannot but be a great advancement and furtherance to his service'.

Chamberlain reported that the general opinion was that the constitution of Bacon's body and mind were too tender for the heavy burdens of the office, and affairs of state would consequently suffer. This soon seemed to be borne out, as Bacon did not appear at various functions. But in fact he was working overtime to eliminate the arrears in the business of the court of Chancery. Swift justice was one of his favourite aims.

He had great satisfaction in expressing his views on how the law should be conducted. He told the judges they were to be careful that 'your hands, and the hands of your hands (I mean those about you), be clean, and uncorrupt from gifts; from meddling in titles, and from serving of turns, be they of great ones or small ones'. He said that 'the King's Prerogative is law, and the principal part of the law'. In the body of man there is not one law for the head, and another for the body, 'but all is one entire law'.

A little further on in the same speech he speaks about whales. Hobbes, who had at one time been employed by him, may perhaps have been influenced by these passages in the choice of the *Leviathan* or whale as an image of human society, conceived as an organic unity.

Bacon soon proudly reported to Buckingham that all outstanding cases in his court had been dealt with. Not one cause was left unheard, the lawyers had no cases, and not one petition was left unanswered. He knew that men thought he could not continue, if he so oppressed himself with business, but the account had been completed, and 'the duties of life are more than life'.

Among all this stir, Bacon nevertheless learned how little he knew about the innermost decisions of the King and his ruling circle. He found that the King was far more deeply committed to a Spanish marriage for the Prince of Wales than he had supposed. He laid the entire responsibility for this policy on the King, and said that now the King had decided on the policy, it was the duty of his privy councillors to be united on it. He carefully avoided expressing his own opinion on the merits of the policy. He took shelter behind the principle of collective responsibility, and busied himself with the consideration of ways in which it could be made more palatable.

For instance, British and Spanish maritime interests might find a common cause in the suppression of the pirates of Algiers. Perhaps the British mariners could do the fighting, if Spain found the money. He suggested a joint war of the Protestant and Catholic powers against the Turks, for the capture of Constantinople and the control of the Middle East. The ideological differences in Europe were to be assuaged by adventures in Asia.

Bacon subsequently discussed the political and moral problems of the proposal in his paper on a *Holy War*. It is written in the form of a dialogue between representatives of moderate and extreme Protestantism, Roman Catholicism, and the military, political and courtiers' points of view, and contains some notable opinions. Concerning the motive for exploration and colonial wars, he says that 'it cannot be affirmed (if one speak ingenuously) that it was the propagation of the Christian faith that was the adamant of that discovery, entry, and plantation; but gold and silver and temporal profit and glory'. He makes his military spokesman speak against the justification of wars on the ground of the alleged superiority of one people over another, and incidentally founds Jeremy Bentham's philosophy: 'I know no such difference amongst reasonable souls, but that whatsoever is in order to the greatest and most general good of people may justify the action, be the people more or less civil.'

But James was not interested in any kind of fighting. He was what is nowadays called an 'unprincipled pacifist'. He hoped for 'peaceful co-existence' between the two religious ideologies which then split Western Europe. The circumstances of his origin had endowed him with conflicting ideas. He was born in a feudal society during a welter of murders, and had been a king since the first year of his babyhood. He was separated from his mother and indoctrinated against her, and forced at the age of twenty-one to acquiesce in her execution. One of the reasons for rearing him with Protestant ideas was to set him against his mother through opposition to her Roman Catholicism. The insecurity of his youth reinforced his emphasis on the feudal rights of a king. He clung to the prerogative as a protection and the legal right to his existence. But his religious ideas were not consonant with his feudal notions of kingship. Very broadly speaking, Protestant ideas are more suited to a trading and capitalist society, while Roman Catholic ideas are more suited to an agricultural society with a land-owning aristocracy.

As James grew older and his personal safety increased, he became less aggressively Protestant and more tolerant to Catholicism. He discovered more and more common ground with kings as such, irrespective of their religions. As the power of the House of Commons increased, a majority of its merchant members and money-making squires used Protestant ideas as an aid to class-independence. James had come to depend on the feudal idea of his divine right to be a king, and found in this the chief guarantee of his personal safety. He felt the growing power of Parliament was encroaching on, and weakening, his main protection. Consequently, as Parliament became more powerful, he became more anti-Parliamentarian, and as a corollary to this, less Protestant.

A marriage alliance with the Spanish monarchy became increasingly attractive to him, for it appealed to his idea of the solidarity of kings, which strengthened his prerogative. At the same time it promised to make him independent of Parliament, through the payment of a huge marriage portion by Spain.

The Spanish Marriage was only one of the major matters on which Bacon had to learn how far the King had gone. Immediately after he had been appointed Lord Keeper, the King left for a six months' visit to Scotland. In the King's absence he was the official head of the government, and as such, began to act with initiative.

The King had signed a proclamation before he departed on his journey, ordering the gentry to leave London and go to their country seats. He regarded them as, in his absence, the provincial custodians of the regime. Their presence at home was necessary to quell any attempts to take advantage of the King's absence to organize anti-government activities.

The Council found that when the Court left London nearly all of the gentry went away also. They, including Bacon, saw no point in issuing an unpopular order interfering with the liberties of the subject when it was unnecessary. The King was informed of this, and Bacon also, in one of his reports to the King, mentioned casually that it had not been issued, as it had been found to be unnecessary.

The King was extremely angry, and ordered that the proclamation be issued at once. He sent a sharp rebuke to his Council, including his new principal minister, in which they were informed that 'obedience is better than sacrifice, and that he knoweth he is King of England'.

It was now obvious to Bacon that he had little political power, and not even much administrative power. But he does not seem to have seen, or not to have recognized, how little power he had until this was repeatedly proved to him by the brutality of events.

32. *The Lawyer Strikes Back*

COKE had not accepted his dismissal from the chief justice-ship as a final defeat. Buckingham, who had been poor himself, and came of a large and impecunious family, felt it a family duty, especially under the pressure of his strong-minded mother, to find financially advantageous matches for his unmarried relatives. Coke saw in this a means by which he might secure his restoration to royal favour. He was rich, he was himself a handsome man and the father of a beautiful young daughter.

Negotiations were begun with Buckingham on the terms on which she might be betrothed to his somewhat feeble-minded brother, Sir John Villiers. Coke, in spite of his recent dismissal, was on good personal terms with the King, who enjoyed his racy dinner-table conversation and stories. The Buckingham family demanded a dowry of £10,000 with a life-allowance of £1,000 a year. Coke, who was one of the keenest men of business, haggled over the terms. At first he would not go beyond £6,666, but presently thought better of it, and in the end paid out £30,000 in cash.

His irascible wife Lady Hatton, the wealthy widow whose hand he had won years before in rivalry with Bacon, was expected to bequeath her fortune to her daughter. She violently objected to the match, especially as it would affect the destination of her wealth. She took the daughter away from the parental home, and hid her at a friend's in the country, alleging that she was pledged to the Earl of Oxford. The Villiers family applied to Bacon on behalf of Coke for a warrant for the return of the girl. Bacon refused this, and was apparently quite unaware of what was going on. He wrote to Buckingham, informing him that it seemed that a match was being arranged between his brother and Coke's daughter.

He believed that Coke was agreeable to it, not out of affection to Buckingham, but to 'make a faction'. Neither the mother nor the young gentlewoman herself had given their consent. He considered the match very inconvenient both for Buckingham and his brother, who would 'marry into a disgraced house', and, referring to the differences between Coke and Lady Hatton, a 'troubled house of man and wife'. It would cause the Earl to lose nearly all of his friends who were adverse to Coke (except himself, who would ever be firm to him 'out of a pure love and thankfulness'). He thought that the results of the match would be bad for the King's service. He advised that the match should not proceed without the consent of both parents, and asked him to believe his faithful advice, 'who by my great experience in the world must needs see further than your Lordship can . . .'.

After Bacon's refusal, a warrant for the recovery of the girl was granted by Winwood. Coke discovered where she had been hidden, and set out with a band of relatives and retainers, one of whom was his son 'fighting Clem Coke', who had a reputation as a pugilist, to regain her, by force if necessary. The ex-Lord Chief Justice and his men hammered on the door of the house, and when it was not opened, battered it down with a large piece of timber, and also broke down several other doors. They seized the girl and conveyed her away.

Lady Hatton drove in a fury to London, to demand of the Lord Keeper, the head of the law, that her daughter should be restored to her. When she arrived at Bacon's house, she was told that the Lord Keeper was unwell and resting, and could not be disturbed. She insisted on being allowed to wait in the room next to his bedroom, so that she would be the first to see him when he emerged. An attendant provided her with a chair. Presently she fell to 'bouncing' against the door. Bacon was awakened, and called his men in alarm. When they opened his door, she pushed her way in with them, and asked for her intrusion to be pardoned on the ground that 'she was like a cow that had lost her calf'.

She had been an old flame of his, even if rather a cool one, and she was now the complaining wife of his great professional rival. Bacon behaved with the delicacy and humane feeling which was characteristic of his judgment in situations that did not appear to him to involve political principles or reasons of state, and assisted her to get a warrant that the girl should be brought under the care of the Privy Council. The Attorney-General was ordered to prosecute Coke in the Court of Star Chamber for 'force and riot'.

Bacon usually had acknowledgments of his letters to Buckingham by return, but after his last blunt advice against the Villiers-Coke marriage, weeks went by and no note came from Buckingham. Bacon then wrote an almost equally blunt expression of his views directly to the King. 'I think it agreeable to my duty, and the great obligation wherein I am tied to your Majesty, to be freer than other men in giving your Majesty faithful counsel. . . .' while policy was being formed; and after it had been formed, to be 'more bond than other men in doing your commandments when your resolution is settled and made known to me . . .'. Bacon had a clear conception of complete loyalty to party decisions—there was to be free discussion before a resolution was made, and after it had been made, complete devotion to it.

This is the explanation of his behaviour, on the many occasions when, after a change of policy had been decided, he as resolutely opposed and prosecuted persons whom he had formerly as devotedly and indefatigably supported.

Bacon submitted his 'honest and disinterested opinion' that the present quiet state of the country was to a considerable degree due to the 'disauthorizing' of Coke. He believed the marriage had been engineered by him to regain his position, and if he did, it would 'give a turn and relapse in men's minds unto the former state of things . . .'. He reminded the King that, in so far as it was fit for him to advise, he 'was ever for a Parliament'. But he believed that the King should have a united Council when he met Parliament, that is, the central executive committee should be united. His Majesty would give Bacon 'leave never to expect, if that man come in', a united Council, for Coke was 'by nature insociable, and by habit popular, and too old now to take a new ply . . .'. If his Majesty decided that the match should proceed, after having heard his reasons to the contrary, Bacon asked that he might receive his decision from himself, so that he might conform thereunto.

As a true friend to Buckingham, he 'had rather go against his mind than against his good', but his Majesty he must obey, and besides he conceived that out of his Majesty's great wisdom and depth, he 'doth see those things I see not . . .'.

How fundamentally different were the ideas of the King and his principal minister is shown by James's reply. He sent a long letter to Bacon, heartily approving of Coke's action in recovering his daughter by force. 'Was not the thefteous stealing away of the daughter from her own father the first ground whereupon all this great noise hath since proceeded?' He had never read any law that signified it was lawful for any person to steal a child from her father (except he be proved lunatic or idiot), or that it was 'streperous carriage' for him to hunt to recover her.

In one of his letters to Buckingham, Bacon had written that the looker-on, meaning himself, sometimes saw more of the game than the 'gamester'. Did not this imply, said James, that the height of Buckingham's fortune might cause him to 'mis-know himself'? Did not this cast an imputation on his discretion?

He accused him of 'pretending ignorance' of his meaning, and of bad manners in crossing Buckingham before he had heard from him.

The King was now on his way back from Scotland. Coke and Yelverton went to meet him at Coventry. Coke was received very cordially, and Yelverton, the Attorney-General, one of Bacon's pupils and nominees, sent Bacon a very confidential account of the atmosphere at Court, and what was being said of him.

Yelverton said that the King's attitude to himself 'was more clouded' than he had looked for. 'Sir Edward Coke hath not fore-borne by any engine to heave both at your Honour and at my-self; and he works by the weightiest instrument, the Earl of Buckingham, who as I see sets him as close to him as his shirt, the Earl speaking in Sir Edward's phrase, and as it were menacing in his spirit.'

Yelverton had assayed the temper of Buckingham himself, and had found that he most fervently believed misinformation. Buckingham said that he would not 'secretly bite' at those who opposed the marriage, but would 'openly oppose them to their faces'.

Yelverton said that he told Buckingham that Bacon and himself had not in any way opposed the marriage, but in several ways had furthered it; they had wished only that Coke might have been more temperate, and have resembled the Earl in his own 'sweet disposition'; that the greatest obstacle was Coke himself, who listened to no advice, and was transported by passion. Finally, he told the Earl that Bacon and himself had been slandered, and it was not consonant with his honour to give credence to these slanders.

He reported that the King had allowed him to kiss his hand, but had said that he had not deserved this favour.

'Now my Lord,' wrote Yelverton, 'give me leave out of all my affections that shall ever serve you, to intimate touching yourself:

1st. That every courtier is acquainted that the Earl professeth openly against you as forgetful of his kindness, and unfaithful to him in your love and in your actions.

2nd. That he returneth the shame upon himself, in not listening to counsel that dissuaded his affection from you, and not to mount you so high, not forbearing in open speech (as divers have told me, and this bearer, your gentleman, hath heard also) to tax you, as if it were an inveterate custom with you, to be unfaithful to him as you were to the Earls of Essex and Somerset.

3rd. That it is too common in every man's mouth in court, that your greatness shall be abated, and as your tongue hath been a razor to some, so shall theirs be to you.

4th. That there is laid up for you, to make your burden the more grievious, many petitions to his Majesty against you.

My Lord, Sir Edward Coke, as if he were already on wings, triumphs exceedingly; hath much private conference with his Majesty; and in public doth offer himself and thrust upon the King with as great boldness as heretofore. . . .'

It was thought that Coke would be recalled to the Council table, and the Earl's eyes and thoughts were never off him.

Yelverton himself advised Bacon not to fail to join his Majesty soon: 'The sight of you will fright some.' He should not single himself from the other Lords, but justify his proceedings as joint acts. He should appear not dismayed, but carry himself bravely and confidently, in which he could 'excel all subjects', and by these means he would 'amaze some and daunt others'.

Yelverton excused the length of his letter by his 'duty and affection' to him, which he described as endless, and he wished his greatness to increase yet more. In a postscript he beseeched Bacon to burn the letter.

It was characteristic of Bacon that he did not burn the letter, and that three years later, he participated in the prosecution of his devoted old friend and pupil, Yelverton, on behalf of the state. Always he placed obedience to the commandments of the King, as the head of the state, above personal loyalty.

By prompt and complete submission to the King's commands, as expressed by the King himself and through Buckingham, he succeeded in retaining his position.

Bacon's apparent lack of insight into the activities of persons around him suggests that his natural perception into human behaviour was not great. The preoccupation in his writings with the explanation of human behaviour, such as his famous description of the effects of organic inferiority on personal psychology, may be regarded as a compensation by intellectual effort for a natural deficiency. His behaviour is often naive. He had the courage of a kind of ignorance in opposing James and Buckingham. Their support of the prerogative was primarily an expression of selfishness, his of the principle of authority. He was absolutely clear on loyally carrying out policies with which he disagreed. He foresaw that Coke was inimical to the King.

Bacon was subject to infantile fixations. He had been reared in ideas of kingship, and desired to grow up worthy of his parents. He aimed at realizing his childhood ambitions, which were in conflict with his understanding of political and social realities. He swung from blunt frankness to transparent dissimulation, which both defeated themselves. His constitution was such that he could not become a creator of a party and a political leader, and he was unable to do more than suggest policy to those in power, and to administer their orders, whether or not these had been influenced by his suggestions.

Bacon's political career was to some extent a construction of the imagination, a play. He was a dramatic performer to himself, and his authority was illusory. One of the motives that prompted him to it was a sense of personal deficiency, which impelled him to a public career in order to prove to himself that he was capable of achieving it. He was not a politician by nature, and attempted to become one by art.

His continual drawing of attention to the excellence of his own performances suggests that he had an inner doubt of his own sufficiency. This appetite for praise was a matter of comment. The financier Cranfield, the Master of the Wards, wrote to Buckingham that he had acquainted Bacon with his plan for relieving the King's debts. 'But your Lordship may guess when he (Bacon) desired to have the handling of it that he may have the honour and thanks from the King. . . .' So far as Cranfield himself was concerned, he would be very well pleased, so long as the thing were done, and his Majesty enjoyed the profit and ease that it would bring.

Ellesmere died, and at last the Woolsack was vacant. Bacon was made Lord Chancellor during a great feast given by Buckingham in celebration of his own reception of a marquisate. It was noted that Bacon was again much in favour with the King and Buckingham, and it was said that he had been granted the nomination of a barony, to assist him to discharge his debts. He had already dismissed sixteen servants as an economy.

Buckingham acquired the habit of writing to Bacon as head of the court of Chancery, to use his influence on behalf of friends who had cases in that court. He sent a stream of letters, dealing with various requests. Bacon received them with as much firmness as was consistent with the retention of his position. In one case, Buckingham asked Bacon to review his decision, and implied that it would be the worse for him if he did not alter it. Bacon did alter his decision, and behaved as if he believed that his revised decision was correct, which is indeed the opinion of some later legal experts.

Buckingham's interference with the course of the law was improper. Bacon showed strong signs that he did not like it, but he no doubt considered that if he refused to take notice of Buckingham's letters he would have been removed from office, and he conceived it more important to stay in office than lose his position in an impracticable attempt to make Buckingham behave. Such an act would have been contrary to the plan of his life, as well as his conception of the nature of political action. He was a statesman before he was a lawyer.

33. *Two Conceptions of Discovery*

BACON as principal minister participated in actions against important enemies of the state. This brought him into the case which led to the execution of Sir Walter Ralegh.

In 1603 Ralegh had been connected with persons engaged in a plot to supplant James by the Lady Arabella Stuart, who was of substantially royal descent. If she married a husband as royal as herself, their son could become a pretender to the throne.

Ralegh was at the time very unpopular, and the case against him was suspicious, but not very convincing. It was conducted by Coke with brutal unfairness. Ralegh defended himself with a courage and ability which changed public opinion in his favour. He was convicted of high treason, and lodged in the Tower while the King's warrant was awaited for his execution. From the legal point of view, he was civilly dead, so no further action of his could be legally construed as a crime.

James left him in this position, a prisoner in the Tower, indefinitely respited, but liable to execution at any time, according to James's decision to sign the warrant.

Ralegh was already over fifty years old, but neither age nor uncertainty of life had weakened his courage and resolution. He devoted his time to the composition of a *History of the World*, to chemical experiments and discussions with his friends. One of these was James's eldest son, Prince Henry, who is reported to have said: 'No man but my father would keep such a bird in a cage.'

So Ralegh passed thirteen years in the exercise of his intellect and imagination. By 1616, he had reached the age of sixty-four, with his body fit and his mind active. The ideas of his younger manhood and the memories of his expeditions to America grew in his imagination. He conceived that a new empire was still to be won in the north of South America, in what he called Guiana, the lands around the mouth of the river Orinoco which now form Venezuela. He proposed that he should lead an expedition to

U

found a base and develop gold mines that he said existed there. A large part of the new wealth was to be assigned to the King, so that the royal finances would be relieved.

James was persuaded to release Ralegh on parole, as it were, to lead the expedition. Ralegh was enthusiastically supported by relatives and friends in search of riches and adventure, and by Winwood and other persons in ruling circles. Some of these hoped that the expedition might destroy the increasingly close relations between James and Spain. It was enthusiastically approved by a large section of the public, which regarded it as a revival of the glorious traditions of the reign of Elizabeth.

In 1617, the grey-haired commander sailed once more to the West, with a fleet of fourteen ships. His commission from the King specifically laid down that he was to discover 'commodities and merchandizes' in countries 'possessed and inhabited by heathen peoples', clearly implying that he must not invade Spanish territory.

He dropped anchor off the Venezuelan coast, after losing many men through sickness, and sent five ships under Captain Keymis up the river Orinoco, to discover a rich gold mine said to exist there in savage territory. When they arrived at the supposed site, they found a Spanish settlement, which they attacked, killing a number of its inhabitants. No gold mine was found.

The party returned, after incurring heavy losses, including Ralegh's own son. Violent disputes followed as to whether they should sail on to Newfoundland, become pirates, escape to France or return to England. Such was Ralegh's strength as a commander that, after all this disaster, and at the age of sixty-six, he still remained in control. He decided to sail for home, and trust to his wit to find some way out of his situation. He planned escapes, applied drugs to himself which created appalling symptoms, and feigned madness. Several of his stratagems were nearly successful, but in the end they all failed. He was imprisoned in the Tower once more. No new legal case could be brought against him because he was 'civilly dead'.

On Ralegh's return the King had issued a proclamation that all subjects who knew anything of the affair were to report to a Privy Council commission of investigation. This contained six members, of whom Bacon was one.

Bacon had not been employed in the prosecution of 1603, but as Lord Chancellor he was necessarily concerned with the affair of 1618. It is known that Ralegh had a long conversation with Bacon in the gardens of Gray's Inn shortly before he sailed in 1617, and that this conversation was so interesting that the Earl of Exeter was kept waiting for a long time in Bacon's rooms in the Inn.

The discovery of the New World had had a profound influence on Bacon's thought. He transferred the spirit of the exploration of the earth to the exploration of the whole universe of nature. The idea of comprehensive discovery was common to the thought of both Ralegh and Bacon, though they saw it in different perspectives, one as the medium of adventure and profitable enterprise, and the other as the means to the control of nature in the interests of man. Ralegh believed that private enterprise was the best method of exploiting resources, and was a forerunner of capitalist development.

While Bacon must have been deeply interested in the exploratory aspects of the expedition, there is vague evidence that he suspected that Ralegh would turn pirate if he failed, and that when he questioned him on this, Ralegh answered: 'Tush, my Lord, did you ever hear of any that was counted a pirate for taking millions?'

Though Bacon had more than the usual official interest in the expedition, Coke seems to have been the leading man in the commission of investigation. Coke suggested on behalf of the commission that, after Ralegh had been examined in respect of his offences subsequent to his conviction in 1603, the King should consider whether he might 'not with justice and honour give warrant for his execution.' The King replied that Ralegh should be called only before those who had already examined him, and after he and others concerned had been heard, the law officers of the Crown should expound his misdemeanours. The warrant for his execution should be sent, and presently an account of the affair should be published. James simply completed the sentence passed on Ralegh in 1603. This had the effect of ordering the long-delayed execution to be carried out.

When Ralegh was taken to the scaffold, he took leave of life with a greatness that has few parallels in history. His departure became an imperishable memory of how a man could die, and decisively won him a place among the nation's heroes.

Ralegh's magnificent last appearance aroused profound indignation against the government, which had issued no

explanation of its action. None was published until several weeks
afterwards. This consisted of a Declaration drafted by the
commissioners. It is some thirty pages long, and though a collective document, shows the influence of Bacon's style. It was
entitled *A Declaration of the Demeanor and Carriage of Sir Walter
Raleigh, Knight, as well in his voyage as in and sithence his return;
and of the true motives and inducements which occasioned his
Majesty to proceed in doing justice upon him, as has been done.*

It is explained that while kings are not bound to explain their
actions, yet his Majesty had thought fit to 'manifest to the world
how things appeared unto himself', and to have the grounds of
his action expounded. Though Sir Walter Ralegh had been convicted of treason, he had been allowed to live under liberal conditions in the Tower. At length, he proposed to exploit a gold
mine in Guiana. This project was recommended to his Majesty
by Sir Ralph Winwood, Secretary of State, who said that Sir
Walter had seen the gold with his own eyes. His Majesty had no
belief in it, and was persuaded that if it did exist, the Spaniards
would have discovered it. But as Sir Walter had 'so enchanted the
world with his confident asseveration of that which every man was
willing to believe', his Majesty felt in honour bound not to 'deny
unto his people the adventure and hope of so great riches',
especially as it was his policy in 'his flourishing times of peace to
nourish and encourage noble and generous enterprizes for plantations, discoveries, and opening of new trades'.

When the Spanish Ambassador heard of the project, he denounced it to the King as piratical and a danger to the peace
between England and Spain. His Majesty thereupon explained
that Sir Walter would go on a limited commission, and if he
committed any such piratical actions he would do justice upon
him. The terms of the commission were given, so that it could be
quite clear to what Sir Walter had agreed.

But the sequel of his actions showed that 'he went his own way
and had his own ends', which were to obtain his liberty, make a
new fortune for himself, have his eye on the Spanish fleet of ships
bringing gold from Mexico, and the sacking of Spanish towns and
ships. He counted on being able to ransom his offences after his
return, and if not, then on fleeing to a foreign country.

Ralegh's progressively decreasing concern with his commission, the events of the voyage and the return were then described,
on the basis of evidence given by participants.

When the news of the sacking of the Spanish town reached Spain, the Spanish Ambassador sought an audience, and demanded justice for the outrages on subjects of the Spanish King.

Nevertheless, his Majesty had 'used a gracious and mild course' towards Sir Walter on his return, sending a Vice-Admiral to bring him in easy stages to London. Then Ralegh's extraordinary drugging of himself, his feigning of madness and his attempts to escape, were described in detail, with many quotations from the depositions of those who had been examined.

Sir Walter Ralegh had by all this made himself 'utterly unworthy of his Majesty's further mercy'. As he could not be legally prosecuted again, his Majesty was enforced to resolve to have him executed upon his former conviction.

The King left it to the world to judge how justice could have been satisfied by any other course. Sovereign princes cannot make a true judgment upon 'the bare speeches or asservations of a delinquent at the time of his death'. Their judgment must be founded 'upon examinations, re-examinations, and confrontments', and such like real proofs, as this *Declaration* was built upon. All these had been attested in the presence of the six commissioners, whose names, including Bacon's and Coke's, were appended.

The cases of Ralegh and of James were each, from their own point of view, unanswerable. Ralegh appealed to the romantic spirit of adventure, acquisition, discovery, and hostility to Spain and Roman Catholicism. Though the gold mine on the Orinoco was not found, Ralegh's belief in the wealth of Venezuela has indeed been borne out by history. Today, Venezuela may not export much gold, but she is the second-largest oil-producing country in the world. A harbour has been built far up the Orinoco, near the place where Ralegh's party looked for the non-existent gold mine, to ship iron ore from the mountain of iron ore that has been discovered not far away. The land has proved to be prodigiously rich in things even more valuable than gold.

Bacon equally supported the policy of discovery, but in a classical rational spirit, reflected in the courteous and reasonable style of the *Declaration* in which he participated. He believed in the principle of authority, of attempting to make the system of government work, of development of the world not by romantic violence but by systematic industry among nations at peace. The apparatus presented by James's government was a weak instrument for the purpose, but it was better to make the best of it, and settle down to quiet steady work rather than depend on violent courses, the age and circumstances for which were now past.

34. *Against Appeasement*

Bacon had achieved his aim of becoming Lord Chancellor, and had thereby made possible the consummation of his life's work. He was now able to publish the *Novum Organum*, containing his plan for the creation of a new life for man on earth by the development of science and its application to the conquest of nature, not as one more academic book, but a programme for mankind, proposed by the principal minister of a state. Without his political experience and position, he could not have spoken with the social authority which is an essential feature of the *Novum Organum*.

While he was perfecting his manuscript and seeing the work through the press, the life around him seethed with corruption and disaster. Nevertheless, he succeeded in launching his great ship safely through this sea of troubles, though not without severe cost to himself.

In 1612, James's daughter Elizabeth had married Frederick, the Elector Palatine and head of the union of Protestant states. Frederick was an energetic and courageous man, whose religion appealed to his neighbours the Slavonic Bohemians. These were suffering from the domination of the German Emperor Matthias, who was also King of Bohemia. The Bohemians rose against the Emperor's government in Prague, captured his ministers in the great castle overlooking the city, and threw three of the most objectionable out of a window overlooking a high cliff. They established a revolutionary government, and appealed to the Protestant powers of the world for support.

The German Emperor attacked Bohemia to re-establish his authority. Spain gave him support, in the interest of Catholicism against the spread of Protestant power. The Bohemians sought

help from Frederick, who in turn looked to his father-in-law to
bring the Protestant country of England in on their side. The
action of the Bohemians aroused great public enthusiasm in
England.

As Lord Chancellor and a member of the Council of State,
Bacon had to consider the wider implications of possible English
intervention in Bohemia. It might provoke a war with Spain.
What would England's prospects be in such a contest? Until these
had been weighed, a correct decision on intervention in Bohemia
could not be made.

He left a paper on the relations between England and Spain,
which may have been part of his notes for the Council's discussions at this time.

He argued that England was more powerful than ever before,
because the whole island was now unified, and Ireland had been
reduced to a more complete state of obedience than heretofore.
The ancient footing in France, which had been withdrawn, had
been a source of weakness rather than strength. We had the
assistance of the valiant Dutch, who were 'the powerfullest
nation at the sea that now is in the world', and whose knowledge
and industry in peace was as great as in war. Their army was 'the
best military school in the world', and would supply the English
army with expert officers.

These points would more than counterbalance any disaffection
among the people caused by the Catholics. Indeed, our strength
was sufficient both to 'spare and suppress' them.

With regard to the wealth of the kingdom, it was such that
the King knew well enough that if Spain attacked us, though he
is poor at the moment, he would soon find himself rich.

As for Spain, if their estate be inquired into, it would be found
that their root would be too narrow for their tops. Their dominions are so dispersed that they cannot be quickly relieved. For
this reason the Spaniards are better able to attack than to defend.
They have to keep up numerous bases and garrisons, which
exhaust their resources. They have more shipping than any other
nation, but few good seamen, whom they must pay at an exhorbitant rate. The cost of their numerous garrisons was so great, that
often they were not paid. This had been the cause of mutinies in
the Low Countries. He could not see how the position of Spain
could improve, for the income from the Indies was a wasting
asset, and without it, she was the poorest country in Europe.

He did not believe that Spain could defy the world at large, and yet retain the Indies. If England and the Low Countries acted together, they could produce two armadas, one to blockade Spain and the other the Indies.

For these reasons, Spain knew that her greatness depended on England, who was in a position to overthrow her.

Spain had followed a more bloody policy than any other Christian nation. Her ministers and negotiators were untrustworthy. She paid punctiliously only those debts used in corrupting the ministers of other countries. She made treaties only to have a better access to those whom she proposed to attack. Marriages did not hinder her from taking an advantage. She disturbed all Christendom with military threats, and yet did least to suppress infidels and pirates.

She had an ambition to rule the whole of Christendom. This involved all Christian princes, exciting their hatred, and necessarily causing them to oppose her.

No nation had spilled so much English blood, and corrupted so many of our people as Spain. If you wanted to find a traitor on a sudden, where would you look? At the door of the Spanish Ambassador. And when? When they come from mass. It continued so, even while the negotiations for the Spanish marriage were proceeding. Their malice is so great that they cannot hide it.

Would it be possible, even if the past were forgotten, to be at peace with her in the future? This will be impossible, because so long as Spain holds the Indies, her imperial ambition will never die.

No matter what things may be dealt in with Spain, her conduct will never be assured as long as the difference in faith endures.

She knew well enough in what danger she stood if she were attacked by England and the Low Countries. Hence, said Bacon, it would be a fit undertaking for his Majesty. He was the greatest islander in Christendom, and a navy was proper to him. He was the Defender of the Faith, as well in understanding, learning and godliness, as in title. The extension of true religion was a work that belonged to him. He was of a great and liberal mind, and the Indies would afford him the means to exercise it.

These considerations, and the multitude of his subjects invited him to undertake the project. In every part of it, considerations of religion, policy and nature seemed to indicate that it was 'a kind of offer preferred unto his Majesty as the Prince the fittest for the entertaining of it'.

Bacon was apparently of the opinion that the outcome of a war with Spain was not to be feared, and that resolute action in support of Bohemia would have successful results.

Evidently, these views had little influence on James. They may well have had far more on Gondomar, who, perhaps, had been picking Bacon's brains when he reported to Madrid at this time that the friendship of James must be secured at any price. It was true that his exchequer was empty, but the nation was rich, and a war with Spain would be immediately followed by a large grant of money. The English navy would rapidly be put into fighting trim, and the seas would swarm with privateers. Whoever was master of the seas would also be master of the land. And never was the Spanish navy, said Gondomar, so unready for such a struggle. The negotiations for the marriage of James's son must continue.

The Spaniards, with an excellent judgment of James's character, proposed that he should be a mediator between the Bohemians and the German Emperor. This appealed both to his pacifism and his vanity. He sent a special ambassador to conduct the mediation, who soon found that no compromise between the two sides was practicable.

Then the German Emperor Matthias died. His cousin Ferdinand, the heir to the Bohemian throne, claimed his crown. But the Bohemians rejected his claim, and offered the crown to Frederick. He accepted it two days before the new Emperor of Germany was elected. The Bohemians expected that now that James's son-in-law was King of Bohemia, James would intervene on their side. They had underrated his attachment to the principle of the divine right of kings. James was angry with his son-in-law for accepting a crown from the hands of rebels. He held that no rebellion against a king, not even against Nero, was justified.

He regarded Frederick as a usurper in this respect, and said he ought to 'resign Bohemia'. Gondomar reported this to Madrid. The Emperor could proceed, and Spain support him, without the fear of being attacked by England.

Neville Chamberlain's shadow had appeared more than three centuries before the man himself.

Bacon expounded his views on policy towards Spain with even

more boldness six years later, after his fall, when he was free from a minister's necessity for adapting the presentation of ideas to the personality of the head of the state. In his pamphlet on *Considerations touching a War with Spain*, written in 1624, he handles the subject with all the strength, flexibility and colour of his style, revealing thereby that he was speaking from the depths of his convictions.

He sent a copy, accompanied by a letter, to the Queen of Bohemia, who then was living in exile with her defeated husband.

35. *Infinite Business and the Abuses of the Times*

WHILE Bacon made proposals on fundamental policy which were ignored, he was engaged in furthering, as far as he could, any kind of request that Buckingham might press on him, or which might be thought to concern the King. He had to deal with such matters as the illegal export of gold by Dutch merchants; 'a poor Yorkshireman' whose house was alleged to have been set on fire by witchcraft; alleged incest by the Countess of Exeter, and corruption by the Lord Treasurer, the Earl of Suffolk. He had occasion to write, in reply to a letter from the King of Denmark, that though he was well and in the greatest comfort from the favour of his King, yet 'I am so pressed and distracted with infinite business that I seem hardly to breathe, or live, only that I regard the duties of life as far more worth than life itself . . .'.

No system of government administration through organized departments of state had as yet been worked out. Bacon proposed to the King that Commissioners should be appointed to deal with particular subjects, so that all questions which bore on them could be referred in the first instance to the particular commissioner concerned. He suggested that in addition to existing commissions for the navy, and for the buildings about London, new ones should be appointed to deal with the development of the textile industry and trade, the control of movements of gold and money, for 'provision of the realm with corn', for the introduction and development of manufactures and the setting of the people to work, and the consideration of all grants and privileges connected with these matters. A commissioner should deal with the prevention of depopulation of towns; another should control highways and drainage. There should be commissions for the 'suppressing of the grievance of informers'; for the better management of plantations abroad, and one for the supply of military equipment, guns, powder, etc.

These conceptions are forerunners of the modern ministries of trade, finance, agriculture, health, transport, works, supply, commonwealth relations and colonies, etc.

Little notice seems to have been taken of these proposals. James was more interested in the case of his Principal Secretary of State, Sir Thomas Lake, who, with his wife, had tried to extort property from his son-in-law Lord Roos by accusing him of incest with his grandfather's second wife, the Countess of Exeter; and conspiring to poison Lady Roos. James insisted on hearing the case himself. The accusations against the Countess of Exeter proved to be unfounded, and the product of a conspiracy between Lady Lake and her daughter, Lady Roos. It was found that the Lakes had also suborned witnesses. Sir Thomas had to surrender his office and submit, with his relatives, to imprisonment.

Arising out of the Countess of Exeter affair, Bacon was involved in a remarkable subsidiary case. A former schoolmaster and minister called Peacock was accused of attempting to infatuate the King's judgment in the Exeter affair by means of sorcery. Preliminary examinations of Peacock convinced Bacon that serious matters were being concealed. He advised that Peacock should be tortured in order to discover them. Torture was then a legal instrument for obtaining information which could show how legitimate evidence might be discovered. The information itself could not be accepted in court as evidence.

Chamberlain reported that Peacock had been 'hanged up by the wrists; and though he were very impatient of the torture and swooned once or twice', nothing much was wrung out of him.

Bacon had more to do with the case of the Lord Treasurer, the Earl of Suffolk, than with the Lake affair. Suffolk was accused by a former servant of illegal exactions. After many misdemeanours had been proved against Suffolk and his wife, the Duke of Lenox called to see Bacon, and suggested that if Suffolk came into court and openly acknowledged his delinquency, this should be considered as a considerable mitigation. Bacon reported the conversation to Buckingham, and said that his answer was that he would not meddle in it; and if he did, it must be to dissuade such a course, 'for that all would be but a play upon the stage, if justice went not on in the right course'.

This could be taken as a hint to Buckingham that he should amend his own conduct in such matters; it could also be taken as a hint that Bacon would not mitigate the case against one who was known to be a political opponent of Buckingham.

After Suffolk had been found guilty, Coke proposed that he should be fined £100,000. The court, including Bacon, agreed on the more reasonable figure of £30,000, and committed the Suffolks to the Tower, to be imprisoned there at their own expense. Bacon reported the sentence to Buckingham, indicating that he had supported the more moderate fine. The King was anxious to have as little trouble over the case as possible.

While these affairs were proceeding, Bacon's theory of the tides was communicated through mutual friends to Galileo, an account of whose own theory was sent in return. Both theories were erroneous.

Bacon was, as usual, forward to draw attention to his services to Buckingham and the King. His deliberate devotion to their interests led him to oppose old friends. He even supported the prosecution of Yelverton, who had been a close colleague of Bacon's from early days in Gray's Inn, and for many years in government service, and had given loyal and great help to him in his struggle with Coke.

Yelverton had got off to a good start as Attorney-General by paying the King £4,000 for the place. When he handed over the money, James had thrown his arms round his neck, and said that now he would be able to buy some new dishes which he badly needed.

Bacon and Yelverton had begun to fall apart. Bacon remarked that Mr. Attorney had been 'pretty pert' with him lately. But, he told Buckingham, he did not care about 'buzzes and stings' in course of anything that concerned his duty to the King and his love of Buckingham.

Yelverton was accused of inserting, without authority, a number of clauses in a new Royal Charter for the City of London.

This was regarded as a grave infringement of the King's prerogative. Bacon in his notes for the case said that he was 'sorry for the person, being a gentleman that I lived with in Gray's Inn; served with him when I was attorney; joined with since in many services, and one that ever gave me more attributes in public than I deserved; and besides a man of very good parts; which with me is friendship at first sight; much more joined with so ancient acquaintance'.

But as a judge he held the offence very great, as it would quickly undermine the authority of the Crown.

Yelverton, with dejected looks and tears, confessed his error in a brief and eloquent oration. He was found guilty, but not of corruption.

Coke proposed that he should be fined £6,000, but the court fixed the fine at £4,000. He was declared unfit for his office, and imprisoned during his Majesty's pleasure.

Bacon reported the result of the case to Buckingham on the next day, and told how he had sat for almost eight hours in order to see it through. 'How I stirred the court, I leave it to others to speak; but things passed to his Majesty's great honour.' He was glad that Yelverton had defended himself, for thereby he had printed more deeply the chief points of the charge against him. He did not like his behaviour, especially as he had chosen Holt as his counsel, 'who is ever retained but to play the fool'.

While Bacon paid the utmost attention to courting James and Buckingham, he wrote, in his recommendation to James to appoint a Lord Treasurer which he had been without for two years, that he should not let the 'regard of persons' be the principal consideration in his choice, but the nature of the 'affairs and the times'.

When a vacancy occurred among the judges, Bacon chose Whitelock, who had long been one of his chief political opponents in the House of Commons. Whitelock had supposed that Bacon's complimentary comments on his abilities had been mere flattery.

In his speech on Whitelock's appointment, Bacon said that a judge must be well-read in the law. He should 'keep no holiday, no not in study, nor go from your books to your brain . . . be patient in hearing causes . . . make no catch hearings . . . keep your hands clean, and the hands of your servants that are about you; keep them in awe, that they may not dare to move you in things that are unfit . . . fly all bribery and corruption, and preserve your integrity, not respecting any in course of justice; for what avails it if you should be incorrupt and yet should be partial and a respecter of persons . . .'.

Bacon made this speech on the same day that he made the final order in one of his own cases, having accepted only a few days before a purse of £100 from one of the litigants.

Overt corruption was one of the characteristics of the politics of the period. The deficiency in social discipline and the lack of an adequate administrative system, caused gross abuses to run wild on every side. The government fell back on force to smother the effects of the anarchic situation.

Bacon recommended the suppression of the 'licentious course of talking and writing'. He told Buckingham that 'My old Lord Burghley was wont to say, that the Frenchman, when he hath talked, he hath done; but the Englishman, when he hath talked, he begins.' In the case of one it evaporated discontent, but in the other kindled it. So it seemed that free speech was all right in France, as it allowed Frenchmen to blow off steam harmlessly, but a bad thing in England, where it fostered trouble.

Bacon also regarded secrecy in the conduct of affairs as of great importance. Secrecy, he said, is 'the high prerogative of kings' affairs'.

36. *The Summit*

As the helmsman of the ship of state, under the capricious captaincy of James and Buckingham, Bacon steered a course between rocks and whirlpools as dexterously as he could.

He drafted suggestion after suggestion, and programme after programme, virtually none of which were adopted, except those which he knew to be already in the minds of the King and his Favourite. Bacon got as far in politics as it is possible to get, trusting to mere intelligence. He shrank from the leadership of any group or party. He had no great natural aptitude for dealing with people. Yet he knew that without being able to 'command wits', the carrying out of any great project was impossible. His life-long attempt to secure a following, though it met with no immediate success either in politics or science, indicated what was required. The conquest of nature, like the conquest of the world, could be achieved only through social organization.

As he had drafted so many suggestive documents for the development of James's kingdom, now he submitted one grand document to all mankind, containing a plan and programme for the achievement of the Kingdom of Man over Nature. He knew from experience how to submit this proposal, not as a technician but as a statesman. The work was published in Latin, so that it could be immediately read in all European countries. The title page was a careful composition, with a picture of a great ship in the centre, about to sail between two pillars, representing the Pillars of Hercules, into the exploration of the unknown world of nature. At the head of the page, Bacon's own name comes first in large letters, and then in smaller letters his title of High Chancellor of England, and under this, in smaller letters still, the title of the work: *Instauratio Magna*, or the Great Instauration. At the bottom of the picture was a quotation from the book of Daniel: 'Many will pass through, and knowledge will be increased.' (See Plate I.) He outlined the six parts of his projects for restoring man to the position of Lord of Creation which he occupied before he was tempted and fell. He referred readers to his *Advancement of Learning* for a sketch of what should be found in Part I.

He called the second part of the work *Novum Organum*, the new method of research. He sketched an exposition of it in two books of aphorisms, 'concerning the Interpretation of Nature and the Kingdom of Man'.

The description of the remaining four parts of the *Great Instauration* consisted of an outline of their contents. The *Novum Organum* was the most substantial contribution, and owing to this, the whole work became popularly known as the *Novum Organum*. The effect of this was to narrow the general understanding of Bacon's object, from a scientific and social plan to conquer nature for the benefit of the human race, to the invention of a new method of research, especially in physics, chemistry and biology. I should not be forgotten, then, that the

proper and most illuminating title of Bacon's chief work is the
Instauratio Magna, the Great Instauration, and not the *Novum
Organum*. The adoption of the narrower and more special title
has been due to a more or less unconscious social motive: a tendency to turn away from the difficult social implications of
science to concentration on technical questions; the same motive
which tends to turn attention today from the implications of
atomic discovery to concentration on its technical development.

Bacon began to distribute copies of his book on October 12,
1620. He had dedicated it to James, and he sent the first copy to
him with a covering letter. He said that 'the work, in what
colours soever it may be set forth, is no more than a new logic,
teaching to invent and judge by induction, (as finding syllogism incompetent for sciences of nature,) and thereby to make
philosophy and sciences both more true and more active'. It
tended 'to enlarge the bounds of Reason and to endow man's
estate with new value', and was no improper oblation to his
Majesty, who of men was the 'greatest master of reason, and
author of beneficence'.

He described how he had 'been about some such work near
thirty years', and he had decided to publish it in its present imperfect state because he numbered his days, and wished it to be
saved. He hoped also that publication would draw attention to
the compiling of 'a natural and experimental history, which must
be the main foundation of a true and active philosophy'.

The project was but a new body of clay, into which his Majesty
could breathe life, if he would further it. He was persuaded that
'the work will gain upon men's minds in ages', and was 'not for
praise or glory, but for practice, and the good of men'.

James acknowledged the receipt of the book four days later,
showing a quick and very creditable interest, in a letter written
in his own hand. He said Bacon could not have sent him a more
acceptable present. He had taken a firm resolution to read it right
through, and send comments on points that occurred to him.
He would do this even if he had to steal some hours from his
sleep, for he had as little spare time to read it as Bacon had had to
write it. He assured him that he could not have chosen a subject
more befitting his place or his 'universal and methodick knowledge', and he hoped that his work would have as good success
as his heart could wish, and as his labours deserved.

Bacon was delighted by this letter, and at once tried to persuade James to participate in his project. He wrote to him again, saying that 'this work which is for the bettering of men's bread and wine, which are the characters of temporal blessings and sacraments of eternal, I hope by God's holy providence will be ripened by Caesar's star'. He hoped that his Majesty would aid him 'in setting men on work for the collecting of a natural and experimental history'. It was the basis of the project, and he assured himself that his Majesty would find it 'an excellent recreation'. Many noble inventions for man's use might be discovered, even in his Majesty's own times, and who can tell, 'now this Mine of Truth is once opened, how the veins go, and what lieth higher and what lieth lower?'

However, James found the *Novum Organum* stiffer going than he had expected. A report stated that in spite of all his favourable disposition to Bacon, he could not 'forbear sometimes, in reading his last book to say that it is like the peace of God, that passeth all understanding'.

Bacon sent a copy to the University of Cambridge. In his covering letter he said that as her son and pupil, he desired to lay in her bosom his new-born child. 'Otherwise I shall hold it for a thing exposed.' They were not to be troubled because his way was new, 'for in the revolution of time such things must needs be'. Nevertheless, the ancients retained their proper honour, 'that is, of wit and understanding; for faith is due only to the Word of God, and to Experience. Now to bring the sciences back to experience is not permitted; but to grow them anew out of experience, though laborious, is practicable.'

Bacon had now achieved the highest ambition of his life, the launching, while England's principal minister of state, of the project for the development of science and its application for the benefit of the human race.

He had adequately acquitted his ambition for mankind. His ambition for himself seemed to be advancing with parallel success.

His sixtieth birthday fell on January 22, 1621. Ben Jonson wrote verses in honour of the event:

> *Hail, happy genius of this ancient pile,*
> *How comes it all things so about thee smile?*
> *The fire, the wine, the men? and in the midst*
> *Thou standst as if some mystery thou didst!* . . .

x

England's High Chancellor, the destin'd heir
In his soft cradle of his father's chair,
Whose even thread the Fates spin round and full
Out of their choicest and their whitest wool . . .

Give me a deep-crowned bowl that I may sing
In raising him the wisdom of my king.

It was celebrated magnificently, and the King announced that he would be raised to the dignity of Viscount St. Alban.

Bacon was invested with his new title a month later, 'with all the ceremonies of robes and coronet, whereas the rest were only done by patent'.

He wrote a letter of the most reverent thanks to the King. He numbered his days both in thankfulness to God, and in warning to himself. The King had advanced him more than scarcely any other of his subjects.

'You found me of the Learned Counsel, Extraordinary, without patent or fee; a kind of *individuum vagum.* You established me, and brought me into Ordinary. Soon after, you placed me Solicitor, where I served seven years. Then your Majesty made me your Attorney or Procurator General. Then Privy Counsellor, while I was Attorney; a kind of miracle of your favour, that had not been in many ages. Thence Keeper of your Seal, and because that was a kind of planet and not fixed, Chancellor. And when your Majesty could raise me no higher, it was your grace to illustrate me with beams of honour; first making me Baron Verulam, and now Viscount St. Alban. So this is the eighth rise or reach, or diapason in music, even a good number and accord for a close. And so I may without superstition be buried in St. Alban's habit or vestment. . . .'

In return he had nothing to offer except 'care and diligence and assiduous endeavour', and he hoped that his Majesty would, finding his heart upright, bear with his other imperfections.

37. *The Fall*

THE Spaniards had convinced James that they were intend-
ing to participate only in the re-occupation of Bohemia.
But they suddenly invaded the Palatinate, of which his son-in-
law was indubitably the rightful prince.

James announced that he would give military support to his
son-in-law. In fact, he had no firm resolution to do so, but this
popular announcement at last gave him a good opportunity for
calling Parliament. Military intervention would place England
once more in the forefront of Protestant powers, prevent the
hated Spanish marriage, provide the young men with exciting
adventures and the merchants with army contracts. The House
of Commons would meet in a mood to relieve his financial
difficulties.

Ultimately, four years later, James's apparent change of
front ended in merely supplying a contingent to the army of
Count Mansfeld, a soldier-of-fortune whose campaigns dis-
integrated in incompetence and disaster, but the immediate
effect was to raise the prospect of a successful Parliament, which
James proceeded to call.

Bacon welcomed the decision, which he had so repeatedly
advised. He drafted a proclamation in which he outlined the
'reasons and respects of religion, nature, honour, and estate',
which called for the recovery of the Palatinate. Constituents
were to choose 'the worthiest men of all sorts', and should not
'disvalue or disparage the House with bankrupts and necessitous
persons', mean lawyers, unripe young men, dependents and
such like inferior persons.

James did not like the draft, because it contained not only
details on how the elections should be conducted, but comments
on policy. He held that the people were not capable of taking a
useful part in discussing policy. Bacon excused himself by remarking that he would not 'have thought of inserting matter of
state for the vulgar, but that now-a-days there is no vulgar, but

all statesmen'; a forerunner of Sir William Harcourt's phrase, two and a half centuries later, that 'we are all socialists nowadays'.

Bacon, Coke and three other councillors discussed 'what is like to be stirred' in the House of Commons. Among such matters were monopolies. They reported to the King through Buckingham that action should be taken, not 'as matter of preparation to a Parliament', but by routine review, of how the monopolies were working in practice. Something should be done about them in Parliament, and something out of Parliament, as the business required.

While these preparations were in hand, Frederick was disastrously defeated in battle at Prague. He became a fugitive. James wished him to abdicate the throne of Bohemia, leaving the way clear, as he considered, for the legitimate recovery of the Palatinate. He believed that Spain, which was still supposed to be in favour of a Spanish marriage for Prince Charles, would facilitate the recovery.

But the fall of Prague infuriated the English people, especially against Gondomar. Bacon suggested and drafted a proclamation against *Excess of Lavish Speech on Matters of State*, aimed at the protection of the Spanish Ambassador.

In this, it was pointed out that during the present reign there had been more liberty for discussing matters of state, which are not 'subjects fit for vulgar persons or common meetings'. Now while 'convenient freedom of speech' was to be allowed, and too much restraint was a sign of weakness, everyone from the highest to the lowest was commanded 'to take heed how they intermeddle by pen or speech with causes of state or secrets of empire'. They were to contain themselves within the modest limits of their callings, and of dutiful subjects. Those who heard such 'lavish discourse' were not to give it any 'applause', but report it to the Privy Council within twenty-four hours, or suffer imprisonment.

At last the Parliament met, on the 30th of January, 1621, eight days after Bacon's triumphant sixtieth birthday. It was the first for six years.

The King in his speech from the throne said that Parliament had been called to assist his finances and support him in his attempts to pacify Christendom. The Palatinate, which was the inheritance of his grandson, had been invaded, and he was determined to assist its recovery, by peaceful negotiation if possible: if not, by the sword. But he could not do this without ample and immediate supplies, for which he looked to them.

His speech was well received, and he was quickly voted £164,000.

Bacon offered advice on how the parliamentary business should be conducted. The speeches should be the speeches of counsellors, and not of orators; their committees should tend to dispatch and not to dispute; public should be put before private business, and liberty of speech should not be turned into licence. Members were to 'represent the people', not to 'personate' them.

So far, all had gone well. But the military experts estimated that an adequate army for recovering the Palatinate would cost at least £500,000 a year. The subsidies already granted would meet only one-third of this for one year, and no other expenses at all.

While military estimates were being considered, the Committee for Grievances drew attention to the monopolies. At the beginning of James's reign there were only eight or nine, but now there were 'so many scores'. Any offence against them was censured by the Star Chamber court. By 1620, its powers were being used in a wholesale manner to enforce the monopolies, and Chamberlain reported that 'the world is now much terrified with the Star Chamber'.

Many of the monopolies had been established since Bacon had become Lord Keeper. He had recommended some of them, and he had strongly supported the most unpopular. Of the latter, the patents for alehouses and inns were particularly notorious. The patent for inns had been suggested by Sir Giles Mompesson, a relative of Buckingham. By this patent, Mompesson was granted the power of licensing inns, through which they could be controlled, so that they should be conducted in an orderly manner, at fair prices.

Bacon and Coke were both of the opinion that the patent was legal. In practice, Mompesson operated it in a manner opposite to its alleged intention. It was found that no one could get a licence unless Mompesson received a bribe. Honest hosts who refused to pay a bribe could not get licences, whereas pimps and bawds flourished.

Such patents caused much scandal, but manufacturing

monopolies raised far more serious opposition, for they interfered with manufacturing and financial interests.

In 1574, Versellini had attempted to introduce the manufacture of Venetian glass into England. He had been granted a
patent by Elizabeth, which passed to Sir Jerome Bowes. The
furnaces used under this patent were fired with wood. In 1611,
Sir Edward Zouch introduced a coal-firing process. A considerable sum was invested in this new industry. The owners then
informed the government that they would not continue the process unless they were given a monopoly of all glass-making.

The Privy Council had been concerned about the steady
destruction of England's woods, and of a possible shortage of
timber for the navy. They saw the advantages of the coal-
firing process, and informed Bowes that his old wood-firing process was injurious to the commonwealth. He lost his patent but
received a state pension. A new patent was issued in the names of
Zouch and of several courtiers. Shortly afterwards, in 1615, the
importation of foreign glass was forbidden.

The monopoly of gold and silver thread manufacture raised
more indignation. These threads, required in court and decora-
tive dress, had been imported. In 1611 four persons under the
patronage of Lady Bedford were granted a monopoly to manufacture such threads. Lady Bedford arranged with the great
French capitalist Burlomachi to send a Frenchwoman to England to teach the process. The patentees were soon engaged in
struggles to prevent the infringement of their patent. In 1616
they obtained a second patent, and added Sir Edward Villiers
to their roll. But the goldsmiths, who claimed that they had long
been engaged in making gold thread, persistently opposed the
legality of the patent. Sir Edward Villiers then complained of the
goldsmiths' attitude to his brother and the King. James ordered
all offenders to be put in prison, but did not state on what
grounds. No action was taken, for his letter was detained by the
Attorney-General, 'thinking the King not well informed'.

James then commandeered the industry. All profits were to
go to him, and handsome pensions were to be paid to the two
Villiers' who were among the patentees. This plan was drawn
up by Bacon, and proclaimed in 1618. It virtually admitted that
the patent of 1616 was illegal. Though Bacon was the instrument
of this extreme monopoly, he left a note in his papers that
'monopolies, which are the cankers of all trading, be not admitted

under specious colours of public good'. However, Yelverton stated in 1621 that in his opinion the thread patent was not a monopoly, and there is indirect evidence that Bacon was of the same opinion.

Bacon had expressed his opinion on the value of patents as an aid to invention and a benefit to the commonwealth in the Commons, as long ago as 1601.

The main ground of the opposition to the gold thread was that its manufacture in England was not new.

Bacon's support for this patent was based on economic theory. He believed that gold and silver were more than commodities, being the pure form of wealth. It was advantageous to bring gold, or foreign wealth, into the country, and it was not permissible to leave the utilization of pure wealth as a raw material to mere artisans. If the country's gold, the essence of its wealth, was to be utilized, it must be done under complete government supervision.

Bacon discovered a law of Henry VII forbidding the use of gold for other than specified purposes, of which gold thread was not one. The views of the law courts on the legality of the patent were therefore irrelevant.

The new patent was put into vigorous operation by Michell and Mompesson. Unauthorized workshops making gold thread were closed and their tools seized. Silkmen selling the thread were arrested. Five of them were brought before Bacon to state their complaints, and were sent back to prison. This caused uproar in the city. Four aldermen offered £100,000 bail, and the King released them.

But there was no change of policy. On October 10th, 1619, there was a new proclamation, drawn up by Bacon.

'Whereas the art or mystery of making gold and silver thread hath formerly been used and made by strangers in foreign parts only, and from thence transported into this our realm, but of late hath been practised by some of our loving subjects, who by their great charge and industry have so well profited therein, and attained to such perfection in that art that they equal the strangers in the making thereof, and are able by the labours of our own people to make such store as shall be sufficient to furnish the expense of this whole kingdom;—And whereas we, esteeming it a principal part of our office as a king and sovereign prince to cherish and encourage the knowledge and invention of good and

profitable arts and mysteries, and to make them frequent among
our people, especially such wherein our people may employ their
labours comfortably and profitably, and many thereby may be
kept from idleness, hereby to preserve and increase the honour
and wealth of our State and people;—And finding that the exercise of this art or mystery (considering the continual use of bullion
to be spent in the manufacture thereof) is a matter of great
importance, and therefore fitter for our own immediate care than
to be trusted into the hands of any private persons, for that the
consumption or preservation of bullion, whereof our coins, the
sinews and strength of our state, are made, is a matter of so high
consequence as it is only proper for ourself to take care and
account of;—We have therefore, to the good liking of the inventors thereof, taken the said manufacture of gold and silver thread
into our hands, and so purpose to retain and continue it, to be
exercized only by agents for ourselves, who shall from time to
time be accountable to us for the same.'

Here Bacon flatly supported what he conceived to be the
interests of the state against private enterprise. Those who did
not accept his theory of the special importance of gold found
his economic argument erroneous, and those who contended that
all questions arising from royal grants should come under the
jurisdiction of the common law, and not under a court stemming
from the Privy Council, believed that his policy struck at the
freedom of private enterprise.

Energetic efforts were made to carry out the proclamation.
Illegal thread was seized; but the manufacture did not pay. The
patentees failed to import bullion, and gold coin was melted
down to provide raw material. City and Parliament were seething
with discontent.

Bacon saw the degree of unrest, and in accordance with his
principle of trying to carry Parliament with the King, by drawing
it into participation in government, he suggested to Buckingham
that it might be wise for the family to withdraw from the patents
and 'put off the envy of these things'. Buckingham coldly rejected this advice.

Bacon believed that the patent was good in principle, but
should be relinquished in face of such intense opposition. He was
in favour of withdrawing it before Parliament was called. But the
King in Council would not accept this proposal.

The gold thread monopoly turned out so badly that the Buckingham family made very little out of it. Nevertheless, Buckingham regarded any opposition to it as a personal insult. Yelverton's lack of enthusiasm for the patent was one of the causes of his disgrace. In the changes that followed, Montagu purchased the Lord High Treasurership for £20,000, and became Lord Mandeville.

In his speech to Parliament in 1621 James explained his view that parliament was an assembly forming part of a monarchy, and acting under a monarch. There might be councils, but there could be no parliament without the king. Parliament was called by the king as the representatives of the various classes of his subjects, to give him advice. This enabled him to make good laws for the benefit of the commonwealth. The House of Commons' special functions were to provide money and bring to light faults in justice and administration. In return it was the king's duty to afford them justice and mercy.

James had so little real intention of fighting for the liberation of the Palatinate that he even allowed English guns, at that time highly esteemed, to be sold to Spain. The Commons strongly protested against this aid to the persecutors of the Protestants.

But on the whole the House had been very complaisant to James on foreign affairs and finance. He declared that if they had any grievances he would be willing to meet them half-way.

The Cornish member Noy proposed that there should be an inquiry into monopolies. He was seconded by Coke, who had returned to the Commons after his ejection from his place as Lord Chief Justice. He was still a Privy Councillor, and the House was overjoyed at having a Councillor in their ranks. Coke brought all of his immense energy and mastery of the common law to the attack on the monopolies, with which he associated Bacon. A committee of the House began to investigate the patent for inns. Mompesson, who was responsible for its conduct, was a member of the House. Plentiful evidence of his disgraceful behaviour was brought forward. The committee condemned the patent and requested Coke to present their report to the House.

Then the patent for alehouses was investigated, and it was proved that the patentees had not suppressed drunkenness but collected fines for those publicans who were willing to pay for the opportunity to ignore the law. Coke moved that Michell, who had operated the patent, should be sent to the Tower. Michell was abused and condemned unheard. The Star Chamber in its worst days was never more contemptuous of human rights. This behaviour gave Bacon cause to doubt the wisdom of placing supreme power in the hands of the Commons.

Mompesson threw himself on the mercy of the House. Coke reported that under his patent 3,320 innkeepers had been prosecuted, and that in Hampshire, of the sixty licensed houses, sixteen had been previously closed as disorderly.

When officers were sent to arrest Mompesson, he retired into his wife's room, where the officers were too polite to follow, and jumped out of a window. He fled to the Continent, probably with the help of Buckingham.

After these proceedings, the attention of the House moved towards Bacon, who had drafted certain of these monopolies, and as a referee had sanctioned their legality.

Noy and Coke had been supported at first by the sole voice of Lionel Cranfield, an able self-made city business man, who hated Bacon's class and cultural superiority, and was contemptuous of his lack of conpetence in business. As Coke opposed the monopolies in the interests of common law, Cranfield opposed them because they were obnoxious to the city business men. He tried to prove that Bacon had unlawfully certified certain patents. He did not secure immediate agreement, but a few days later the unravelling of the scandals of the gold and silver thread patents began.

The champions of the common law were horrified by the arbitrary proceedings of the patentees. The business men were horrified by the interference with business, described as interference with the freedom to labour, while the economists were horrified by the melting of coin.

The Commons sent a demand to the Lords for an inquiry. It was evident that it was reviving the old principle of parliamentary impeachment, which had been systematically evaded by the Tudors. This revival implied a limitation of the royal prerogative which had been the core of James's thought and life. He summoned the Commons before him, and wished to know on what they founded their claim to omnipotence. There was no precedent for what they were doing, except in times of anarchy. Formerly, his subjects had asked any favours they desired either of himself or Buckingham. 'But now, as if we had both ceased to exist, they go to the Parliament. All this is most disrespectful. I will, therefore, tell you a fable. In the days when animals could speak, there was a cow burthened with too heavy a tail, and, before the end of the winter, she had it cut off. When the summer came, and the flies began to annoy her, she would gladly have had her tail back again. I and Buckingham are like the cow's tail, and when the session is over you will be glad to have us back again to defend you from abuses.'

The Commons were not impressed. In the afternoon they sent representatives to lay their complaints on the monopolies before the House of Lords. Bacon and Mandeville rose to reply to the charges, but were ruled out of order and compelled to apologize to the House for attempting to speak at a conference without permission.

It is said that Bacon told the King that 'those that will strike at your Chancellor it is much to be feared, will strike at your crown'. If the King surrendered his authority to decide for himself whether to accept the advice given him by the Commons on, for example, the question of referees, the Commons would, in effect, become the sovereign power. At this time, Bacon seems to have believed that he was engaged only in a constitutional struggle. He wrote to Matthew that he would not have his friends apprehensive either of or for him, 'for I thank God my ways are sound and good'.

The King decided to try to shield the referees by supporting the abolition of the monopolies. Coke brought in a bill to that effect. The Commons did not proceed against the patentees, but made a law which established that all disputes concerning commercial privileges should come under the jurisdiction of the common law. This was an important step towards the bringing of the control of business into the hands of business men, and away from the control of the Chancery courts. It eased the way towards the supremacy of private enterprise.

In the hostility towards Bacon suspicious eyes were looking for faults in the court of Chancery. Cranfield and Coke criticized its protection of insolvent debtors, which was described as no better than stealing.

The Commons' interest in the referees was transferred to this further and graver cause of scandal. As none of the referees, except Bacon, was ever proceeded against as such, the Commons was evidently primarily concerned with attacking Bacon as the chief instrument of the actions they disapproved. Scandals in Bacon's court of Chancery were a far more effective means than the monopolies for overthrowing him, so the Commons concentrated its attention on them.

The new charges of corruption in the Chancery court were brought forward on information provided by John Churchill, a former Deputy Registrar of the Chancery, who had apparently been sacked by Bacon for irregularities in his work. Churchill said that he would 'not sink alone', and offered confessions not only of his own misdeeds, but accounts of those of others.

Bacon seems to have had no inkling at first that there was a suggestion that he was implicated, and he announced 'that any man might speak freely anything concerning his court'.

Then one Christopher Aubrey appeared at the House of Commons with a petition charging the Lord Chancellor with bribery.

Aubrey stated that he had sent £100 through Sir George Hastings to the Lord Chancellor to secure a favourable decision in an appeal against him, which was before Bacon's court. The money had been accepted, but it did not secure a favourable decision. Aubrey had received 'a killing order', ejecting him from his post. Hastings was a member of the House of Commons and was immediately asked for an account of the affair. He said that Aubrey gave him a box, the contents of which he was unaware, and requested him to hand it to Bacon. He did so, and Bacon hesitated, saying it was too much, and then accepted it only from himself and not from Aubrey.

Then one Edward Egerton appeared. He was a foolish man who had conveyed away his estate, and then wanted it back. The case had first come before Ellesmere who had decided against Egerton. In the later developments the case was to have been transferred to the court of King's Bench.

Egerton called to see Bacon, and was told that the Lord Keeper was engaged. He produced a bag containing £400, which was taken by Sir Richard Young and given to Bacon in the presence of Hastings. Egerton had been a client of Bacon's in the earlier stages of the case, while Ellesmere was still Lord Chancellor. He sent the message that the money was a present for his earlier services, and he desired he would buy some hangings for his house with it. Bacon poised the purse in his hand, and accepted it only after repeated assurances that it was for past services. He sent a message to Egerton that he had not only enriched him, but had laid a tie on him to do him justice in all his rightful causes.

Egerton's case came before Bacon some months later, but Bacon did not award him anything more than was strictly his due. Egerton re-opened the case no less than three times in subsequent years, but Bacon's judgment was not upset.

The report on the two cases was made to the House of Commons by Phelips. He pointed out in most moderate language that a complete investigation was absolutely necessary. He said that 'It is a cause of great weight. It concerns every man here. For, if the fountains be muddy, what will the streams be? If the great dispenser of the King's conscience be corrupt, who can have any courage to plead before him?'

The Commons decided to lay the report before the Lords 'without prejudice or opinion'. As Bacon was a peer, only the peers could try him.

He regarded the accusation as a revenge for failure to overthrow him on the question of the patents. At first he had shown no sign of awareness that the action was more than a factious attack on authority, the King and himself, and had said to his colleague Hastings: 'Well, George, if you lay it on me, I must deny it on my honour.' Two weeks of the preliminary House of Commons inquiry completely dissipated this apparent unconcern. He wrote to Buckingham: 'Your Lordship spoke of purgatory; I am now in it, but my mind is in a calm, for my fortune is not my felicity. I know I have clean hands, and a clean heart; and, I hope, a clean house for friends or servants. But Job himself, or whoever was the justest judge, by such hunting for matters against him as hath been used against me, may for a time seem foul, especially in a time when greatness is the mark, and accusation is the game. And if this be to be a Chancellor, I think if the Great Seal lay upon Hounslow Heath nobody would take it up.' He hoped that the King and Buckingham would put an end to his straits 'one way or other'. His greatest fear was that his health would break down under all his business and these cares, and 'it will be thought feigning or fainting'.

His health did break down temporarily under the strain. His opponents received news of this with sharp suspicion, but it seemed to be genuine. It conveniently excused him from attending the House of Lords, and being personally requested to vacate the Lord Chancellor's seat, the Woolsack. In his letter of apology to the Lords, he wrote that though sick in heart and back, it was joined 'with that comfort of mind, that persuadeth me that I am not far from Heaven, whereof I feel the first fruits'. He asked for an opportunity to answer the charges, and said he would not 'trick up an innocency with cavillations; but plainly and ingenuously (as your Lordships know my manner is) declare what I know or remember . . .'. He mentioned that he had made 'two thousand decrees and orders in a year', and implied that among so many, there might well be more than one that was open to question.

James proposed that he should appoint a commission of eighteen, six from the Lords and twelve from the Commons, to investigate the charges. It would have been easy to choose eighteen friends from the total membership of both houses. Coke successfully opposed the proposal, saying: 'Let us see that this gracious message taketh not away our parliamentary proceeding.'

A fresh petition was then presented to the Commons, demanding an inquiry into Bacon's acceptance of a bribe of £300 from Lady Wharton. This woman had been three times married, and spent her life in litigations. A discontented servant discovered among her papers evidence that she might not be entitled to lands she had inherited from her second husband. The case came before Bacon.

He delivered a judgment which had the effect of allowing Lady Wharton to retain the lands, but this did not satisfy Lady Wharton. She wished the deed on which evidence had been given against her to be invalidated. The case was re-opened, and Lady Wharton intended to make sure this time that the result should be exactly as she wished. She called on Bacon with a purse containing £100 in her hand. 'What is that that you have in your hand?' asked Bacon. She replied that it was a purse she had made herself, which she hoped he would accept. Bacon replied: 'What lord could refuse a purse of so fair a lady's working?' She said that she would send £200 more on the successful conclusion of her case. Bacon re-affirmed his previous decision, and received the further £200. This was at the time Bacon had told the new judge, Whitelock, that as a judge he must not only be pure, but see that the hands of his servants were likewise pure. But it was then discovered that Bacon's previous decree had not been properly entered in the records of his court, and that the Deputy Registrar, John Churchill, had been bribed by Lady Wharton to alter the decree. The case had to be re-opened yet again. Lady Wharton complained that though she had paid her money, she had not got what she wanted.

Bacon was glad to hear that he was not to be judged by the Commons but by the Lords. Brent wrote that 'his most judicious friends have already given him for gone. Notwithstanding, himself is merry, and doubteth not that he shall be able to calm all the tempests raised against him.'

Bacon wrote to the King that 'when I enter into myself, I find not the materials of such a tempest as is comen upon me'. He had never 'been the author of any immoderate counsel'. He had 'been no haughty or intolerable, or hateful man' in his conversation or character.

'For briberies and gifts wherewith I am charged, when the book of hearts shall be opened, I hope I shall not be found to have the troubled fountain of a corrupt heart in a depraved habit of taking awards to pervert justice, however I may be frail and partake of the abuses of the times. And therefore I am resolved, when I come to my answer, not to trick my innocency, as I writ to the Lords, by cavillations or voidances; but to speak to them the language which my heart speaketh to me, in excusing, extenuating, or in ingenuous confessing; praying God to give me the grace to see to the bottom of my faults, and that no hardness of heart do steal upon me under show of more neatness of conscience than is cause.'

Bacon said that he had first made his reputation in the Commons, 'and now it must be the place of the sepulture thereof'. Yet in the current Parliament, the Commons had said that he was the same man still, 'only honesty was turned into honour'.

The House of Lords proceeded to judgment on the patents. It ordered Mompesson to be imprisoned for life, degraded from knighthood and generally held in infamous person. This was the first time for two centuries that a case of malversation by an official had been judged not by the King, but by Parliament. It was a serious inroad on the scope of the royal prerogative established by the Tudors.

James cancelled several of the most obnoxious patents before the Lords' consideration of Bacon had begun. They appointed committees of investigation, and made no provision for the defence of the accused. They specially ordered that 'no witnesses were to be examined what they received themselves, but only what bribes were given the Lord Chancellor'.

Bacon asked that he should hear through the medium of his 'matchless friend' Buckingham what was the King's attitude to him, for 'I have ever been your man'. The events increased Buckingham's anxiety, for he perceived that the methods which were being used against Bacon might be used against himself. He pleaded with the King for the dissolution of Parliament, so that the inquiries should stop, but it was impossible for his plea to be granted. The magnitude of his failure appeared all the greater because the King had nearly always granted his pleas.

So Buckingham swung over from ardent support for Bacon to alleged disapproval of his conduct.

Bacon hastily drafted a will: 'I bequeath my soul to God above, by the oblation of my conscience. My body to be buried obscurely. My name to the next ages, and foreign nations. . . .'

He composed a psalm to God, in which he said:

'The state and bread of the poor and oppressed have been precious in mine eyes: I have hated all cruelty and hardness of heart: I have (though in a despised weed) procured the good of all men. . . . Besides my innumerable sins, I confess before thee, that I am debtor to thee for the gracious talent of thy gifts and graces, which I have neither put into a napkin, nor put it (as I ought) to exchangers, where it might have made best profit; but misspent it in things for which I was least fit; so as I may truly say, my soul hath been a stranger in the course of my pilgrimage. . . .'

In this period of acute depression Bacon doubted whether he had been correct when he had decided to secure political place and experience. He felt he should have devoted himself exclusively to science and learning. In this state of mind he showed the conventional reaction towards abasement of one who had been brought up as a Christian.

Bacon could not see the evidence collected against him, so in ignorance of official information he asked for an audience with the King. In his notes for the interview he gave the lines of the defence he would have pursued, if he had had the opportunity.

'There be three causes of bribery charged or supposed in a judge.

The first, of bargain or contract for reward, to pervert justice.

The second, where the judge conceives the cause to be at an end by the information of the party or otherwise, and useth not such diligence as he ought to enquire of it.

And the third, when the cause is really ended, and it is *sine fraude*, without relation to any precedent promise.

Now if I may see the particulars of my charge, I shall deal plainly with your Majesty, in whether of these causes my particular case falls. But for the first of them I take myself to be as innocent as any born upon St. Innocent's Day in my heart. For the second, I doubt, in some particulars I may be faulty; and for the last, I conceived it to be no fault, but therein I desire to be better informed, that I may be twice penitent, once for the fact, and again for the error. For I had rather be a briber than a defender of bribes.

I must likewise confess to your Majesty that, at new year's tides, and likewise at my first coming in (which was, as it were, my wedding), I did not so precisely, as perhaps I ought, examine whether those that presented me had causes before me, yea or no. And this is simply all I can say for the present concerning my charge, until I may receive it more particularly.'

If the King were prepared to retain him in his present position, he hoped he would be a new man, and reform himself. If he had to be relieved of some of his offices, then he would be more strong and 'delivré' to perform the rest. He would deal ingenuously with his Majesty, 'without seeking fig-leaves or subterfuges'.

The King, who was said to have wept when he heard of the situation of Bacon, received him privately, and treated him kindly, giving him 'comfortable access'.

The Lords appointed a joint committee of sixteen peers and prelates to draw up the report on the investigation. It contained the saintly and learned Bishop Lancelot Andrewes, one of Bacon's best friends, and none of the Villiers family or their followers. Bacon informally received copies of the depositions before them, and after studying them gave up all further effort of defence. He saw that his case was legally indefensible, so he tried to resign with the hope that he would be spared further disgrace.

He suggested to the King that dismissal from the Lord Keepership, after confession, would be a sufficient punishment, 'if it be reformation that is sought'. This would be as severe a punishment for such offences as any that had been given during the last four hundred years. The suit was the last he would make to his Majesty, after serving him fifteen years. As 'I presumed to say to your Majesty, am still a virgin for matters that concern your person or crown.'

Y

He decided to make a confession and submission on these lines to the House of Lords.

He said that, in the midst of as great an affliction as 'mortal man can endure (honour being above life) . . .' he would begin by confessing gladness that, after the example of himself, the greatness of a judge's position would be no sanctuary against guiltiness, which is 'the beginning of a golden world', and judges would fly from corruption as from a serpent. Though he was 'the anvil whereupon these good effects are beaten and wrought', he took no small comfort from it.

He sent his submission to the House of Lords, where it was presented by the Prince of Wales.

In it he wrote that: 'it resteth therefore that, without fig-leaves, I do ingenuously confess and acknowledge that, having understood the particulars of the charge, not formally from the House, but enough to inform my conscience and memory, I find matters sufficient and full, both to move me to desert the defence, and to move your lordships to condemn and censure me'. He humbly pleaded that his removal from the Lord Chancellorship would be a sufficient punishment.

The reading of his letter was followed by a long silence. It did not satisfy the Lords, who desired definite answers, yes or no, on the truth of each of the charges. Among those who were determined not to allow Bacon any mitigation was Lord Southampton, who had been one of the chief associates of Essex in his rebellion. Unlike Essex he had not been executed but imprisoned in the Tower. He was released when James came to the throne. He had never forgiven Bacon for his part in the trial of Essex. The sole vote against the acceptance of the report by the House of Lords was given by Buckingham.

A copy of the evidence was officially sent to Bacon. He asked for time to consider it, which raised the suspicion that he intended to make a defence. In reply to a direct question, Bacon wrote: 'The Lord Chancellor will make no manner of defence to the charge, but meaneth to acknowledge corruption, and to make a particular confession to every point, and after that an humble submission. . . .'

In the confession he said: 'Upon advised consideration of the charge, descending into my own conscience, and calling my memory to account so far as I am able, I do plainly and ingenuously confess that I am guilty of corruption; and do renounce all defence, and put myself upon the grace and mercy of your Lordships.'

He confessed to twenty-eight items, involving gifts and loans to a total value of about £11,630. They included a gift of gold buttons worth £50; hangings for York House worth £160, and a rich cabinet said to be worth £800. Most of the gifts were of about one or two hundred pounds. Some of the gifts had been made when he was Lord Keeper, and at the time of the New Year.

Finally, Bacon confessed that he had given way 'to great exactions by my servants, both in respect of private seals, and otherwise, for the sealing of injunctions'. It was 'a great fault of neglect in me, that I looked no better to my servants'. He pointed out that he was not an avaricious man, implying that he had not been collecting wealth merely for hoarding; and that few or none of the items were less than two years old. This seemed to indicate that he had recognized the existence of irregularities two years ago, and had since restored order in his affairs.

The Lords sent a commission to ask whether he would stand by his confession. He replied: 'My Lords, it is my act, my hand, my heart. I beseech your Lordships, be merciful to a broken reed.'

Another commission was sent to relieve him of the Great Seal. They found him very sick, and wished he had been better. He replied: 'The worse the better. By the King's great favour I received the Great Seal; by my own great fault I have lost it.'

After agreeing without dissent that Bacon was guilty, the Lords discussed his sentence. They decided that he should not be deprived of his title, but should be fined £40,000, be imprisoned in the Tower during his Majesty's pleasure, should be incapable of holding any office in the state, and never sit in Parliament, nor come within the verge, that is, within twelve miles, of the Court. As Bacon was ill, the King respited his conveyance to the Tower, but a fortnight later he was imprisoned there, at the end of May, 1621.

So Bacon departed from public life. In social affairs no degree of solitary ability can be a successful substitute for co-operation between the members of a group. Even the most transcendent abilities, in isolation, are betrayed by lack of criticism. Bacon tried to govern a corrupt society by his own ability alone, acting through the King and one or two other powerful persons.

He had no collaborating equals who could insist on the

correction of the mismanagement of his personal finances, and help him where he was weak.

The offences through which his political fall was encompassed, and the rising business men and Puritans were enabled to strike a blow at the prerogative, were in fact relatively trivial money matters, though they were dressed to appear as the depths of immorality. It was an unfortunate political mistake to have presented his opponents with such an easy way of getting rid of him.

38. *Criminal or Invalid?*

THERE is no evidence that any of Bacon's thousands of legal decrees were reversed on appeal, as a result of his conviction for bribery. Though he had accepted presents or 'compliments' before cases had been decided, his legal judgment had not been influenced by them. In several cases, the judgments were of outstanding legal excellence. This made many of those who had given him bribes particularly bitter, for they regarded him as having broken faith with them. They considered they had been swindled.

Shady financiers, some of the most prominent of whom were in Parliament, regarded him as one of themselves, and hated him for his superior airs, which they considered hypocritical.

Bacon's financial irregularities were not very large compared with those common at the time. He was almost alone in not paying the King for his offices and promotions. Some considered that he was open to reprehension for having accepted high office without making payments to the King. He probably believed that his financial probity was higher than was customary.

The passage of time steadily confirms the truthfulness of Bacon's writings. Fundamentally, he was incorruptible. As Feuerbach remarked, he had an essential nobility of mind that shines through his works.

The Spaniards, and their ambassador Gondomar who admired him so greatly, never pensioned him, though they paid Sir Robert Cecil and others.

When the House of Lords condemned Bacon, acting as its own

prosecutor, judge and jury, and not granting him the usual means of defence, they were engaged in making a political rather than a legal judgment. The prosecution was conducted more like an investigation by a political commission. The Marconi affair is a rough modern parallel. In this, the Chancellor of the Exchequer, Lloyd George, and the Attorney-General, Rufus Isaacs, were accused of speculation in Marconi shares, while the Government was negotiating with the Marconi Company of Great Britain. The commission of inquiry divided on party lines, and as the Liberals and their supporters had a small majority, the two ministers were not condemned. If the Liberals had not had a majority the decision would almost certainly have gone against the ministers, who would have been forced to retire from public life. Asquith, who was their Prime Minister, said that the incident was the most unpleasant in his experience.

Bacon, like the Liberal ministers, was rather insensitive to the financial conventions of his day. The attitude towards the acceptance of gifts by statesmen and judges in feudal times differed from that which emerged in a money economy. It had been customary to present gifts to dispensers of justice. It was regarded as a mark of respect. With the development of the use of money, actions were measured more and more in terms of money values.

A considerable part of the change from the feudal attitude on gifts occurred during Bacon's lifetime. In his youth, Burghley was accepting gifts recognized as proper, which forty years later would have been regarded by the new business men as questionable. Statesmen and judges were not paid more than token salaries by the state. According to feudal conceptions they were landlords who had their own means of support, and dispensed justice as part of their social duties, for which they were not additionally paid.

Bacon was a man of genius with little inherited wealth, lacking in common perceptions, and deficient in business ability, who engaged in statesmanship when the state had not yet worked out a system of administration and salaries appropriate to the new economy. He was brought up in Burghley's household, and the Court, where his feeling for 'magnificence' was nourished. This notion, feudal in ancestry, had been taken over by the Renaissance and developed in its own way. Bacon regarded it as a concomitant of greatness. He was conscious of the magnitude of his own gifts, and he considered it a point of principle to live in an appropriate style.

Bacon's passion for magnificence was reflected in his ideas as well as his tastes. His *Great Instauration* was the apotheosis of grandeur in ideas. He said of Xenophanes of Colophon that he was 'a man of vast conception, breathing nothing but infinity'. This was also true of himself. The *Great Instauration* is a sublimation of his subjective aspirations.

As he had not sufficient means to support what he considered to be the appropriate style, he borrowed. Through the whole of his adult life he was never out of debt, on a considerable part of which he perpetually paid ten per cent interest.

His personal accounts from June to September, 1618, at the time when he was accepting some of the presents later described as bribes, are known.

During those three months his receipts totalled £4,160. This included a sum of £400 from Toby Matthew, which was probably one of the bribes. He gave £302 in tips, and paid out £3,711 for household expenses. Thus he was living at a rate of £12,000 a year.

Some typical items from his accounts are:

GIFTS AND REWARDS

	£	s.	d.
June, 1618			
26. To one that brought your Lp. cherries and other things from Gorhambury by your Lp.'s order		6	0
July, 1618			
5. To Mr. Recorder's man that brought your Lp. a salmon		10	0
5. To my La. Poyznes her man that brought your Lp. a stag	2	0	0
14. To the King's trumpeters by your Lp. order	2	4	0
14. To the Prince's trumpeters by your Lp. order	3	6	0
31. To Sir Edward Carew's man that brought your Lp. boxes of orange flowers, by your Lp. order		10	0
August, 1618			
1. To a poor pilgrim by your Lp. order		2	4
September, 1618			
10. To a Dutch musician by your Lp. order	1	2	0
14. To Mr. John Murray's man, that brought your Lp. a book from the King, by your Lp. orders	4	8	0
17. To a poor woman, one Knight's wife, by your Lp. order	1	2	0
17. To one that brought your Lp. strawberries from Hackney		11	0

PAYMENTS

	£	s.	d.
June, 1618			
25. Paid the Lining draper and sempster's bill for cloth and lace and making your Lp. Ruffs, & Cuffs, & Shirts, as appears by the particulars	29	8	10
July, 1618			
9. Paid Mr. Parkinson the Linen draper by your Lp. order in part of his bill of 158 lb.	50	0	0
25. Paid Mr. Pemberton silkman in part of his bill of 130 lb. by your Lp. order 50 lb. So there remains due to him 80 lb.	50	0	0
25. Paid Mr. Markham silkman in part of his bill of 326 lb. 4s 6d. by you Lp. order 50 lb. Rem. 276.4.6. ..	50	0	0
25. Paid Mr. Askew the silkman by your Lp. order in full of his bill of all due to him	48	0	0
August, 1618			
15. Paid Mr. Wells your Lp. Butcher at Gorhambury in part of his bill of a greater sum due unto him by your Lp. order	100	0	0
22. Paid Mrs. Harris by your Lp. order for a fair ruby set in a ring	20	0	0

Interest at 10 per cent was paid on £1,000 and many other sums. One of his most interesting items was £33, 'paid the picture drawer for your Lp. picture', probably for the portrait by Somers. His domestic staff consisted of about 150 persons.

His passion for grand houses, beautiful things, fine clothes, exquisite flowers, odours and tastes was taken by many for vanity, and was supposed by some to reflect vices.

Before his impeachment, Bacon seems to have believed that the gifts he received were legitimate. Afterwards he recognized that at least some of them fell within the definition of bribery.

The acceptance of gifts for which he was condemned occurred about the time when he became Lord Keeper. He spared no expenses in maintaining his position in the manner he considered essential to the dignity of the state and himself. Having little means of his own, he probably took it for granted that presents which enabled him to maintain this dignity were justified. But the fact that he seems soon to have stopped accepting such presents suggests that he had doubts about them. Bacon's recognition of some of the presents as bribes was due in part to a change of social values in assessing acts.

Bacon remarked after his condemnation that the sentence was just and for reformation's sake fit, but he never admitted that he had allowed justice to be swayed by one whit. Rawley reported that he had said: 'I was the justest judge that was in England these fifty years, but it was the justest censure in Parliament that was these two hundred years.'

Bacon's personal psychology was slightly abnormal. Different activities of his mind were kept in separate compartments. As he made a complete division between the acceptance of gifts and the dispensation of justice, so he made an absolute cut between personal and state interests. He even felt it necessary to pass on secretly to official quarters information which he had received from his dearest personal friend, Toby Matthew, when he believed it might have a bearing upon matters of state.

This psychology of a divided mind may have contributed to the distrust in which he was held. Elizabeth never gave him any power though she was fascinated by his conversation, and was glad to make use of his intelligence.

Simonds D'Ewes and John Aubrey state that Bacon was addicted to homosexual practices. In all Bacon's extensive writings, including his intimate notebooks, there is no evidence for this, though in his psychology he showed homosexual tendencies. D'Ewes and Aubrey mixed up fact and gossip which make their books more valuable as records of what people were saying and thinking, than of historical facts. John Ray once told Aubrey: 'you are a little too inclinable to credit strange relations'. Stories of alleged secret vices are commonly in circulation about eminent persons especially after conviction for some offence. They are to be taken with great reserve.

Some of Bacon's servants became so prosperous that they kept racehorses, and retired with considerable estates. Perhaps they were homosexual blackmailers, who forced him to collect money from all directions, legitimate and illegitimate. Speculations of this kind can be built up on the basis of occasional remarks by persons other than Bacon himself, and on coincidences such as the execution for unnatural vice of his brother-in-law Mervyn Touchet, second Earl of Castlehaven, in 1631. But they are not well-founded, and consequently not very interesting or important.

In Bacon's case, they are to be particularly distrusted because they were embroidered in the midst of the struggle against

Stuart feudalism. The Puritan mind was probably even more un-
healthy on such matters than the Stuart society which was being
overthrown.

The absence of good portraits of Bacon in adult life may have
arisen from the difficulty, recorded by Hilliard, of conveying
an impression of his extraordinary mind. Bacon's attempts to
construct a synthetic personality by means of intellectual arts
was not completely successful. He was aware of the danger of the
rationalist fallacy: 'It is a great mistake to suppose men too
rational.' The portrait that does most justice to Bacon is the terra-
cotta bust made when he was twelve. It expresses his intellectual
power, and it also reveals his resemblance to his mother.

Bacon was an autodidact who thought everything out for himself. When this kind of man possesses great mental power his
work has a perpetually stimulating originality, because it owes
exceptionally little to conventional ideas. All topics are seen in a
fresh perspective unique to the author. But it is easy for him to
lose touch with common opinion.

'For my own part at least,' Bacon wrote, 'I have committed
myself to the uncertainties and difficulties and solitudes of the
ways, and relying on the divine assistance have upheld my mind
both against the shocks and embattled ranks of opinion, and
against my own private and inward hesitations and scruples, and
against the fogs and clouds of nature, and the phantoms flitting
about on every side; in the hope of providing at last for the present and future generations guidance more faithful and secure.'

His absorption in the development of ideas is seen in the
nature of his speech and conversation. Ben Jonson described how
he could hold an audience, but this did not prove that he could
learn in give-and-take discussion.

His secretary Rawley said that 'though he was a great reader
of books, yet he had not his knowledge from books, but from some
grounds and notions from within himself'. When he entertained
friends, he led the conversation ever as 'a Countenancer and
fosterer of another man's parts'. He did not 'appropriate the
speech wholly to himself, or delight to outvie others, but leave a
liberty to the co-assessors to take their turns'.

He drew men out on their specialities, and 'contemned no
man's observations, but would light his torch at every man's
candle'. His opinions and assertions were generally not contradicted and were more 'like oracles than discourses'. There was

little argument, and if there happened to be any, it was conducted with 'much submission and moderation'.

Able men were known, after rising from his table, to retire to their rooms and make notes of his conversation. It was observed that when he had to repeat other men's words and ideas, he often expressed them better than the speakers or authors themselves.

Bacon guided his discussions courteously, but they were aimed more at elucidating the development of his own thoughts than at placing himself in a position to look at things with the eyes and in the perspective of others. By keeping complete control over conversation, Bacon limited its usefulness to himself. He politely listened to what people said, but was often psychologically deaf to it. He particularly needed close candid criticism to illuminate areas of abnormal opacity in his mind. He knew he needed it, but he had great difficulty in securing it in a form he could bear.

One of the penalties of Bacon's personal psychology was social isolation. He had few friends and was unqualified to be a leader. As he was deficient in the aptitude for leadership he tended to become an administrator. He was loyal to the principle of social authority; he did not allow personal affection to interfere with it. A man like Buckingham, who understood nothing more than the most primitive personal relations, could not make proper use of him, though he owed so much to him for help in the conduct of public business.

His limited emotional contact with others restricted his intuitive understanding. He tried to make up for this by intellectual effort. His repeated boasting to the King and Buckingham on the amount of work he was doing, and his claiming of credit for innovations and clever manoeuvres in policy, indicate that he had a feeling of inadequacy. He was not confident that what he did would effectively speak for itself. He had an inferiority complex, engendered by the inborn qualities of his mind and especially by his relations in boyhood with his cousin Robert Cecil.

He never lacked confidence when he spoke on intellectual and scientific matters.

Paul Langevin remarked, after having been imprisoned by the Nazis, that it is necessary to have been in prison once in order to complete one's experience of life. Bacon through his tragedy had this completed experience, which has greatly enhanced the interest of his personality.

It was part of his genius to keep a remarkably complete and unreserved record of his most confidential thoughts and acts. He scrupulously kept document after document which the average man would have hastily destroyed. He impartially completed all the evidence which would be regarded as telling against himself. As a consequence his writings trace a vast maze of turnings of the human mind and heart, both creditable and discreditable.

Bacon was a kind of modern Faust. In a sense, he successfully bartered his reputation for immortal fame. He wrote some of the boldest words ever uttered by man: his fall, like Marlowe's death, might be regarded as a punishment by fate for his presumption. He made almost superhuman efforts to advance science, by improving its aim and method, and claiming social utility for it, so that the energy of human society could be harnessed to its development. The dual effort was too much for him. In attempting so much, he overreached himself, and to some extent fell back on illegitimate means for trying to accomplish his ends.

If he could have had a competent modern business secretary to manage his financial affairs, he probably would never have been impeached. But then he would probably have been less interesting and influential.

Kennedy has described a mental patient who had been a student, and after losing interest in his surroundings, said he was pre-occupied with a 'thought machine'. This kind of mental disorder can sometimes be improved by shock treatment.

The actions of Bacon which led to his fall, like his autodidacticism, show symptoms of a slightly abnormal detachment. He seems to have been not very conscious of how his acts appeared to others.

Then his fall gave him a profound shock. Perhaps it brought into communication areas of his mind which had lost contact with each other. The relief of tension is reflected in the tranquil style of the *New Atlantis*, and the great mental industry, for a man in his sixties, during the last years of his life. He was himself so much impressed by this, that he felt it was an indication of divine approval. However, most of the work done in these last years was lower in quality and principle than his earlier work.

It seems possible that for most of his life Bacon's personality was not completely integrated, and he was suffering from a slight form of mental disorder that was cured only by the shock of his fall. The existence of such an abnormality would help to explain the attitude of Elizabeth and Burghley. His behaviour was not wholly normal and intelligible.

He tried to make up for his deficiencies by tremendous efforts, and strained himself so far that he succumbed to temptation and mental stress. He confessed to financial irregularities, and was to some extent a mental invalid. These were the social and mental costs of probing the uttermost ends of knowledge, and projecting the Kingdom of Man over Nature.

39. *Bacon and Coke*

THE legal aspects of the impeachment of Bacon were guided by his rival, Coke. Their lifelong conflict ended with Bacon's expulsion from public life. Coke went on to further triumphs, helping the Commons in their struggle against the prerogative. His efforts culminated in the *Petition of Right*, the most important legal document since *Magna Carta*, which was passed in 1628, two years after Bacon's death.

But the struggle between their respective conceptions of law did not end with Bacon's death; it continued for centuries, and is going on still.

Coke was a Norfolk man, fierce, tall and strong, like the Vikings who had settled in those parts centuries before. He was exceptionally vigorous and healthy. When he was nearly eighty, he mentioned that he had never taken medicine in his life. He was descended from lawyers on both sides of the family, and educated at Norwich Grammar School at a period when the city was full of self-confidence and prosperity, after having taken a leading rôle in the break-away from feudalism. The hard-working craftsmen, merchants and professional men were ardent Puritans, and their children naturally acquired their habits and outlook. Coke was a thoroughly orthodox son of this society.

He never lost his local dialect. He learned Latin, and at an early age acquired the habit of taking extensive notes. For the rest of his life he was rarely without pen-in-hand, even in the

busiest situations, making notes of the salient points in everything that he read, and that passed in court and committee. This
note-taking, combined with a strong memory, helped him to
become a most formidable antagonist, for he was usually better
informed on details than anyone else. It made others cautious
of challenging him, because they might easily be shown to be
wrong on a matter of fact. Coke took advantage of this prestige.
When he found he was ignorant on some point, and saw that his
opponents were also ignorant, he invented convenient fictions.
If no law existed, he was capable of inventing it on the spur of
the moment, and pronouncing it with such authority that few
dared to object until they had looked up the books.

After a good grounding at school, he was sent to Trinity
College, Cambridge, where he worked with characteristic
industry. He found his aptitudes particularly well-suited to the
atmosphere of theological disputation which then dominated
Cambridge. The ancient weapon of Aristotelian deductive logic,
inherited from the medieval schoolmen, had been taken over, and
was being enthusiastically applied to Protestant ends.

Coke ever afterwards believed that deductive logic was a
powerful weapon for discovering truth, and said in his *First
Institute* that 'our student should (as Littleton did) come to the
study of the common law from one of the universities, where he
may learn the liberal arts, and especially logic for that teacheth a
man not only by just argument to conclude the matter in question,
but to discern between truth and falsehood, and to use a good
method in his study, and probably to speak to any legal question . . .'.

It was just this confidence in deductive logic which Bacon had
devoted the greatest effort of his life to overthrow, and which
had led to his development of inductive logic.

Coke was the conservative in logic, Bacon the revolutionary
innovator. As their philosophical outlooks were incompatible, so
were their social origins. Coke was bourgeois, Bacon a gentleman
with an aristocratic education, who would never have dreamt of
practising law if he had not been forced to do so by circumstances.

Coke had an intense interest in, and appetite for, the details
of cases. They were of immense importance in practising the law
and winning cases.

When Coke came to London to practise, English law had not

yet been codified. It was an accumulation of laws made by Parliament, decisions made by judges in particular cases, and opinions expressed by eminent lawyers. Coke pursued his note-taking through all this accumulation from the past, and daily in his practice, with a dedicated intensity, for sixty years. He continued it while occupying the highest positions of the law, and through periods of extreme political tension. Out of these notes and practical experience he composed his *Institutes*, which were the first comprehensive work on the laws of England. He said that he had written the books 'to break the ice herein'. The common law consisted, in Coke's phrase, of a body of 'almost infinite particulars'. It had accumulated during centuries, and was rooted in custom.

He traced the origins of the English laws from Saxon times, not only giving the facts as derived from ancient records, but freely expressing his opinions on laws, judges and lawyers.

His great work had an eclectic quality, deriving from the miscellaneous nature of the origins of its contents. By putting down everything that seemed salient, Coke hoped that a system would appear in the English laws, not made by any man, but by the people operating through centuries. Law was the production of ages of unconscious reasoning by the people. He said that 'the laws, that by long experience and practice of many successions of grave, learned and wise men, have grown to perfection, are grounded no doubt upon greater and more absolute reason than the singular and private opinion or conceit of the wisest man that liveth in the world can find out or attain unto. Therefore the law shall stand for reason'.

The laws are not to be discovered by pure reason, but are seen to be reasonable after emerging from practical experience. Burke had a similar conception of political principles. These emerged from experience and were seen to be reasonable, but could not be discovered by pure reason. As Coke was fundamentally conservative in law, so Burke was in politics.

With his lack of aptitude for, and distrust of, general ideas, Coke more or less unconsciously replaced them by the general ideas of his social class. His great work was a review of a thousand years of English law from the standpoint of the social class to which he belonged. He was the master of the legalities of middle-class life. His mind ranged with delight on all the details and complications of the law of property, which in the course of centuries had become more complex than criminal justice, and seemed to make land more important than the people who lived on it. Coke's practical interest in property and his skill in business were so great that he augmented his estates to a size which frightened James.

He understood the heart of the Commons, whose members, it was estimated, already then owned three times as much property as the Lords.

As a fundamentally conservative lawyer, Coke was able to endow the Parliamentarians with a conservative legal tradition, which was an important factor in enabling them to carry through a revolutionary policy successfully.

Bacon belonged to the aristocratic side of legal society. He was inclined by his social upbringing to be interested in those aspects of law concerning authority, system and order. From these, he naturally advanced to considerations of general principles of justice, to be derived from the comparative study of the laws of all nations. Unlike Coke, he believed that the individual human mind, using the appropriate methods of research, could discover fundamental principles not hitherto recognized.

Coke's insistence on the law's infinity of particulars, and his theory that general principles could arise out of it unconsciously in the course of centuries reflected his own lack of aptitude for abstract thinking. Because he was unable to do it, he believed that abstract thinking by other men was not to be trusted, and general ideas could emerge only by unconscious processes, rather as competition in the market is supposed to lead to organization of the economy without any conscious planning. Coke's theory of law and Adam Smith's theory of economics have something in common.

Coke had a command of short-range logic, and a tactical mind. Bacon's logic was long-range, and his mind was strategic. He was no match for Coke in the smaller things of life.

In Coke's time, the common law was as varied and contradictory as any other natural growth. It contained numerous inconsistencies and was often entirely lacking in the kind of law required in societies that were not feudal. It shed little light on the law of overseas trade, law at sea, or the law of an industrial society.

New branches of law were needed to meet these new social requirements. Ellesmere established the new court of equity to carry out tasks hitherto performed by the Lord Chancellor as the monarch's deputy, to remedy injustices arising from the inadequacy of the common law. Bacon defined its function as the conscience of the law.

Bacon was in agreement with Ellesmere both intellectually and emotionally. Besides sharing his ideas, he mentioned in 1596 that Ellesmere 'doth succeed my father almost in his fatherly care and love towards me'.

Coke and the practitioners of the common law were professionally jealous of the upstart court. Bacon succeeded at first in repelling these attacks, but after his fall, Coke, with the support of the Commons, made ground against it, under the plea of protecting the liberties of the subject which, he contended, were enshrined in the common law.

Thus Coke, though conservative in law, emerged as the champion of liberty and progress. In fact, his conception of law never changed, but the political situation changed. This caused him to see the law in new perspectives, and hence apparently to change his opinion on many important points in constitutional law. As Holdsworth has remarked, the situation changed, but not Coke.

Bacon, following Ellesmere, developed the court of equity and the new law required by the society of the future. As a practising lawyer, Bacon consolidated the initiatives of Ellesmere. James settled the right of equity to exist as an independent system. This provided the means by which the future law of trusts and mortgages, partnership, and administration of assets could be worked out. Under the common law, the law of bankruptcy was highly inconvenient to a developing capitalist state.

Though, through Coke, the common law was a great weapon of the Parliamentarians, it was in fact unsuited to the kind of society that the Parliamentarians were fighting to bring into existence.

Bacon viewed the law in a philosophical, historical and comparative spirit which was entirely different from Coke's narrow practical intensity. His *Maxims of the Law*, written before he was thirty-five, showed that he alone had the philosophical, historical and literary capacity required for a restatement of English law after five hundred years of feudal accumulation, in preparation for the modern era. But he had not the leisure or encouragement to carry out the task, which was not adequately done until the nineteenth century.

Bacon boasted to James that he could be a greater lawyer than

Coke. Holdsworth considers that his legal arguments and writings show that he was 'a skilful lawyer, a great jurist, and an un-equalled expositor of the law'. Few could doubt that if he had given all his energies to the law, he would have been a greater lawyer than Coke. But he gave law only his second thoughts, and Coke became the legal champion of the new society coming into being.

Coke's later contention that the king must operate according to the rule of law as interpreted by the judges, has had great influence. Following him, Judge Marshall in the United States established the doctrine that the Supreme Court should decide the legality of laws, and thereby established the supremacy of the law over the executive.

Bacon brought into his consideration of the law the same atti-tude as to his consideration of science. Coke and his colleagues could see his legal ability, but they did not understand his philo-sophy. Their attitude and conservatism were well-expressed by William Hale in the eighteenth century: 'It is a reason for me to prefer a law by which a kingdom hath been governed four or five hundred years than to adventure the happiness and peace of a kingdom upon some new theory of my own, though I am better acquainted with the reasonableness of my own theory than with that law.'

Bacon, on the other hand, fully appreciated the legal merits of his rival. He said that if it had not been for Coke's *Reports* 'the law by this time had almost been like a ship without ballast; for that the cases of modern experience are fled from those that are adjudged and ruled in former times'.

Though he was unable to carry out his restatement of the law, he outlined how it should be done.

Bacon was a far more many-sided lawyer than any of his con-temporaries. His analysis of the law was continued by Thomas Hobbes, who had been his amanuensis. Hobbes selected Coke's works as 'examples of the obsolete'. He elaborated the theory of sovereignty, or social authority, and foreshadowed Bentham.

Bacon launched a general theory of law, abstracted from the infinite particulars of the common court, and from the comparison of the main legal systems of the nations in present and past times.

In spite of appearances, Coke was the man of the past, though his legacy has flourished for three centuries, because it aided capitalism to gain power.

z

Bacon seemed to nearly all in his own day to be a servile tool of royal despotism. But in fact he was the man of the future. He was concerned with the development of the law. Coke's vast importance was due to his being the legal spokesman of the triumphant new business and middle-class society. When this kind of society has passed away, his importance will be seen to be transient rather than fundamental.

Bacon belonged only in small part to the superstructure of the society of his day. He was in it but not of it. He identified his personal interests with James I and his depraved Court, as it was the only way in which he could secure the necessary experience of statesmanship. In spite of his utmost efforts to adapt himself to their level, he failed and fell. But the important part of his legal achievement did not belong to the social superstructure of the society of his day, or even of modern capitalism. It was a generalization and development from the experience of many nations and times.

Bacon's legal theory applies to various systems of social organization, with differing methods of production. It is for this reason that his legal as well as his scientific work has an inspiring significance, because it belonged not to the changing conditions of his time, but to the future.

40. *Entrance Halls of a Better Life*

As soon as Bacon was in the Tower, he wrote to Buckingham asking for his help in securing his release. Death, he said, had been so far from being unwelcome to him during the last two months, as Christian resolution would permit. 'But to die before the time of his Majesty's grace, and in this disgraceful place, is even the worst that could be; and when I am dead, he is gone that was always in one tenor, a true and perfect servant to his master, and one that was never author of any immoderate, no, nor unsafe, no (I will say it) not unfortunate counsel; and one that no temptation could ever make other than a trusty, and honest, and thrice loving friend to your Lordship; and howsoever I acknowledge the sentence just, and for reformation sake fit, the justest Chancellor that hath been in the five changes since Sir Nicholas Bacon's time. . . .'

This was one of the letters that he described as 'written *de profundis*'. Three centuries later Oscar Wilde used the same phrase for the title of his reflections on a comparable experience.

He was released in a day or two, on the King's order. To the King he sent his thanks: 'your Majesty that did shed tears in the beginning of my trouble, will I hope shed the dew of your grace and goodness upon me in the end'.

The King assigned the fine of £40,000 to persons nominated by Bacon. In this way, he pointedly did not exact the money. As other creditors could not secure their money until the King's assignees had been paid, Bacon was protected, and could not be thrown in prison in default of payment.

One of the first to condole with Bacon was Gondomar, who offered to ask the King of Spain to intercede for him. Bacon declined the offer, and thanked him for his love towards him in times of adversity as well as prosperity. 'For myself, my age, my fortune, yea my Genius, to which I have hitherto done but scant justice, calls me now to retire from the stage of civil action and betake myself to letters, and to the instruction of the actors themselves, and the service of Posterity. In this it may be I shall find honour, and shall pass my days as it were in the entrance halls of a better life. . . .'

In another letter to Gondomar, he thanked him for obtaining for him things which other friends had not ventured to try. His friendship had strengthened one who had been somewhat in the living generation, and in the next would not be altogether dead. Beneath the ashes of his fortune the sparks of his affection would ever remain alive.

The King's first thought was to make use of Bacon's political and legal advice in his retirement. He requested him to expound his views on, of all things, the reform of the courts of justice; and on political policy. Bacon replied that the King should announce that he would 'pursue the reformation which the Parliament hath begun'. He repeated the general advice which was the foundation of his political policy: 'all great reformations are best brought to perfection by a good correspondence between the King and his Parliament, and by well sorting the matters and the times'. For advice on particular matters, his Majesty would appreciate 'how improper and how unwarranted a thing it is for me, as I now stand, to send for entries of Parliament, or for searches for precedents . . .'.

It is evident that James did not consider that Bacon had committed any fundamental fault. No doubt he and Buckingham also felt partly responsible for his position, by encouraging and pressing him to go to the limits of propriety and beyond, in protecting the prerogative, and helping Buckingham's relations and friends.

During his remaining years, and especially in the first after his fall, he wrote numerous letters to them, begging for help of various kinds. He felt the expulsion from the verge of the Court, which meant that he must live outside London when the King was in residence, particularly hard, as it prevented him from using libraries, and hindered him in literary work. One of his earliest requests was that he should be relieved of this handicap. The King thought it unwise so soon after his release, so he left London for Gorhambury. He departed in style, creating the general impression, according to Chamberlain, of 'having (as should seem) no manner of feeling of his fall, but continuing as vain and idle in all his humours as when he was at highest'.

He occupied the next four months in writing his *History of Henry the Seventh*, which he presented to the King as a new kind of service which he could still perform, even in his present circumstances. It was a demonstration that his faculties were resilient and undamaged, and there to be used. Their exercise was a reaffirmation of his powers, and a refuge from self-doubt and misery.

The book is written in an unbroken narrative style. The characters and their policies are clearly evoked, and analysed with a statesman's insight. Weight is given to social and economic forces in shaping history.

The accomplishment of such a work after the shock of such a fall, and in spite of the difficulties in his domestic establishment, the limitation on his movements, and the contemptuous attitude of mankind in general, shows the strength of his mind. The deepest foundations of his life were unshaken by his political and social fortunes.

He petitioned the House of Lords for release from his exclusion from the verge of the Court. He was 'old, weak, ruined, in want, a very subject of pity'. Being excluded from London he was unable to see his physicians, and deal with his creditors and affairs. The weather was very cold, and at Gorhambury he lived 'upon the sword-point of a sharp air'. One of his greatest griefs was 'my wife that hath been no partaker of my offending, must be partaker of this misery of my restraint'. The petition was rejected.

It was arranged that Lady St. Alban should apply to Buckingham for his support in obtaining a sinecure of £1,000 a year to relieve her husband. Bacon's secretary and friend, Thomas Meautys was within earshot at the interview. Buckingham 'spake so loud as that what passed was no secret' to him. One can imagine the feelings of Lady St. Alban at having her solicitations treated in this manner. It appeared that Buckingham was making himself difficult because he wanted York House. He thought that an offer to acquire it would have given Bacon welcome financial relief. But Bacon was deeply attached to the house for his own reasons, and for the sake of his wife, who found the prospect of having to move from her London home very hard.

The situation was eased when the Duke of Lenox applied for York House. Bacon said that he was sorry to deny his Grace anything, but this he must pardon him. 'York-house is the house where my father died, and where I first breathed, and there will I yield my last breath, if it so please God, and the King will give me leave. . . .'

When Buckingham heard that Lenox had also been turned down, he became affable once more. The King ordered all the arrears on Bacon's pension of £1,200 a year to be paid.

Buckingham had meanwhile found another London house, but he insisted that though neither he nor Lenox were to have York House, one of his nominees should have it. This was Cranfield, now Lord Treasurer, who so deeply hated Bacon and had been one of the leaders in his impeachment. It was understood that, after York House had been handed over, the Lord Treasurer would do something to relieve Bacon's financial difficulties. Bacon saw that further opposition was impossible, and acquiesced.

After this, he received permission to return to London. He thought of trying to recover Buckingham's complete good will by presenting his Gorhambury estate to him. He was advised by Meautys to write a letter to Buckingham 'made all of sweetmeats'. 'Low as I am,' Bacon wrote to Buckingham, 'I had rather sojourn in a college at Cambridge than recover a good fortune by any other but yourself.'

After Cranfield had got York House, Bacon took a house in the suburbs. His wife was unhappy at the change. 'My Lady hath seen the house at Chiswick, and can make a shift to like it, only she means to come to your Lordship thither, and not to go first and therefore your Lordship may please to make the more haste, for the great Lords long to be in York-house.'

Bacon made careful notes of what he should say to the King, in case he were again granted access to him. He noted qualifications by which he could still be of service, pre-considered compliments and forms of flattery, and works that he might write for him. His Majesty's business had never miscarried in his hands, not because of 'any extraordinary ability in myself, but to my freedom from particular either friends or ends, and my careful receipt of his Majesty's directions . . .'.

Among literary projects, he included works on legal and educational subjects, and on the regulation of trade. He thought also of a history of Henry VIII, and a treatise on the Holy War. He wished to 'live to study, and not study to live'.

His mind was now more and more concentrated on books. He had mislaid one of Matthew's books: 'But sure it is safe; for I seldom leese books or papers.' He wrote to the King that he had now, 'by God's merciful chastisement (and by his special providence) time and leisure to put my talent, or half-talent, or what it is, to such exchanges as may perhaps exceed the interest of an active life'.

He wrote to the Queen of Bohemia that Leisure with Honour was a great bliss, but had never been his fortune. He had had Honour without Leisure, and now he had Leisure without Honour, but his desire was to have Leisure without Loitering, and not to become 'an abbey-lubber', but to yield some fruit of his private life.

He meditated on other eminent men who had been convicted of bribery, such as Demosthenes, Cicero and Seneca, though he 'durst not claim affinity' with them. These examples confirmed him in a resolution to spend his time wholly in writing, and to invest his talent in an intellectual bank which would be permanently solvent and never break. He therefore proposed to pursue the following programme. He would add new parts to his *Instauration*, his chief work. He knew that the general reader found it abstruse, so he intended to express his main ideas in a simpler form, through a book on *Natural History*.

As he could not 'altogether desert the civil person' he had been, he proposed to write a book on *Laws*, in a manner between the philosophical, and the practical of the working lawyers. He had hoped to compile a digest of the laws of England, but had laid this project aside, as he could not carry it out without assistance. The *Instauration* 'had in contemplation the general good of men in their very being, and the dowries of nature; and in my work of laws, the general good of men in society, and the dowries of government'. He counted his *Essays* 'but as the recreations' of his other studies. He accounted the reputation an author gains before his death 'an untimely anticipation of that which is proper to follow a man, and not to go along with' him.

Bacon's replies to letters he received from abroad contain some of the most concise and illuminating expositions of his views. No doubt he felt freer to express himself in communications to foreigners. Father Baranzano, professor of philosophy and mathematics at Anneci, had read the *Novum Organum* and had written to Bacon for further elucidation of his method of investigation. Bacon gave him very careful and valuable answers, and invited him to participate in the programme of the *Instauration*; unfortunately, this talented and understanding young man, who was only thirty-three years old, died almost immediately.

Bacon pushed on with the extension, and translation into Latin, of the *Advancement of Learning*. This was published under the title *De Dignitate et Augmentis Scientiarum* in 1623. He proffered it as a sketch for the first part of the programme of the *Great Instauration*.

He longed for collaborators in the work, but had neither the influence nor the means for securing them. His financial situation grew yet more difficult, and Cranfield, as was to be expected, did nothing for him.

He drafted yet another appeal to the King. He had not committed a major crime, and he had been rewarded with honour and profits. Indeed, 'the then profits might have maintained my now honour, if I had been wise'. Bacon was not wise, in the sense of being shrewd.

His own means, he said, through his own improvidence, were poor and weak, little better than his father had left him. His dignities, which were marks of the King's favour, were now burdens on his present fortune. He had sold his jewels and plate to 'spread upon poor men unto whom I owed, scarce leaving myself bread'. He hoped that his 'extreme misery' might be relieved by compassion of the House of Lords. 'For there is, as I conceive, a kind of fraternity between great men that are and those that have been, being but the several tenses of one verb.' Many of the lords had excused the severity of their sentence by saying that they knew they had left him in good hands.

Bacon scrapped this draft and sent in a much more formal petition, laying emphasis on receiving his rights, in the form of arrears of pension.

He succeeded in seeing Buckingham once more, and after this, the King issued a warrant dealing with his debts. He was 'one whom, howsoever he offended in judicature, yet in matter of counsel and our commission of treasure we found faithful and very careful and diligent, running courses entire and direct for the good of our service . . .'. The King would have liked to have assisted him with his liberality, but 'the times being as they are', he could only require that he should be assisted to come to a reasonable composition with his creditors, which he would regard as a service to himself.

While he was pursuing relief in every quarter he could think of, Bacon devoted his intellectual energy to the compilation of the works on natural history, which he conceived as a necessary collection of preliminary data for the advancement of science, and also as an easy introduction to the new notions in the *Novum Organum.*

He proposed to write books on the various departments of the subject at the rate of one a month, and thought that he might have six completed in six months. In modern terms, these would cover meteorology, gerontology, the properties of matter, attractions and chemical reactions.

These works were expositions of current scientific knowledge, interspersed with occasional original observations and experiments. They were not a sustained breaking of new ground, like the *Novum Organum.* They correspond more to the expositions of current scientific knowledge produced by the modern scientific writers.

Bacon did his best thinking before the age of thirty, and his best writing before the age of sixty. His large output after his fall was a moral rather than an intellectual triumph.

He retired to his ancient and modest rooms in Gray's Inn,

'for quiet and the better to hold out', for when his 'chief friends were gone so far off', he thought it was time 'to go to a cell'.

His attempts to secure more relief through the Court were interrupted by the fantastic incognito journey of Buckingham and Prince Charles to Madrid, to try to secure the hand of the Infanta in marriage. He kept in touch with the party through Matthew, but he made no progress through this contact.

About this time, the Provost of Eton became very ill. Bacon revived his old idea, which he had noted fifteen years before, of securing this place. When he approached Buckingham he was told that he was already pledged to support another candidate. Bacon's application was mentioned to the King, who said 'that he could not value you so little, or conceive you would have humbled your desires and your worth so low', but he would study whether it was possible to accommodate him. Bacon evidently did not consider his condemnation was a disqualification for supervising the education of the young. The place was ultimately given to Sir Henry Wooton.

Bacon in the meantime sent a tractate on *Usury* for the King, as one of his suggestions for political consideration. He excused its deficiencies, as he was 'solitary and hear not things debated', so he may have missed obvious points, for 'as iron sharpeneth iron, so one man's wit edgeth another'.

Usury must be permitted, as necessary for trade. There had been few useful discussions of the subject, though he noted that some had 'made suspicious and cunning propositions of Banks, Discovery of men's estates, and other inventions . . .'. He pointed out that usury leads to a concentration of capital. 'It brings the treasure of a realm or state into a few hands. For the usurer being at certainties, and others at incertainties, at the end of the game most of the money will be in the box, and ever a state flourisheth when wealth is more equally spread.'

Matthew's presence in Madrid enabled Bacon to send a flood of letters to the party there. He was conscious of 'cloying' them, but he could not forbear to offer his advice to Buckingham yet once more. 'Somewhat I have been, and much have I read; so that few things which concern states or greatness, are new cases unto me. And therefore I hope I may be no unprofitable servant to your Lordship. I remember the King was wont to make a character of me, far above my worth, that I was not made for small matters. . . .'

Bacon described Buckingham's negotiations as 'the most important business in Europe'. If the marriage could be arranged it might lead to the establishment of peaceful co-existence be tween Protestantism and Catholicism.

While Buckingham was in Madrid, the King raised him to a dukedom to increase his prestige, but without avail. The Spaniards had long since decided not to allow the marriage unless it led to an official recognition of the Roman Catholic faith, with the aim of the ultimate conversion of England to the Catholic religion. Buckingham waited until his pride could stand the delay no longer. He returned with the Prince, in high dudgeon, to England. James was deeply disappointed, but for a brief interval, the two young men were taken to the heart of the Protestant nation, and received as heroes.

Matthew, as an associate of Buckingham's small group in Madrid, had also, like Buckingham, been raised in rank while he was there; the King knighted him. The reason was not obvious to outsiders. As Chamberlain remarked, 'for what service God knows'.

Shortly after the return of Buckingham and the Prince, Bacon published *De Augmentis*. He described it to the King as a Latin translation of his *Advancement of Learning*, but enlarged almost to the scale of a new work. A feature of the book is the elimination of passages from the *Advancement* which Catholics might find offensive. 'I have been also mine own *Index Expurgatorius*, that it may be read in all places. For since my end of putting it into Latin was to have it read everywhere, it had been an absurd contradiction to free it in the language and to pen it up in the matter.'

Bacon was prepared to accommodate the expression of his ideas to the feelings of his readers. If one form of words was considered offensive, then he was quite willing to substitute another, and he would leave out particular points which might be found objectionable, as long as the main ideas of the work remained.

He told the Prince that he thought the book would live, 'and be a citizen of the world, as English books are not'. To Matthew, he explained that in his opinion 'these modern languages will at one time or other play the bankrupts with books, and since I have lost much time with this age, I would be glad as God shall give me leave to recover it with posterity'.

He sent complimentary copies of *De Augmentis* to the universities of Cambridge and Oxford, and to Trinity College. As a son of Cambridge, he exhorted them to apply themselves strenuously to the advancement of the sciences, and not to lay up in a napkin the talent entrusted from the ancients. They were to make a legitimate and dexterous use of the keys of sense, put away the spirit of contradiction, and dispute only as if they were disputing with themselves.

He exhorted Oxford likewise, and not to regard the work of the ancients as nothing, nor yet as all; to weigh their own powers modestly, and yet make trial of them. And all would succeed best, if instead of turning their arms against each other, they joined their forces to make an impression on the nature of things. This would be sufficient for honour and victory.

He recommended co-operative research in the investigation of nature, and indicated that, in that, men could find all necessary recompense.

To Trinity College, from which he drew his beginnings of knowledge, he thought it right to return the increase of the same, hoping that it would grow and flourish in its native soil. He exhorted them to study, after the word of God and the Scriptures, but before all other books, the great volume of the works of God and His creatures.

He went on compiling notes for hoped-for interviews with the King and Buckingham. If the King would put a hook into the nostrils of Spain, he might lay a foundation of greatness for his children here, in these western parts of the world. For himself, his call was for book-learning; as the King had said: if good for anything, for great volumes. He told Buckingham that he differed from other favourites in being loved by both the King and the Prince.

This was indeed unique in history, for James and Charles were not only father and son, but of contrary dispositions, James being affable and gross, and Charles reserved, precise and pure. Buckingham seemed to cut across the usual psychological relationships, besides appealing to men of contrasting characters.

Besides flattering Buckingham's double status as a favourite, he fed his social prejudices. He had, he said, 'the hearts of the best subjects (for I do not love the word People)'.

Bacon's indefatigable application for financial relief, for re-admission to the House of Lords and for a general pardon was accompanied by personally dignified behaviour. He had complete command of himself. The style of his suits was determined by his conceptions of politics and diplomacy. These were formed during the reign of Elizabeth, when the ruling personages had indeed earned, and justified, the profound deference they received and exacted. Bacon had also been influenced by his early diplomatic training, and his reading of Guicciardini and Machiavelli.

When the news came that one of his last requests to James had been finally rejected, he happened to be in the midst of dictating accounts of experiments for his *Natural History* to Rawley. He left his desk to receive the friend who brought the message that the King could not help him, howsoever his fortunes required it. 'Be it so,' said Bacon cheerfully. After thanking his friend, he returned to Rawley and said: 'Well, Sir, yon business won't go on: let us go on with this, for this is in our power.' He sat down and resumed his dictation, speaking without the least hesitation, for several hours.

Bacon's personal apothecary Peter Boener recorded that though Bacon's fortune changed, he never saw any change in his mien, his words, or his deeds towards any man.

James died on 27th of March 1625, prematurely aged and worn out. His passionate desire for an accommodation with Spain had been disappointed, and his attempts, against his will and aptitude, to retrieve the Palatinate for his son-in-law had collapsed disastrously.

Bacon hoped that the new King, Charles I, whom he had known long and well, might be more helpful, but Charles was soon absorbed in his own troubles.

Bacon set his thoughts yet more in the future. He was now sixty-four, and frequently ailing. But he gave expression to his intellectual plans with as much vigour as ever. A divine in Venice, Father Fulgentio, had entered into a correspondence with him. Bacon replied with a letter which, like that to his other Italian correspondent, Baranzano, gave some of the best information on his work and its progress. He had been unable to reply to him earlier because of a severe illness, and he now described the works he had in mind and in hand, not hoping to perfect them, but to try, because he worked for posterity, 'these things requiring ages for their accomplishment'. He intended to have his main works translated into Latin. *De Augmentis* was, as Fulgentio knew, already published. It included the review of the various sciences, and formed the first part of the *Instauration*. The *Novum Organum* should have followed, but he interposed his moral and political writings, as these were readier for the press. These included his *History of Henry VII*, and his *Faithful Discourses*. He would include in the same volume (which would not be part of the *Instauration*), his *Wisdom of the Ancients*. The next volume would contain the *Novum Organum*, to which a second part was to be added. 'I have already compassed and planned it out in my mind.' This would complete the second part of the *Instauration*. The third part, consisting of *Natural History* was 'plainly a work for a King or a Pope, or some college or order: and cannot be done as it should be by a private man's industry'. The fourth part would contain examples of 'intellectual machinery . . . more exact and more applied to the rules of induction', and the fifth would consist of the *Precursors of the Second Philosophy*. Finally, there would be the sixth part, which would consist of the *Second Philosophy*, of which he had 'given up all hope; but it may be that the ages and posterity may make it flourish'.

He believed that these things proceeded from the providence of God, 'first because of the ardour and constancy of my own mind, which in this pursuit has not grown old nor cooled in so great a space of time: it being now forty years, as I remember, since I composed a juvenile work on this subject, which with great confidence and a magnificent title I named "The Greatest Birth of Time."' Secondly, he saw in its infinite utility the sanction and favour of God.

He composed his will on the 19th of December 1625, hopefully remembering his best friends and servants, and making provision for his relatives. He requested that he should be buried in the same church as his mother, and that the funeral expenses should be modest.

'For my name and memory, I leave it to men's charitable speeches, and to foreign nations, and the next ages.'

He asked that Buckingham should 'reach forth his hand of grace to assist the just performance of this my will . . .'.

He requested that two lectureships should be endowed, one in Cambridge and the other in Oxford, for 'natural philosophy, and the sciences in general thereunto belonging'. He hoped that the stipends would be two hundred pounds a year, and he suggested that the lecturers might be foreign or English.

At the end was a codicil: 'Whatsoever I have given, granted, confirmed, or appointed to my wife, in the former part of this my will, I do now, for just and great causes, utterly revoke and make void, and leave her to her right only.'

Bacon's buoyancy remained with him to the end. In March 1626 he was driving near Highgate, while snow was lying around. He had given most profound attention to the problem of the nature of heat, and had indeed proposed the modern theory of heat as a mode of motion. He repeatedly commented on the importance of refrigeration both for chemical processes, and in the preservation of food. It was entirely in line with his life's thought on heat and refrigeration that he should have stopped his coach, procured a chicken, had it killed, and helped to stuff it with snow, to see how far this would be effective in keeping it fresh.

He suddenly became ill, and was taken to Lord Arundel's house nearby, and put to bed. He was quite unaware that he might be seriously ill, and dictated a letter to Arundel, excusing his unannounced descent on his house.

'My very good Lord,' he wrote, 'I was likely to have had the fortune of Caius Plinius the elder, who lost his life by trying an experiment about the burning of the mountain Vesuvius. For I was desirous to try an experiment or two, touching the conservation and induration of bodies. As for the experiment itself, it succeeded excellently well; but in the journey (between London and Highgate) I was taken with such a fit of casting, as I knew not whether it were the stone, or some surfeit, or cold, or indeed a touch of them all three. But when I came to your Lordship's house, I was not able to go back, and therefore was forced to take up my lodging here, where your house-keeper is very careful and diligent about me; which I assure myself your Lordship will not only pardon towards him, but think the better of him for it. For indeed your Lordship's house was happy to me; and I kiss your noble hands for the welcome which I am sure you gave me to it. . . .'

He apologized for not writing the letter with his own hand, as he could not hold a pen steadily.

This was Bacon's last letter, for his illness became far more serious than he had expected. The house-keeper had put the distinguished visitor in the best bed, which had been unused for a long time, and was probably not well-aired. His attack turned to bronchitis, and he died in a sudden fit of choking and suffocation, early in the morning of April the 9th 1626.

His assets amounted to about £7,000, and his debts to £22,371 1s. 3d., so that the generous intentions of his will could not be realized, especially the foundation of the lectureships in natural philosophy at Cambridge and Oxford. More than three centuries have gone by since he died, and no institution or person has thought fit in all that time to endow two such lectureships in Bacon's memory.

References

1. (a) *The Works of Francis Bacon.* Edited by James Spedding, Robert Leslie Ellis and Douglas Denon Heath. 7 vols. London 1857–9.
   (b) *The Letters and the Life of Francis Bacon.* By James Spedding, 7 vols. London 1861–74.
2. *The Works of Francis Bacon.* Edited by Basil Montague. 17 vols. London 1825–34.
3. *The Philosophical Works of Francis Bacon.* Edited by Peter Shaw. 3 vols. London 1733.
4. *The Complete Works of Francis Bacon.* Edited by John Blackbourne, London 1730.
5. *Francis Bacon: A Bibliography of his Work and of Baconiana to the year 1750.* By R. W. Gibson. Oxford 1950.
6. *Bacon's Novum Organum.* Edited by Thomas Fowler. Oxford 1878.
7. *The Posthumous Works of Dr. Robert Hooke.* London 1705.
8. *The Plan of the French Encyclopaedia.* Translated from the Preface of the French Editors. London 1752.
9. 'Preliminary Dissertation' by John Playfair, prefixed to the 2nd vol. of the Supplement to the *Encyclopaedia Britannica*, 6th edition. Edinburgh 1824.
10. 'Discourse on the Study of Natural Philosophy.' By Sir John Herschel. Lardner's *Cabinet Cyclopaedia*, London 1831.
11. 'The Development of the Main Problem in the Methodology of Francis Bacon.' By Tadeusz Kotarbinski, *Studia Philosophica*, Poznan 1935.
12. *The Philosophy of Francis Bacon.* By C. D. Broad. Cambridge 1926.
13. *Science: Its Method and its Philosophy.* By G. Burniston-Brown. London 1950.
14. 'Lord Bacon as Natural Philosopher.' By Baron Liebig. *Macmillan's Magazine.* London 1863.
15. *The Century of Science: 1840–1940.* By F. Sherwood-Taylor. London 1941.
16. *The Philosophy of the Inductive Sciences, founded on their History.* By William Whewell, 2 vols. London 1840.
17. *The Philosophy of Francis Bacon.* By F. H. Anderson. Chicago 1948.
18. *Geschichte der neuern Philosophie von Verulam bis Benedict Spinoza.* Von Ludwig Feuerbach. Leipzig 1847.
19. *Bacon.* By Thomas Fowler. London 1881.
20. *Francis Bacon: Philosopher of Industrial Science.* By Benjamin Farrington. London 1951.
21. 'The Life and Writings of Francis Bacon.' By T. B. Macaulay. *Edinburgh Review*, 1837.

22. *Francis Bacon.* By Mary Sturt. London 1932.
23. *Personal History of Bacon.* By W. H. Dixon 1861.
24. 'Historia vitae et regni Richardi II, etc.' Edited by Thomas Hearne (with extract on Bacon from the *Autobiography of Sir Simonds D'Ewes*). Oxford 1729.
25. *Brief Lives.* By John Aubrey. Edited by Andrew Clark. Oxford 1898.
26. *Queen Elizabeth.* By J. E. Neale. London 1934.
27. *Memoirs of Queen Elizabeth.* By Thomas Birch. London 1754.
28. *The Great Lord Burghley.* By M. A. S. Hume. London 1898.
29. *Sir Walter Raleigh.* By Milton Waldman. London 1943.
30. *The Letters of John Chamberlain during the Reign of Elizabeth.* Camden Society. London 1861.
31. *A History of England: 1603–1642.* By S. R. Gardiner, 10 vols. London 1883.
32. *The Early Stuarts.* By Godfrey Davies. Oxford 1737.
33. *The Court and Times of James I.* Compiled by T. Birch. Edited by R. F. Williams, 2 vols. London 1848.
34. *A Jacobean Letter Writer: Life and Times of John Chamberlain.* By Edward Phillips Statham. London 1920.
35. 'Life and Character of King James.' By Sir Anthony Weldon in *Secret History of the Court of James the First*, 2 vols. Edinburgh 1811.
36. *The Romance of George Villiers: First Duke of Buckingham.* By Philip Gibbs. London 1908.
37. *The Murder of Sir Thomas Overbury.* By William McElwee. London 1952.
38. *Business and Politics under James I.* By R. H. Tawney. Cambridge 1958.
39. *The Works of Ben Jonson.* With a memoir by William Gifford. London 1816.
40. *The Lion and the Throne: A Biography of Sir Edward Coke.* By Catherine S. Drinker Bowen. London 1957.
41. *A History of English Law.* By W. S. Holdsworth, 13 vols. London 1937.
42. *The Levellers.* By Joseph Frank. Harvard 1955.
43. *The English Revolution: 1614.* Three essays. Edited by Christopher Hill. London. 1940.
44. *The Good Old Cause: The English Revolution of 1640–1660.* Extracts from contemporary sources. Edited by Christopher Hill and Edmund Dell. London 1949.
45. *Puritanism and Revolution.* By Christopher Hill. London 1958.
46. 'Sir Nicholas Bacon.' Vol. I: *Biographia Britannica.*
47. 'Sir Nicholas Bacon.' *Dictionary of National Biography.* London.
48. 'James I'. *Dictionary of National Biography.* London.
49. 'Sir Tobie Matthew.' *Dictionary of National Biography.* London.

INDEX

Abstract natures, 58

Advancement of Learning, the, 24, 47, 49, 219, 221 ff., 225, 249, 303

Aerodynamics, 130

Agricola, 70

Airy, G. B., 23

Alexander, the Great, 42, 67, 113

Alphabet of Nature, 57

Anderson, F. H., 64

Andrewes, Bishop Lancelot, 229, 248, 321

Animal breeding, 34

Aphorisms as means of exposition, 96 f.

Aristotle, 11, 22, 42, 51, 53, 65 f., 69 f., 96, 102, 141, 145, 157

Asquith, Lord, 325

Association for advancement of science, 36

Astrology, 68

Astronomy, 67

Athletics, 74

Atoms, Atomism, Atomic Energy, 58, 65 f., 68 f., 114

Aubrey, Christopher, 316

Aubrey, John, 11, 14, 328

Augustus, 141

Babbage, C., 9

Bacon, Anthony, 156, 159, 166 ff., 171, 178, 181, 187, 201 f., 209, 250

Bacon, Edmund, 228

Bacon, Francis:
character, 17
on the Fall of Man, 21, 48 f.
and the industrial revolution, 40, 49
religion, 41, 48, 49, 88
not a *bourgeois*, 50
on his debt to Aristotle, 70
against fortuitous organization of universe, 70
on mathematics, 71, 118
on social class, 86

Bacon, Francis—*contd.*
prophetic forecast of his fall, 87
preference for early Greek philosophers, 93
atomicity of his ideas, 95
as statesman of science, 105 f., 112, 127
a materialist, 115
on motion, 126, 232
style, 135, 168
influence of his class origin, 145
birth, 154
his estate, 155
marriage, 156, 223
education, 156
verses, 158
M.P. for Melcombe, 160; for Middlesex, 173
on himself, 161, 213, 222, 242, 277 f., 319 f., 320, 329, 343, 345
on controversy, 162, 171
on leadership, 163
on democracy, 164
on dictatorship, 164
clerkship of the Star Chamber, 165, 184, 225, 234
seeks position, 167
on Elizabeth I, 169, 191
on conspirators, 170
on Spain, 171
on the Pope, 171
on Burghley, 171
on Cecil, 172
on his father, 172
contributes to power of Commons, 174
Elizabeth's attitude to, 175
and democratic rights, 175
candidate for attorneyship, under Elizabeth, 176–9; under James, 240, 245
his servants, 178
proposes to retire to Cambridge, 179

Bacon, Francis—*contd.*
candidate for the solicitorship, under Elizabeth, 179–84; under James, 223 f.
on secret service, 180
on education, 182, 221, 231
suspicion of the Cecils, 183
attitude to Essex, 185
lectures on law, 187
on his *Essays*, 188, 343
candidate for Mastership of the Rolls, 188
on Essex's sack of Cadiz, 189
advice to Essex, 190
on enclosures, 193, 242
arrested for debt, 196
deficiency in ordinary perception, 203
in prosecution of Essex, 205 ff., 208
inherits Gorhambury, 210
on weights and measures, 210
on patents, 211
on commercial assurance, 211
becomes incoherent through excitement, 211
on post-war policy, 212
on secrecy, 215
letter to John Davies, 216
on James I, 217, 262
knighted, 218
contemplates marriage, 218
parliamentary services, 219
work on union of England and Scotland, 219, 221
his disinterestedness, 219
on population problem, 220
on unity in the Church, 220
gains confidence, 221
King's Counsel, 221
on marriage, 224
appointed Solicitor, 224
his frankness, 226
self-advancement, 227
lacking in natural cunning, 227
on endowment of research, 231
on imperial policy, 233, 274, 280
his pleasure house, 233
his health, 234
his finances, 234, 236
on technique of public speaking, 235
relations with James I, 237
relations with Cecil, 237
work on monopolies, 237
Commons' confidence in him, 239, 258
on Cecil, 241

Bacon, Francis—*contd.*
calls for a new Parliament, 241, 243, 284
improves administrative procedure, 242
on banks, 242
on private industry, 242
on relations between lawyer and client, 243
on managing Parliament, 244
appointed Attorney-General, 246
his friendships, 247
on seeking criticism from friends, 248
aims at future fame, 249
on religion and science, 250
moral courage, 250 f.
Matthew on his character, 251 f.
and bribery, 252, 302, 316–24, 327, 342
differences with Coke, 254
his affections, 255
change in Commons' attitude to him, 256
on the 'Undertakers', 257
his conception of Parliament, 257
on apologies, 258
on relations between Crown and Parliament, 259
on torture, 259, 299
and duty to state, 260, 287, 328
on supremacy of politics over the law, 261
candidate for Lord Chancellorship, 262
on government initiative in trade and industry, 263
his indebtedness to Villiers, 264
on Overbury, 266
refers to his exclusion from political confidences, 267
on management of state prosecutions, 268
on the best kind of authors, 272
and qualification as a statesman of science, 273
on Villiers, 273, 277
on the Cecils, 273
on using cunning and corrupt men, 273
on rules for dealing with suits, 273
on civil war, 274
on his position at Court, 274
on Coke's *Reports*, 275
becomes Lord Keeper, 277
and democracy, 278

Bacon, Francis—*contd.*
and collective responsibility, 279, 284
his lack of political power, 282
on Coke's character, 284
receives letter from Yelverton, 285
his psychology, 287, 328, 330
becomes Lord Chancellor, 288
pressure from Buckingham, 288
on reasons for resisting appeasement, 295 ff.
on reforming the system of government administration, 298 f.
attitude to Yelverton, 300 f.
on duties of a judge, 301
on free speech, 302, 308
on the *Great Instauration*, 304
becomes Viscount St. Alban, 306
on conduct of Commons, 309
on monopolies, 310
his impeachment, 314–25
drafts a will, 320
James's attitude to him after his impeachment, 321
his submission presented to House of Lords by Prince of Wales, 322
his confession, 322
his sentence, 323
political character of his impeachment, 325
'magnificence', 325 f.
his personal accounts, 326 f.
a modern Faust, 331
James's attitude after his fall, 340
attitude to academic life, 341
candidate for provostship of Eton, 345
on concentration of capital, 345
on peaceful co-existence, 346
his last will, 349
revokes gifts to his wife, 350
his death, 350
dies insolvent, 351
Bacon, Lady (Alice Barnham), 156, 223 f., 341 f., 350
Bacon, Lady (Anne Cook), 154, 156, 167 ff., 177 f., 182, 184
Bacon, Sir Nicholas, 60, 153 f.
Bancroft, Archbishop, 248
Baranzo, Father, 343
Bedford, Lady, 310
Bellarmine, Cardinal, 252
Bentham, J., 337
Bettenham, J., 247
Biological processes for industry, 135
Birch, T., 153

Black, J., 124
Blount, Sir Christopher, 197 f.
Bodleian Library, 222
Bodley, Sir Thomas, 13, 222
Body and mind, 72
Boener, Peter, 348
Bohr, Niels, 96
Bondi, H., 104
Bowes, Sir Jerome, 210
Boyd Orr, Lord, 147
Boyle, Robert, 14, 22
Brent, 319
Buckingham, Duke of (George Villiers), 4, 15 f., 128, 142, 188, 251 f., 254, 263, 265, 268 f., 271 ff., 275, 277 f., 280–5, 288, 298, 300, 308, 314, 317, 320, 322, 330, 338, 341, 344–7
Burghley, Lord (William Cecil), 12, 153 f., 156, 164–7, 170, 173, 175 f., 178, 182 f., 196, 273, 325, 332
Burlomachi, 310

Caesar, Julius, 42, 81, 84
Caesar, Julius, 81, 249
Cardan, 145
Carleton, D., 223
Carlini, 123
Carnegie, Dale, 85
Carr, Robert (Lord Rochester, Earl of Somerset), 246, 254, 263 ff., 267 f., 270 f., 275
Cartwright, 160
Cecil, Sir Robert (Lord Salisbury), 13, 154, 156, 167, 175, 177, 179, 182 f., 186, 192, 200, 203, 205, 207, 209, 217, 221, 223 ff., 227, 232 ff., 236 ff., 241 ff., 245, 273, 324, 330
Census of the sciences, 46, 61
Chain-reactions, 126
Chaloner, Sir Thomas, 228
Chamberlain, John, 246, 251, 270, 279, 299, 309, 340, 346
Chamberlain, Neville, 297
Chancery Court, scandals in, 315
Charles I (Prince of Wales), 142, 252, 279, 322, 345 ff.
Charterhouse School, 230
Churchill, John, 316, 318
Cicero, 85, 342
Code Napoleon, 87
Coke, Clem, 283
Coke, Sir Edward, 175 f., 178 f., 201, 205 f., 229, 234, 241, 245 f., 253 f., 259 ff., 263 ff., 268 f., 275 ff.,

282, 284 ff., 289, 300 f., 308, 313 ff., 318, 332–5, 338
Coke, Lady, *see* Lady Hatton
Coke's *Institutes*, 333 f.
Coke's *Maxims of the Law*, 336
Coke's *Reports*, 272, 275 f., 337
Colours of Good and Evil, 187
Columbus, C., 36, 107, 112 f., 129
Comedy of Errors, 181
Commentarius Solutus, 226
Common Law, 234, 245 f., 273
Compiling and Amendment of the Laws of England, 275
Conservation, principle of, 131
Considerations touching a War with Spain, 298
Continuous creation of matter, 68
Cook, Anne, *see* Lady Bacon
Co-operation in learning, 43
Copernicus, N., 68
Cosmic radio, 69
Council, of, 272
Cranfield, Lionel, 17, 287, 314 f., 341 ff.
Cuffe, Henry, 207, 229
Cultural diffusion, 63

D'Alembert, 3 f., 14
Dairy products, nutritive value of, 147
D'Ewes, Simonds, 264, 328
De Augmentis, 156, 343, 346 ff.
Declaration of the Demeanor and Carriage of Sir Walter Raleigh, etc., 292 f.
Declaration of the Practices and Treasons, etc., 208
Democritus, 51, 57, 66, 69 f., 106
Demosthenes, 342
Densities, experimental determination of, 133
Descartes, R., 4, 75, 19
Description of the Intellectual Globe, 95
Dialectics, 85, 97
Diderot, 3
Dignity and Advancement of Learning (De Augmentis), 61, 90, 156, 343, 346
Donne, Dr. John, 248
Dorset, Lady, 228, 233
Dreams, 149, 157
Drugs, synthetic, 34, 38, 62

Eddington, A. S., 124
Education, views on, 46, 156
Egerton, Sir Thomas, *see* Lord Ellesmere

Egerton, Edward, 316
Einstein, A., 68, 94, 103
Elastase and prolongation of life, 139
Elizabeth, 249 f.
Elizabeth I., 42, 154, 160, 164, 166 f., 170, 173 ff., 177–80, 182 ff., 186, 188 f., 193, 197–204, 208, 211 f., 225, 274, 290, 310, 328, 332
Elizabeth's last Parliament, 210
Elizabeth, Princess, later Queen of Bohemia, 237, 294, 298, 342
Ellesmere, Lady, 223 f.
Ellesmere, Lord (Sir Thomas Egerton), 188, 199, 204, 207, 233, 254, 262, 267, 270, 272, 276 f., 288, 316, 335 f.
Ellis, R. L., 54 f.
Engels, F., 98 f.
Engineering development Research, 130
Essays, 87, 187 f., 240, 251, 343
Essex, Earl of, 165 f., 176–80, 182–5, 188 f., 192 f., 195, 197–208, 225, 254, 275, 322
Evolution, Theory of, 120
Excess of Lavish Speech on Matters of State, 308
Exeter, Countess of, 298, 299
Exeter, Earl of, 29

Faithful Discourses, 349
Feuerbach, L., 324
Final causes, 70
Forms, 69
Franklin, Benjamin, 85, 146
Frederick, Elector Palatine, later King of Bohemia, 294, 297 f., 307 f.
French Encyclopaedia, 2, 4, 26
Friendship, of, 251
Fulgentio, Father, 348

Galen, 69
Galeria Copiola, 141
Galileo, 5, 10, 54, 103, 111, 240, 300
Gardiner, S. R., 5
Garrard, 277
Gerontology, 73 f., 137
Gilbert, W., 10, 102, 111, 131 f.
Gondomar, Count, 252, 297, 308, 324, 339
Goodman, Bishop, 154
Gravitation, 66
Gravity, effect of on pendulum, 123

Great Instauration, 21, 23 f., 144, 225, 227, 229, 240, 249, 303 f., 326, 342 f., 349
Greatest Birth of Time, 12, 159, 349
Greniewski, 127
Guicciardini, 348
Gunpowder Plot, 222, 228, 249

Hadamard, J., 6
Hale, William, 337
Hamlet, 82
Harcourt, Sir William, 308
Harrington, Sir John, 202
Harriot, Thomas, 228
Harvey, William, 10 f., 14
Hastings, Sir George, 316 f.
Hatton, Lady (Lady Coke), 282 f.
Heat, 7, 40, 58, 117
Heat from sun and fire the same, 122
Heath, Archbishop, 153
Henry, Prince, 240, 289
Heraclitus, 98
Herbert, George, 159
Hero, 70
Herschel, J., 127
Hilliard, N., 157, 329
Hippocrates, 141
History, 61 f., 64
History of Henry VII, 340, 349
History of Life and Death, 137
History of the World, 289
Hitlerism, 148
Hobbes, Thomas, 279, 337
Holdsworth, 336 f.
Holy War, 56, 280
Hooke, Robert, 8 f., 90
Hopkins, F. G., 57
Howard of Effingham, Lord, 192, 194
Howard, Thomas, Lord Suffolk, 235
Hubbard, 235, 241, 245, 262 f.
Humboldt, A. von, 129
Hume, David, 232
Hydrogen fusion, 68

Idols, doctrine of, 56, 79, 101
Imagination, force of, 147
Impeachment, 314
Impositions, 239, 258
Induction, 304
Industrial Revolution, 40, 97
Information services, 35, 78
Information theory, 9, 80
Instances, doctrine of, 119 ff.
International scientific organization, 46
Interpretation of Nature, 213

Inventions needed, 38, 70
Inventions, science of, 76
Inventions, inventory of, 71
Inventors, 50, 76
Irish problem, 194–201
Isaacs, Rufus (Lord Reading), 325

James I, 4, 13, 15, 47, 66, 83, 92, 128, 137, 142, 175, 216–19, 229, 234, 237, 240, 246, 253 f., 256, 262 ff., 270 ff., 275–80, 284 f., 287, 289, 297, 304, 307 f., 313, 318, 330, 335 f., 344–8
Jonson, Ben, 235, 305, 329

Kennedy, 331
Keymis, Captain, 290
Kotarbinski, T., 126

Lake, Sir Thomas, 299
Langevin, Paul, 330
Latent properties, 116
Lavoisier, A., 124
Law, science of, 87
Laws, 343
Leicester, Earl of, 191
Lenox, Duke of, 300, 341
Leucippus, 65
Leviathan, 279
Liebig, J. von, 23
Light, nature of, 35
Light, velocity of, 125
Livia, 141
Livy, 113
Lloyd George, 325
Locke, John, 4
Logarithms, 72
Logic, 75, 77, 93, 100
Logic, inductive, 8, 24, 53, 89, 118, 126 ff.
Lopez, Dr., 180
Lysenko, T. D., 145

Macbeth, 82
Machiavelli, N., 81, 84, 348
Magellan, 107
Magna Carta, 332
Mandeville, Lord, 315
Marlowe, Christopher, 240, 331
Marriage and Single Life, of, 224
Marshall, Judge, 337
Marx, K., 98 f.
Mary, Queen of Scots, 154, 160
Masques, 161, 168, 181, 185
Mass-action, law of, 136
Mathematics, its rôle in science, 71

Matthew, Toby, 216, 247, 249–52, 315, 326, 328, 345 f.
Matthias, German Emperor, 294, 297
Maxims of the Law, 187
Maxwell, J. Clerk, 58, 94
Meautys, Thomas, 341
Medicine, 73
Memory and association, 120
Metaphysics, 67
Meteorology, 129 f.
Michell, 311
Mill, J. S., 127
Milton, John, 21, 48, 55
Mompesson, Sir Giles, 309, 311, 313 f. 319
Monopolies, 275, 309, 313
Montaigne's *Essays*, 157
Mountjoy, Lord, 192, 196, 200, 202 f., 209, 211
More, Sir Thomas, 188
Myths, 64

Napier, J., 72
Natural history, 25 f., 36, 92, 128, 149
Natural History, 342, 348 f.
Nero, 297
New Atlantis, 3, 17, 28, 36 f., 128, 331
Newton, Isaac, 4, 6, 8, 35, 67, 94, 103
Nicod, 127
Northampton, Lord, 237
Northumberland, Lord, 237
Novum Organum, 24, 54, 56, 89 ff., 93, 97, 116, 128, 229, 293, 303 ff., 343 f., 349
Novum Organum, James's view on, 304 f.

Oil, synthesis of, 135, 146
Olbers, 103
Olympic games, 74
On Canvassing, 85
Orinoco, 289 f.
Outer space, 110, 114
Overbury affair, 265–72

Palatinate, 307, 313
Paracelsus, 147
Paradise Lost, 48
Paradise Regained, 48
Parasceve, 25
Parliamentary Privilege, 174
Parsons, Robert, 248
Pasteur, L., 6
Paulet, Sir Amias, 157

Pavlov, I. P., 75
Peacham, 259 f.
Peacock, 299
Peel, Sir Robert, 275
Petition of Right, 332
Philosophy, 61 f.
Philosophy of the Inductive Sciences, 97
Planning of science, 1 f., 14
Planning of Society, 1, 14
Plant breeding, 34
Plant-growth, stimulation of, 34
Plastic surgery, 140
Plato, 22, 51, 65, 69 f., 96, 106, 141, 147
Playfair, John, 11
Playfer, Dr., 225
Pliny, 26, 145
Poetry, 61
Polymerization, 134
Porta, 145
Posterior Analytics, 53
Prague rising, 294, 308
Prerogative, 173, 188, 211, 234, 243, 245, 254, 261 f., 276, 279 f., 287
Primeval atom, 68
Propaganda, principles of, 187
Propaganda, technique of, 22, 67
Proust, M., 264
Psychoanalysis, 81
Puckering, Sir John, 177, 184, 188
Pythagoras, 166
Pythagorean philosophy, 147

Quantum of nature, 66
Quantum theory, 96

Ralegh, Sir Walter, 174, 192 f., 203, 205, 216, 228, 289–93
Ralegh's expedition to Guiana, 289–293
Ramus, Peter, 11, 53, 157
Rawley, 28, 36, 90, 144, 328 f., 348
Reflex action, 75
Rejuvenation, 140
Relativity, theory of, 68, 103
Religion and science, 59, 87
Repressed complexes, 82
Rochester, Lord, *see* Robert Carr
Roos, Lord, 299
Royal Society, 2 f., 5, 7, 135

St. Alban, Lady, *see* Lady Bacon (Alice Barnham)
St. Ambrose, 64

St. Augustine, 64
St. John, Oliver, 261 f.
Salisbury, Lord, *see* Sir Robert Cecil
Sandys, Sir Edwin, 248
Science, a democracy, 51, 104
  and curiosity, 49 f., 52
  and morality, 15, 37
  and politics, 16, 112
  and social conditions, 59 f., 63, 105
  Arabian, 106
  co-operation in, 72, 113
  fiction, 18
  for profit, 4, 40, 150
  fundamental, 65
  Greek, 106
  history of, 106
  impediments to, 56, 58 f., 62, 67, 79, 101, 111, 122
  justification of, 49
  motives for, 52, 89
  nature of, 62
  planning of, 1 f., 14, 46 f., 51, 60, 61, 136
  Roman, 106
  social responsibilities of, 15
  social status of, 20, 109
Scientific laws, 69
Scientific method, 1 f., 5–8, 12, 22, 24, 89, 93, 104, 109, 116
Scientists' conditions of work, 44
Scientists' salaries, 45
Scientists, social status of, 41
Second Philosophy, 349
Secrecy, 30, 35, 55, 302
Secret police, 166
Sectarianism, 42
Self-advancement, 83
Semantics, 79
Seneca, 240, 342
Sense-impressions, 62
Senses, the, 77, 105
Shakespeare, William, 82, 156, 181, 240, 264
Shaw, Peter, 22
Sherrington, C. S., 75
Silencers for guns, 146
Smiles, Samuel, 85
Smith, Adam, 335
Social organization, 85
Somerset, Countess of (Lady Frances Howard), 246, 265, 268–71
Somerset, Earl of, *see* Robert Carr
Sound, 146
Southampton, Earl of, 198, 205, 322
Spain, situation of, 295

Spanish marriage, the, 267, 279, 281, 296, 307, 345 f.
Species, differences between, 66
Species, transmutation of, 147
Spedding, J., 36, 54 f., 144, 173, 195, 226, 229, 232, 235
Sprat, Thomas, 2, 22
Stalin, J., 98
Stuart, Lady Arabella, 289
Subsidies, 161 f., 173 f., 176, 193, 210, 238
Substances, preparations in which they exist, 66
Suffolk, Lord, *see* Thomas Howard
Sutton, Thomas, 230
Sylva Sylvarum, 26, 37, 144 f.
Synthetic fibres, 122

Taylor, F. Sherwood, 37, 39
Tenison, 135, 225
Thought-reading, 148
Transformation of nature, 62
Trollope, Anthony, 236
Tyndall, J., 116
Tyrone, Earl of, 194 f., 198 f., 211

'Undertakers', 255, 257
Usury, 345

Valerius Terminus, 47, 54, 56, 60, 90, 97, 116
Venezuela, 293
Vernalization, 145
Versellini, 310
Villiers, George, *see* Duke of Buckingham
Villiers, Sir Edward, 310
Villiers, Sir John, 282
Vivisection, 73
Vorstius, 262

Wales, Prince of, *see* Charles I
Walsingham, 159, 161, 164
Water, compression of, 125
Watt, James, 6, 76
Wealth, 86
Weather, control by 'seeding', 130
Weather, effect of explosions on, 129
Weather, synthetic, 34, 39
Wegener's hypothesis, 121
Wharton, Lady, 318
Whewell, W., 97
Whitelock, 301
Whitgift, John, 160, 162

Wilde, Oscar, 339
Winwood, Sir Ralph, 255 f., 259, 283, 290, 292
Wisdom of the Ancients, 64, 251, 349
Wooton, Sir Henry, 345
Wright, von, 127

Xenophanes, 141, 326

Yelverton, 276, 285 ff., 300 f., 311
Young, Sir Richard, 316

Zouch, Sir Edward, 310